The complete *joy of sex*

THE CLASSIC **JOY OF SEX** AND **MORE JOY OF SEX** IN ONE VOLUME

Alex Comfort M.B., Ph. D.
Illustrated by Charles Raymond and Christopher Foss

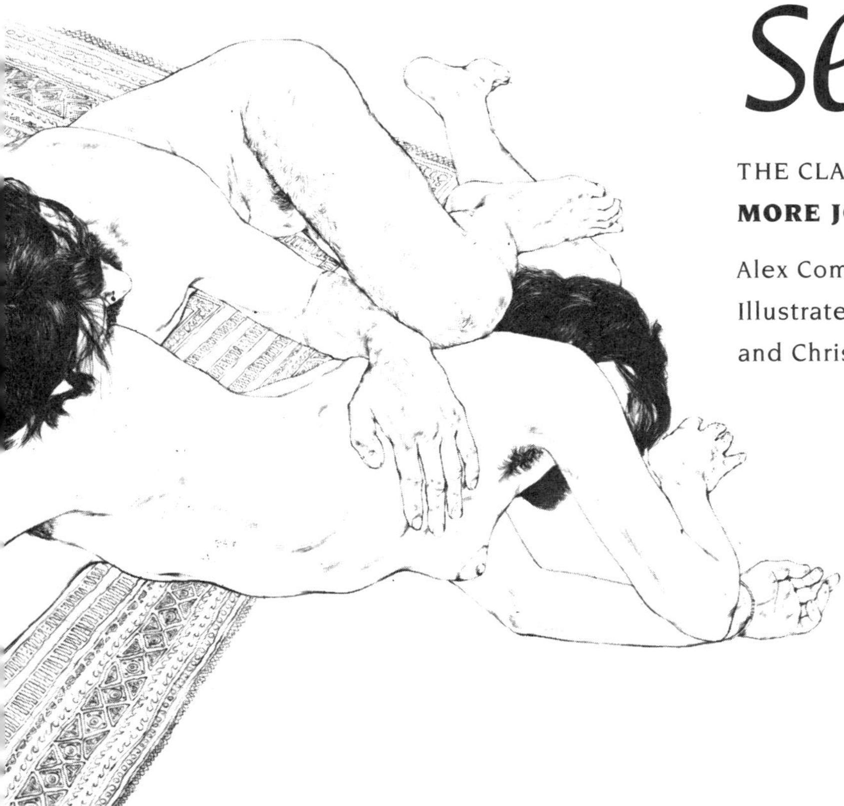

CHANCELLOR PRESS

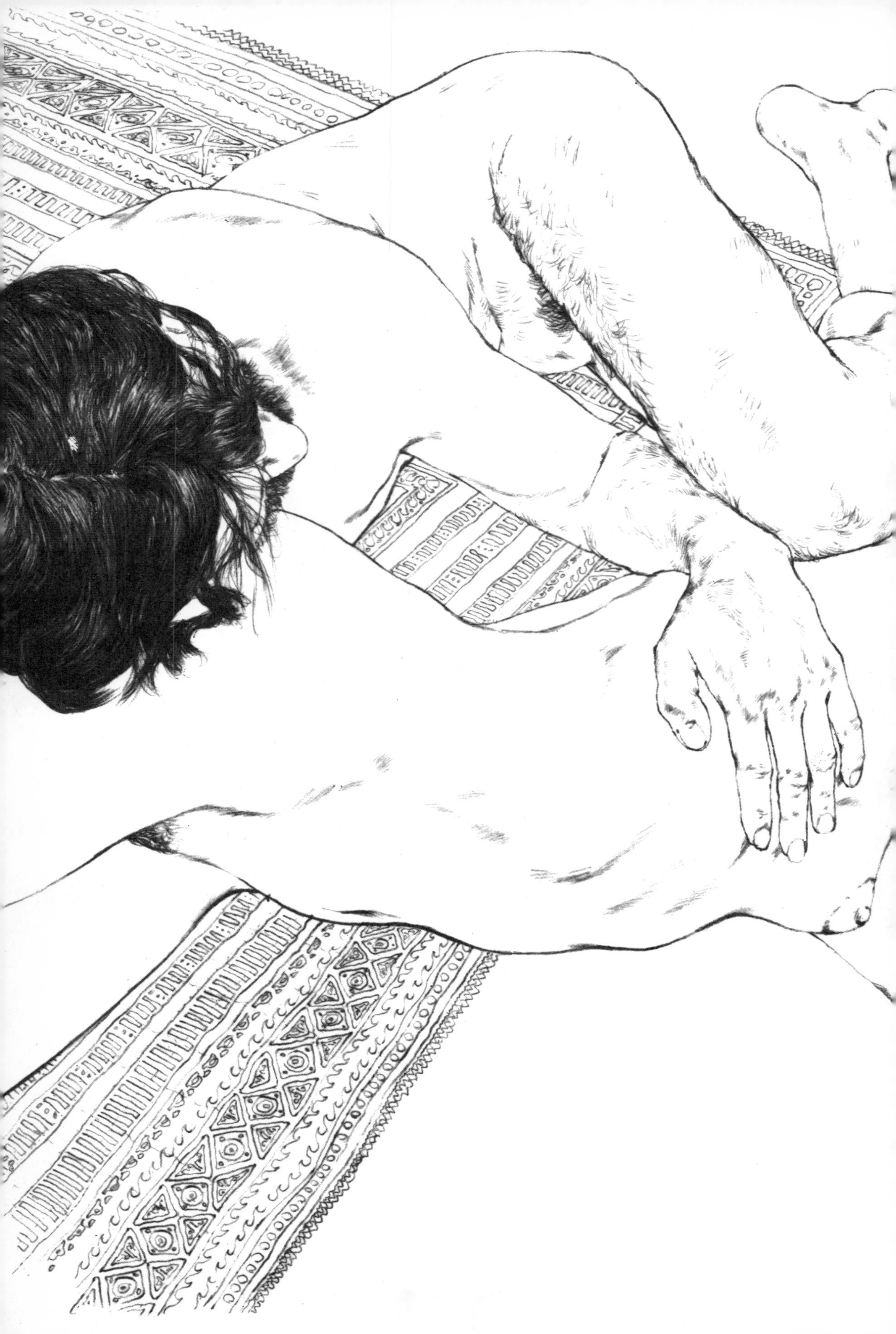

The complete joy of sex

First published in Great Britain by Mitchell Beazley Limited in two separate volumes under the titles:

The Joy of Sex 1972
More Joy of Sex 1973

This updated and revised edition published 1993 by
The Chancellor Press
an imprint of Reed Consumer Books Limited
Michelin House
81 Fulham Road
London SW3 6RB
and Auckland, Melbourne, Singapore
and Toronto

ISBN 1 85152 443 6

A CIP catalogue record for this book is available at the British Library

Produced by Mandarin Offset

Contents

The publishers would like to thank the artists, Charles Raymond and Christopher Foss, for the care and devotion they have lavished on their illustrations for *The Joy of Sex*. They have throughout worked closely with the Editor to reflect the style of this book – its humor, honesty and directness. The results are a magnificent tribute to their skill and dedication.

This book was originally published prior to the recent identification of Acquired Immune Deficiency Syndrome(AIDS) and other medical conditions that may be sexually transmitted. The advice and/or information included in this book should be considered in the light of the present understanding of such health risks. The reader is advised to consult a physician about these risks.

Sauces & Pickles 157

Problems 219

Index 255

Preface

A biologist-writer interested in human sexual behavior is asked to read many prospective books – admonitary, weird, religious, naive, conventional or just plain ignorant – all of them aiming to be helpful, and none of them getting the key quite right.

My wife and I started to compile a book of our own, found it could be expanded to cover tastes other than our own, and that other couples found it helpful – in fact, it has sold over 5,000,000 copies. I am a practicing physician: when the book first came out I appeared as editor, not author. The anonymity was professional, but since I do not practice sex counseling it now seems unnecessary.

The analogy to a cookbook seemed appropriate: this is a book about sexual cuisine, not sexual indigestion. A cookbook is an unanxious account of available dishes which people enjoy – culinary fantasies as well as staple diets, with practical details provided. Cookbooks do not make people anxious. This is an equally unanxious account, I hope, of the full repertoire of human heterosexuality. As such it was overdue. A cookbook tells the novice how to deal with a live lobster, what to do if the mayonnaise separates, how to fix a chateaubriand. In this book we describe, hopefully in the same unruffled detail, and with a sense of fun, what to do about impotence or premature ejaculation, how to manage oral sex, how to play symbolically aggressive games, how to treat a partner who is hip for 'discipline,' how not to be bothered by fetishes, how to use kinky clothes as sex stimuli. A good many professional counselors react to such questions – when clients have the pluck to ask them – if not with psychiatric and moral anxiety, at least with a lack of detailed knowhow. Doctors, moreover, can't necessarily know your needs and resources from their own sex lives, and not all of them have much idea of the range and variety of human sexual behaviors. I know that I could have done with such a book as a medical student.

The thing that has pleased us most about this book is the number of total strangers of all ages who say that they have found it helpful. It is difficult to produce anything new in the field of 'sex education.' The permissive society has permitted nearly everything from po-faced admonition to eccentric porn, including 'straight' books which stop short of answers and counseling magazines full of unpractical, if not pathological, fantasy. Adults deserve better treatment. Sexual profiles are quite as diverse as tastes in cooking, but nobody is guilty or obsessed over the fact that they hate curry and like tripe. Of course sexuality is a different case – in fact, such is the human capacity for anxiety that whereas people formerly worried if they did the things described in this book, some will now worry if they don't do all of them. That we can't help – but experience has shown that professional counselors use the book to widen their clients' sexual perspectives. However, it is the ordinary, sexually active, reader – who wants both to enjoy sexuality and to be responsible about it – who seems to benefit most. This book, as the title implies, is about joy through play. Children are not embarrassed by their games: adults often are. So long as they are not hostile, cruel or unhappy games, they need not be. Our society could do with a lot more unembarrassed playfulness.

Alex Comfort M.B., Ph.D.

On Advanced Lovemaking

All of us who are not disabled or dumb are able to dance and sing – after a fashion. This, if you think about it, summarizes the justification for learning to make love. Love, like singing, is something to be taken spontaneously. On the other hand, the difference between Pavlova and the Palais de Danse, or opera and barber-shop singing, is much less than the difference between sex as the last generation came to accept it and sex as it can be.

At least we recognize this now (so that instead of worrying if sex is sinful, most people now worry whether they are 'getting satisfaction'– one can worry about anything, given the determination). There are now enough books about the basics: the main use of these is to get rid of worries over the normality, possibility, and variety of sexual experience. The people who go to Masters and Johnson are getting over hangups so basic that in past generations the folk tradition would have taken care of them. At least the 'permissive' scene in publishing removed some of this cover-up. Our book is slightly different, in that there are now enough people who have the basics and really need hard information (not simply reassurance).

Chef-grade cooking doesn't happen naturally: it starts at the point where people know how to prepare and enjoy food, are curious about it and willing to take trouble preparing it, read recipe hints, and find they are helped by one or two detailed techniques. It's hard to make mayonnaise by trial and error, for instance. Cordon Bleu sex, as we define it, is exactly the same situation – the extra one can get from comparing notes, using some imagination, trying way-out or new experiences, when one already is making satisfying love and wants to go on from there.

It is always sad when a love relationship runs aground through non-communication (fear of rejection over some fantasy need, inability to come to terms with aggressive needs through a misplaced idea of tenderness, inability to accept sexuality as play). These hangups, plus monotony, are a large part of all five or seven year itches, and, between loving and tolerant people, avoidable.

We shall have four sorts of readers; those who don't fancy it, find it disturbing and would rather stay the way they are, with Reuben sandwiches – these should put it down, accept our apologies, and stay the way they are: those who are with the idea, but don't like our choice of techniques – these should remember it's a menu, not a rulebook. We have tried to stay wide-open, but it is always difficult to write about things one doesn't enjoy, and we have left out long discussion of the very specialized – one-legged ladies, mackintoshes – and things like S and M, which aren't really love or even sex in quite our sense of the word. People who like these know already what they want to try. One aim of this book is to cure the notion, born of non-discussion, that common sex needs are odd or weird. As to the general repertoire, the whole joy of sex-with-love is that there are no rules, so long as you enjoy, and the choice is practically unlimited. This is the way most people will use our notes – as a personal one-couple notebook from which they might get ideas. Then there are the hardy experimentalists, bent on trying absolutely everything. They too will do best to read this exactly like a cookbook – except that sex is safer in this respect, between lovers, in that you can't get obese or atherosclerotic on it, or give yourself ulcers. The worst you can get is sore, anxious or disappointed. Sex must be physically the safest of all human activities (leaving out social repercussions). You can have infinite variety to suit every taste. But one needs a steady basic diet of quiet, night-and-morning matrimonial intercourse to stand this experimentation on, simply because, contrary to popular ideas, the more regular sex a couple has the higher the deliberately-contrived peaks – just as the more you cook routinely, the better and the more reliable banquets you can stage.

Finally, the people we are addressing are the adventurous and uninhibited lovers who want to find the limits of their ability to enjoy sex That means we take some things for granted – having intercourse naked and spending time over it; being able and willing to make it last, up to a whole afternoon on occasion; having privacy and washing facilities; not being scared of things like genital kisses; not being obsessed with one sexual trick to the exclusion of all others, and, of course, loving each other.

This book is about love as well as sex as the title implies: you don't get high quality sex on any other basis – either you love each other before you come to want it, or, if you happen to get it, you love each other because of it, or both. No point in arguing this, but just as you can't cook without heat you can't make love without feedback (which may be the reason we say 'make love' rather than 'make sex'). Sex is the one place where we today can learn to treat people as people. Feedback means the right mixture of stop and go, tough and tender, exertion and affection. This comes by empathy and long mutual knowledge. Anyone who *expects* to get this in a first attempt with a stranger is an optimist, or a neurotic – if he does, it is what used to be called love at first sight, and isn't expendable: 'skill', or variety, are no substitutes. Also one can't teach tenderness.

This is a book about valid sexual behaviors, plus a certain amount about how and why they work. It isn't a dictionary: in particular we've avoided a lot of the name-entries attached to particular sorts of performance at the start of the century – the reason is that they are largely out of date. Rather than sticking on labels like narcissism or sadomasochism, biologists and psychiatrists now tend to start by looking at actual behaviors and seeing what use they are or what they signify. Lump names are a handy shorthand, but they tend to be offputting, especially when very general human behaviors get a label which makes them sound like an illness, and they tend to trigger pointless collectors'-piece arguments, for example whether 'women are naturally masochistic' because they get penetrated rather than doing the penetrating.

We haven't started with a short lecture on the biology and psychology of human sex: instead we've put a little about it into the various entries. Most people now know that man's 'sexuality' starts at birth and runs continuously from mother-child to man-woman relations, that it involves some periods of programmed anxiety about the genitals ('castration fears') which probably served originally to stop young apes from falling foul of their fathers, but which, in man, are building stones for a lot of other adult behaviors; and that the wide range of human sex needs of all kinds controlled by this unique developmental background – long childhood, close mother-child contact but a taboo on mother-child or father-child sex, close pair-bonding which centers in sexual play, the way bird pair-formation centers in nest-building and display (this is the phenomenon more often described as love), and so on. Without going into details we've mentioned throughout the book how parts of this human background fit into the pattern of what humans enjoy sexually. Most human sex behaviors 'mean' a whole range of different things (the in-word is that they are 'overdetermined'– for examples of what this means in practice see what we've written about *Clothes*, for instance).

A little theory makes sex more interesting, more comprehensible, and less scarey – too much is a put-down, especially as you're likely to get it out of perspective and become a spectator of your own performance. If you have really troublesome hangups you need an expert to hold the mirror for you and go personally into what they mean – self-adhesive labels are actively unhelpful. All humans are sadistic, narcissistic, masochistic, bisexual and what have you – if you stuck on all the labels you would look like a cabin trunk. What matters is whether any of the behaviors in which you engage are bothering you or other people – if so, they are a useful pointer to what the problem is, but no more than that.

The starting point of all lovemaking is close bodily contact. Love has been defined as the harmony of two souls and the contact of two epidermes. It is also, from our infancy, the starting point of human relationships and needs. Our culture ('Anglo-Saxon'), after several centuries of intense taboos on many such contacts – between friends, between males – which are used by other cultures, has cut down 'intimacy' based on bodily contact to parent-child and lover-lover situations. We're getting over this taboo, or at least the part which has spilled over into baby-raising and explicit lovemaking, but coupled with our other cultural reservation, which says that play and fantasy are only safe for children, it has dealt us a bad hand for really full and personal sex. Our idea of sex wouldn't be recognizable to some other cultures, though our range of choice is the widest ever. For a start it's over-genital: 'sex' for our culture means putting the penis in the vagina. Man's whole skin is a genital organ. As to touching, proximity and so on, see Desmond Morris's brilliant account in *Intimate Behavior*, which catalogues our hangups. Good sex is about the only adult remedy for these.

There isn't too much point in crying over cultural spilt milk. *Our* sex repertoire has to be geared to us as we are, not to Trobriand Islanders (who have their own different hangups). *We* need extensive sex play which is centered in intercourse and in doing things. At the same time we might as well plan our menu so that we learn to use the rest of our equipment. That includes our whole skin surface, our feelings of identity, aggression and so on, and all of our fantasy needs. Luckily, sex behavior in humans is enormously elastic (it has had to be, or we wouldn't be here), and also nicely geared to help us express most of the needs which society or our upbringing have corked up. Elaboration in sex is something we need rather specially (though it isn't confined to our sort of society) and it has the advantage that if we really make it work it makes us more, not less, receptive to each other as people. This is the answer to anyone who thinks that conscious effort to increase our sex range is 'mechanical' or a substitute for treating each other as people – we may start that way, but it's an excellent entry to learning that we are people – probably the only one our sort of society can really use at the moment. There may be other places we can learn to express all of ourselves, and do it mutually, but there aren't many.

Those are our assumptions. Granted this feedback and

mutual exploration, there are two modes of sex, the duet and the solo, and a good concert alternates between them. The duet is a cooperative effort aiming at simultaneous orgasm, or at least one orgasm each, and complete, untechnically-planned let-go. This in fact needs skill, and can be built up from more calculated 'love-play' until doing the right thing for both of you becomes fully automatic. This is the basic sexual meal. The solo, by contrast, is when one partner is the player and the other the instrument; the aim of the player is to produce results on the other's pleasure experience as extensive, unexpected and generally wild as his or her skill allows – to blow them out of themselves. The player doesn't lose control, though he or she can get wildly excited by what is happening to the other. The instrument *does* lose control – in fact, with a responsive instrument and a skillful performer, this is the concerto situation – if it ends in an uncontrollable ensemble, so much the better. All the elements of music and the dance get into this scene – rhythm, mounting tension, tantalization, even actual aggression: 'I'm like the executioner,' said the lady in the Persian poem, 'but where he inflicts intolerable pain I will only make you die of pleasure.' There is indeed an element of aggression or infliction in the solo mode, which is why some lovers dislike it and others overdo it, but no major lovemaking is complete without some solo passages.

The antique idea of the woman as passive and the man as performer used to ensure that he would show off playing solos on her, and some marriage manuals perpetuate this idea. In a more liberated scene she is herself the soloist par excellence, whether in getting him excited to start with, or in controlling him and showing off all her skills. In fact there is only one really unmusical situation, and that is the reverse of a real solo, where one uses the other to obtain satisfaction, without any attempt at mutuality. True, one may say, 'Do it yourself this time,' as a quick finish, but it is no more than that.

In the old world extended solo techniques have never quite died as a male skill: in Europe at one time calculated solo skill among women was supposed to be limited to prostitutes (most of whom conspicuously lack it, for lack of empathy). Now it is on the way back, starting halfheartedly with 'petting to climax,' but getting today to be a polite accomplishment: we shall probably have extension courses soon. This, as usual, will likely go too far, and become a substitute for full, let-go intercourse – whereas in fact it's a preparation, supplement, overture, bridging operation, tailpiece, interlude. The solo-given orgasm is unique, however – neither bigger nor smaller in either sex than in a full duet, but different. We've heard both sexes call it 'sharper but not so round,' and most people who have experienced both like to alternate them; it is also quite different from self-stimulation, which most people like occasionally too. Trying to say how they differ is a little like describing wines. Differ they do, however, and much depends on cultivating and alternating them.

Solo devices are not, of course, necessarily separate from intercourse. Apart from leading into it there are many coital solos – for the woman astride, for example – while mutual masturbation or genital kisses can be fully-fledged duets. Nor is it anything to do with 'clitoral' versus 'vaginal' orgasm (this is only a crass anatomical way of trying to verbalize a real difference), since the man feels the same distinction, and you can get a roaring solo orgasm from the skin of the fingertips, the breasts, the soles of the feet, or the earlobes of a receptive woman (less commonly extragenitally in the man). Coition which ought to be mutual but gives a solo feeling (to her) is what people who talk about 'clitoral orgasm' are trying as a rule to verbalize. Solo-response can be electrifyingly extreme in the quietest people. Skillfully handled by someone who doesn't stop for yells of murder, but does know when to stop, a woman can get orgasm after orgasm, and a man can be kept hanging just short of climax to the limit of human endurance.

Toplevel enjoyment doesn't *have* to be varied, it just often is. In fact, being stuck rigidly with one sex technique usually means anxiety. In this book we have not, for example, gone heavily on things like coital postures. The non-freak ones are now familiar to most people from writing and pictures if not from trial – the freak ones, as a rule, one could think of spontaneously, but few of them have marked advantages except as a spectator sport. Moreover, the technique of straight intercourse, which needs a suspension of self-observation, doesn't lend itself to treatment in writing, except for elementary students. This explains the apparent emphasis in our book on extras – the sauces and pickles. Most of these are psychologically and biologically geared to cover specific human needs, often left over from a 'civilized' childhood. Individuals who, through a knot in their psyche, are obliged to *live* on sauce and pickle only are unfortunate in missing the most sustaining part of the meal – kinks and exclusive obsessions in sex are very like living exclusively on horseradish sauce through allergy to beef; fear of horseradish sauce as indigestible, unnecessary and immature is another hangup, namely puritanism. As to our choice of needs and/or problems, we've based it on a good many years of listening to people.

In writing descriptively about sex it is hard not to be solemn, however unsolemnly we play in bed. In fact, one of the things still missing from the 'new sexual freedom' is the unashamed ability to use sex as play – in this, psychoanalytic ideas of maturity are nearly as much to blame as oldstyle moralisms about what is normal or perverse. We are all immature, and have anxieties and aggressions. Coital play, like dreaming, is probably man's programmed way of dealing acceptably with these, just as children express their fears and aggressions in games. If they play at Indian tortures, out of jealousy of their little brother or the opposite sex, we don't call that sadism: adults are unfortunately afraid of playing games, of dressing up, of acting scenes. It makes them self-conscious: something horrid might get out.

Bed is the place to play all the games you have ever wanted to play, at the play-level – if adults could become less selfconscious about such 'immature' needs we should have fewer deeply anxious and committed fetishists creating a sense of community to enable them to do their thing without feeling isolated. We heard of a frogman who used to make his wife sleep in rubber bedsheets; he had to become a frogman for real, because dressing in a diving-suit for kicks was embarrassing and made him look odd. If we were able to transmit the sense of play which is essential to a full, enterprising and healthily immature view of sex between committed people, we would be performing a mitzvah: people who play flagellation games and are excited by them bother nobody, provided they don't turn off a partner who finds the scenario frightening. People who enact similar aggressions outside the bedroom are apt to end up at My Lai or Belsen. The aim of this book is pleasure, not psychiatry, but we suspect that the two coincide. Play is one function of sexual elaboration – playfulness is a part of love which could well be the major contribution of the Aquarian revolution to human happiness. Hence the association with pregenital and immature sauces and pickles.

But still the main dish is loving, unselfconscious intercourse – long, frequent, varied, ending with both parties satisfied but not so full they can't face another light course, and another meal in a few hours. The *pièce de résistance* is the good old face-to-face matrimonial, the finishing-off position, with mutual orgasm, and starting with a full day or night of ordinary tenderness. Other ways of making love are special in various ways, and the changes of timbre are infinitely varied – complicated ones are for special occasions, or special uses like holding off an over-quick male orgasm, or are things which, like pepper steak, are stunning once a year but not dietary.

If you don't like our repertoire or if it doesn't square with yours, never mind. The aim of *The Joy of Sex* is to stimulate your creative imagination. You can preface your own ideas with 'this is how *we* play it,' and play it your way. But by that time, when you have tried all your own creative sexual fantasies, you won't need books. Sex books can only suggest techniques to encourage you to experiment.

There are after all only two 'rules' in good sex, apart from the obvious one of not doing things which are silly, antisocial or dangerous. One is 'don't do anything you don't really enjoy,' and the other is 'find out your partner's needs and don't balk them if you can help it.' In other words, a good giving and taking relationship depends on a compromise (so does going to a show – if you both want the same thing, fine: if not, take turns and don't let one partner always dictate). This can be easier than it sounds, because unless your partner wants something you find actively off-putting, real lovers get a reward not only from their own satisfactions but from seeing the other respond and become satisfied. Most wives who don't like Chinese food will eat it occasionally for the pleasure of seeing a Sinophile husband enjoy it, and vice versa. Partners who won't do this over specific sex needs are usually balking, not because they've tried it and it's a turn-off (many experimental dishes turn out nicer than you expected), but simply through ignorance of the range of human needs, plus being scared if these include things like aggression, cultivating extragenital sensation, or play-acting, which the last half-century's social mythology pretended weren't there. Reading a full list of the unscheduled accessory sex behaviors which some normal people find helpful might be thought a necessary preliminary to any extended sex relationship, particularly marriage if you really intend to stay with it, but so far the books haven't helped much in this respect. If anything they've scared people rather than instructed them.

Couples should match up their needs and preferences (though people don't find these out at once). You won't get to some of our suggestions or understand them until you've learned to respond. It's a mistake to run so long as walking is such an enchanting and new experience, and you may be happy pedestrians who match automatically. Most people who marry rightly prefer to try themselves out and play themselves in. Where a rethink really helps is at the point where you've got used to each other socially (sex needs aren't the only ones which need matching up between people who live together) and feel that the surface needs repolishing. If you think that sexual relations are overrated, it does need repolishing, and you haven't paid enough attention to the wider use of your sexual equipment as a way of communicating totally. The traditional American expedient at the point where the surface gets dull is to trade in the relationship and start all over in an equally uninstructed attempt with someone else, on the offchance of getting a better match-up by random choice. This is emotionally wasteful and you usually repeat the same mistakes.

One specific group of readers deserves a special note. If you happen to be disabled in any way, don't stop reading. It's particularly important for you to realise that there are more ways of skinning a cat than one. In sex, as in other activities, a physical disability is an obstacle to be outwitted. In counseling disabled people, one repeatedly finds that the real disability isn't a mechanical problem, but a mistaken idea that there is only one 'right' – or enjoyable – way to have sex. The best technique with this book is probably to go through it with your partner marking off the things you *can* do. Then pick something appealing which you think you can't quite do, and see if there is a strategy you can develop together. Talking to other couples where one partner has a problem similar to yours is another resource.

The implications of AIDS

When this book was first written, in 1973, sex was an extremely safe occupation, and any hazards attending it were social and emotional. The major venereal diseases, especially syphilis, which had caused death and disability for the previous four hundred years, were curable: those which had replaced them, nonspecific urethritis and herpes, though troublesome, were not life-threatening. This picture was changed in the late 1970s by the introduction to Western societies of the disease AIDS – Acquired Immunodeficiency Syndrome. The arrival of this disease totally alters the sexual landscape. There is a full discussion of AIDS on page 251. Read it, preferably before you read anything else in this book.

What does AIDS mean to the sexually active adult, and how does it modify the advice we give? The simplest way of looking at it is that there are now two populations – those who do not carry the virus and those, luckily still a small minority, who do. Between any two people who are virus-free, all sexual activities are as safe as they ever were. This applies to the vast majority of married couples. If either partner is a carrier, then virtually no sexual activity, other than mutual masturbation, is safe. "Safe" sex ideally involves staying clear of any potential carrier – this means not only bisexual males and intravenous drug users but also those who may have been the partners of a high-risk subject during the last ten years.

That said, there is no occasion for panic, or for losing out on the joy of sex – simply for informed caution. A crimp on the candy-store exploitation of sexual freedom may give us time and motive to redevelop its affectional side. Now read on.

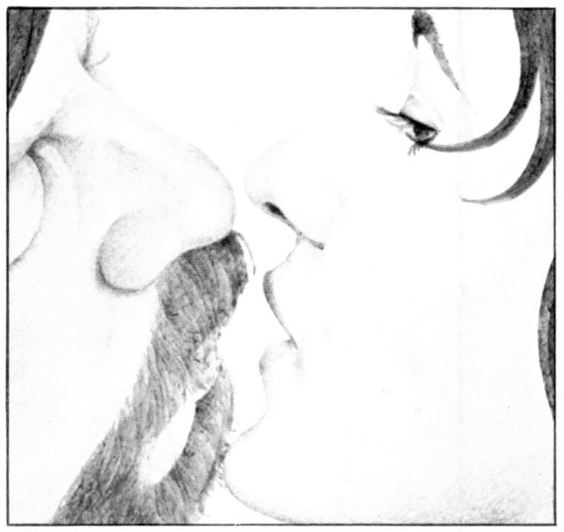

The Art of Making Love

The whole joy of sex-with-love is that there are no rules, so long as you enjoy, and the choice is practically unlimited.'

'You don't get high-quality sex without love and feedback. Feedback means the right mixture of stop and go, tough and tender, exertion and affection.'

'Bed is the right place to play all the games you have ever wanted to play. This is essential to a full, enterprising and healthily immature view of sex between committed people. Take off your shell along with your clothes.'

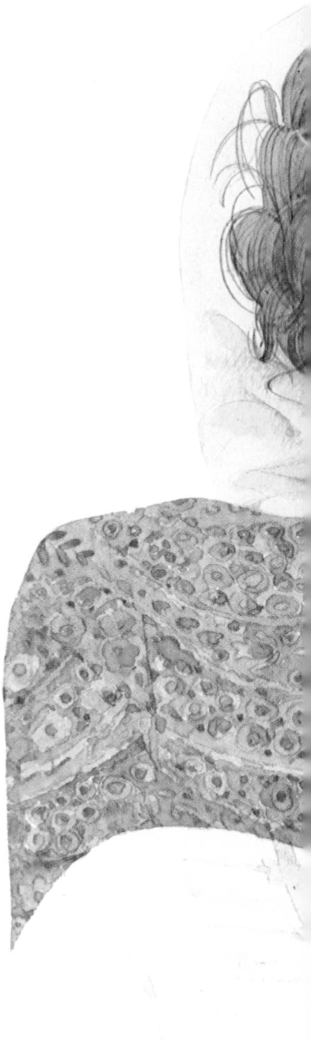

'There are only two guidelines in good sex, "Don't do anything you don't really enjoy", and "Find out your partner's needs and don't balk them if you can help it."'

'Finding out someone else's needs and your own, and how to express them in bed, is not only interesting and educative, but rewarding, and what sexual love is all about.'

'We must learn to use the whole of our skin surface, our feelings of identity, aggression and so on, and all our fantasy needs.'

'A woman's greatest asset after her beauty is her natural perfume—it comes from the whole of her, hair, skin, breasts, armpits, genitals. The smell and feel of a man's skin probably have more to do with sexual attraction than any other single feature.'

'Sex ought to be a wholly satisfying link between two affectionate people from which they emerge unanxious, rewarded and ready for more.'

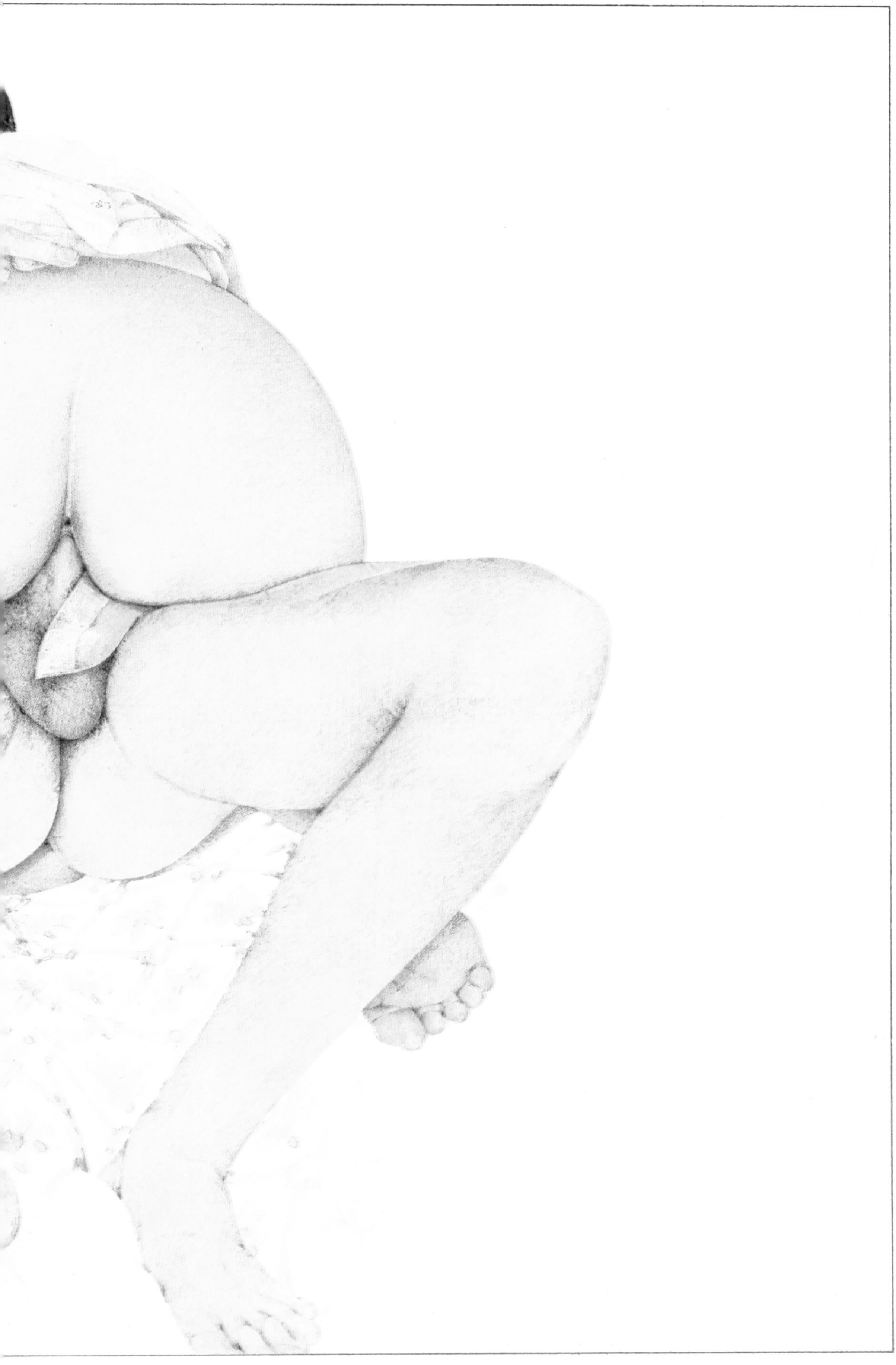

'Women who have really learned to enjoy sex are usually fascinated by their partner's penis, as men are by women's breasts, shape, odor and feel, and learn to play with it fully and skillfully. Good hand and mouth work practically guarantee a good partner.'

'Tenderness does not exclude extremely violent games (though many people neither need nor want these) but it is shown fully in the way you touch each other.'

'Women often fail to use enough pressure, especially in handwork, though the light variety is a sensation on its own. Start very gently, making full use of the skin surface and work up. Male strength, on the other hand, is a turn-on in sex, but it isn't expressed in clumsiness, bear hugs and brute force.

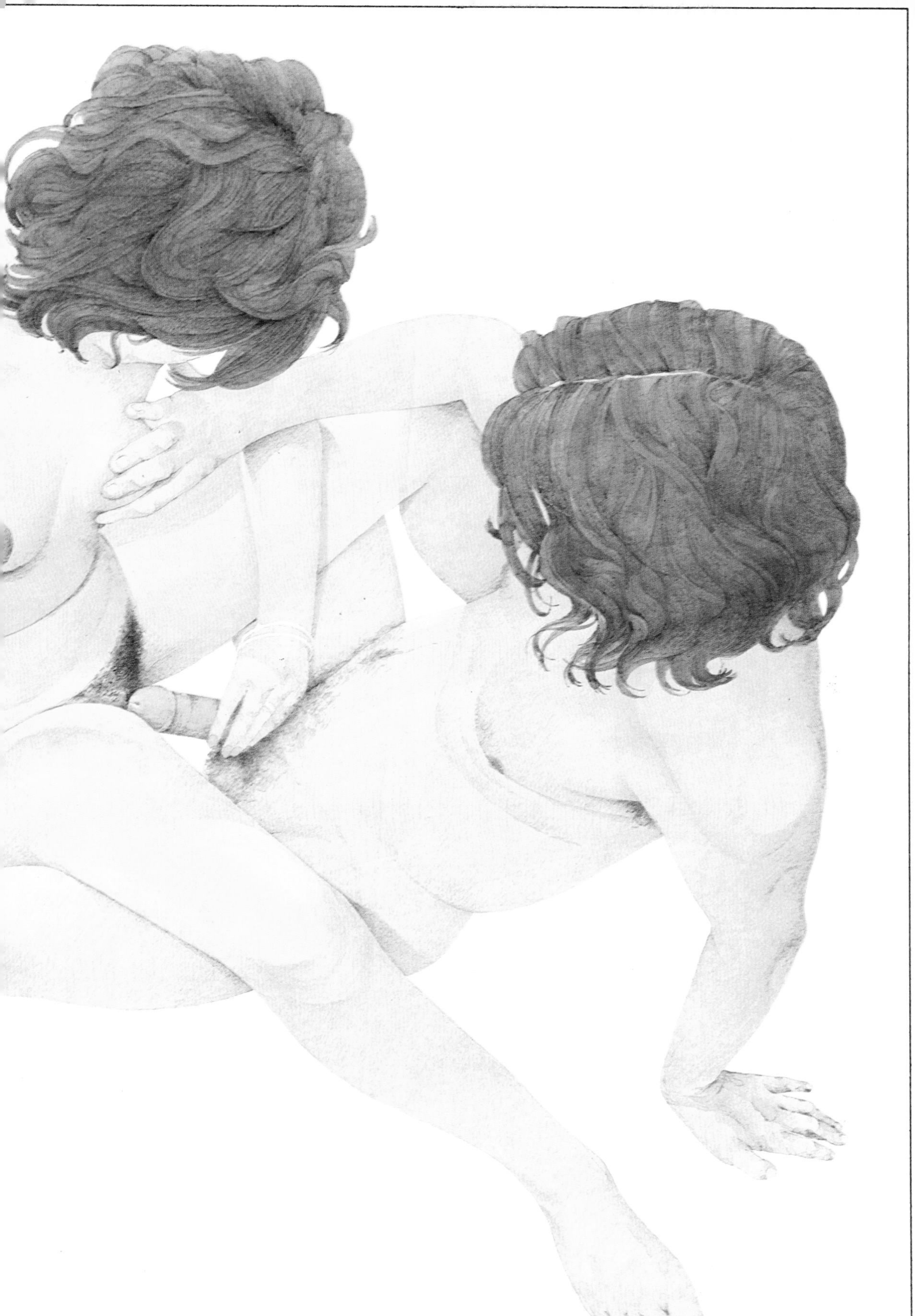

'Male sexual response is far brisker and more automatic than women's: it is triggered by *things*. Your clothes, breasts, odor, etc. aren't what he loves instead of you–simply the things he needs to set sex in motion to express love.'

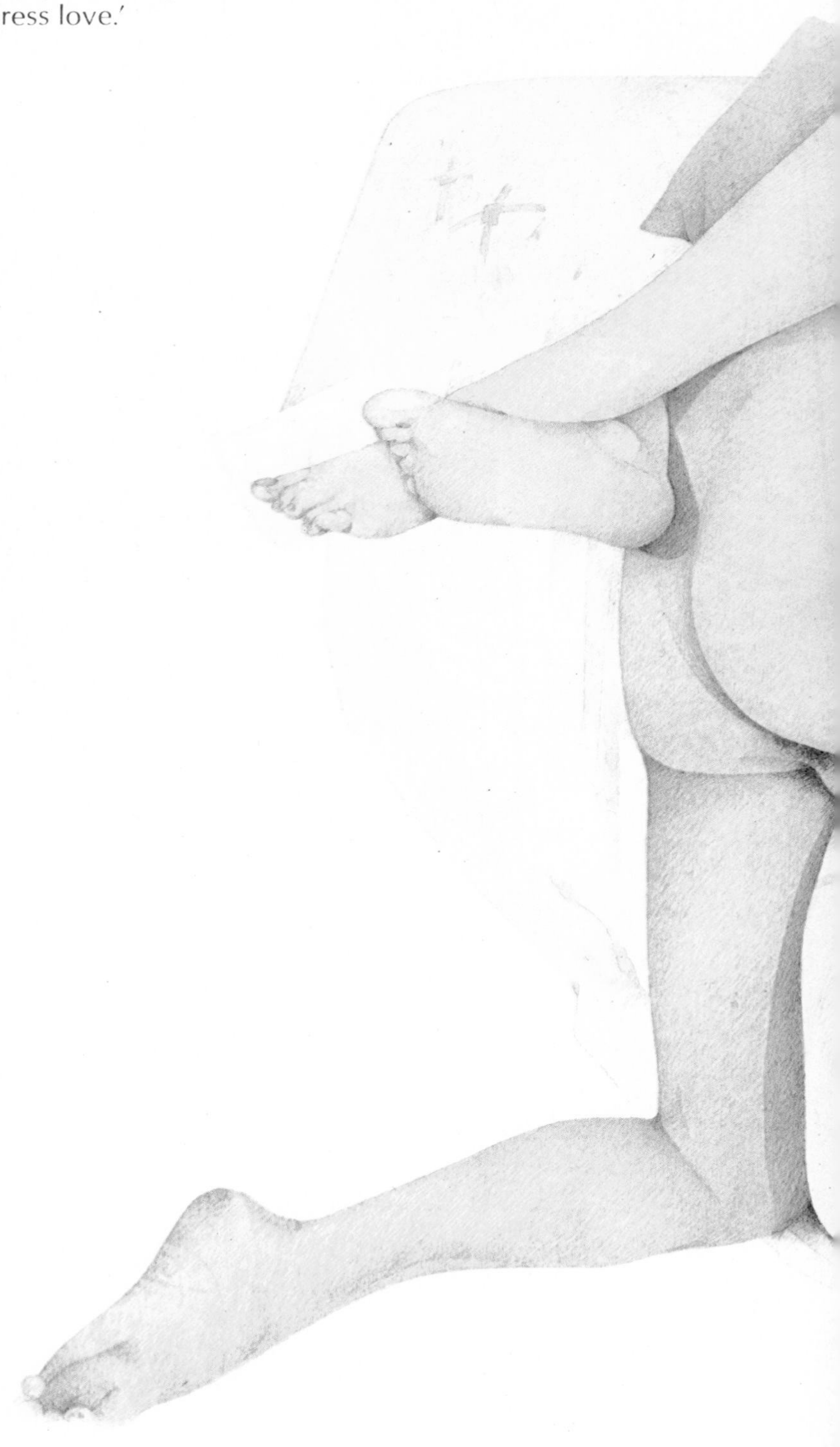

'Uninhibited partners will tell each other about their fantasies (try free-associating just before orgasm if you are shy). Really communicating partners look for them and put them on the menu unannounced–there is no more complete communication.'

'Women probably differ sexually more than men. Never assume that you don't need to relearn for each person.'

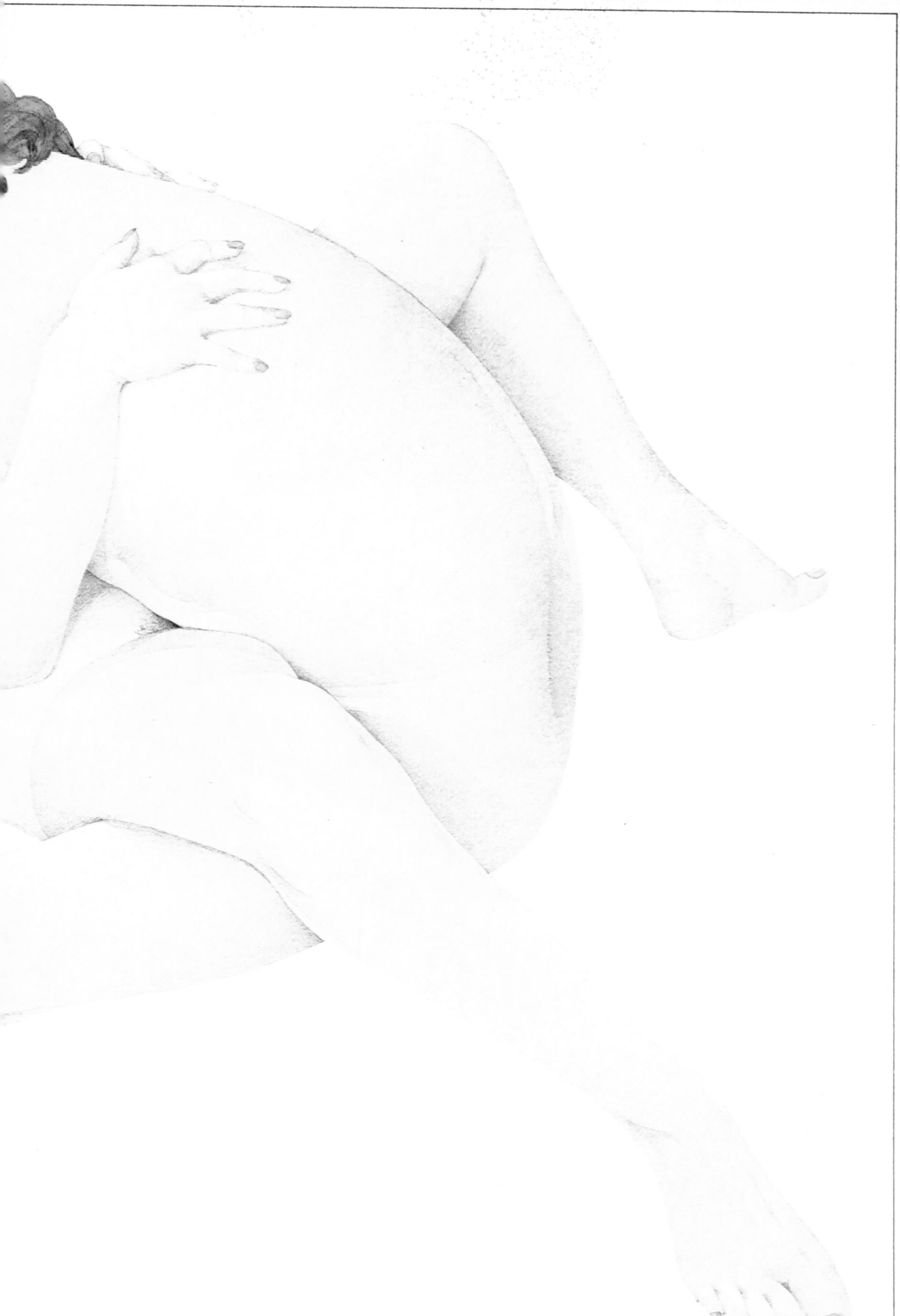

‘Planning and thinking about sex to come is part of love. So is lying together in complete luxury afterwards.’

'Cordon bleu sex is the extra one can get from comparing notes, using some imagination, trying way-out or new experiences, when one is already making satisfying love and wants to go from there.'

Starters
the basic ingredients

beds

Still the most important piece of domestic sexual equipment. Really enthusiastic sex usually involves at one time or another almost every piece of furniture in the house, at least experimentally, but the bed is its commonest venue. Most beds on the market are designed by people who think they are intended to sleep on. The problem arises from the fact that the ideal surface for most kinds of intercourse needs to be rather harder than is comfortable for a whole night's sleep. One solution is to have two beds, one for sex and the other for sleeping, but this is a counsel of luxury, and in any case the need to move disrupts the best part of the night, the total relaxation which follows complete love.

The best advice is probably to settle for a compromise and have a mattress on the floor as well. Enormous or circular beds look suggestive but have no real advantages over a full-size double bed. There are a few points we would consider before giving a seal of approval. First, since one uses the sides as well as the surface, the height needs to be right. The top of the mattress should be exactly level with the man's pubic bone – then, if you put your partner on or over it, she will be at the right height from in front or from behind. For some operations, especially bondage scenes if you like them, bedposts are essential, preferably tall ones, like those which hold up the canopy of old European beds, but not, for choice, a foot-board, as you may want to use the end edge to start with, moving directly to full-length. Massive old bed-frames have great advantages, in that they don't rattle or collapse. The mattress needs to be as hard as you can tolerate for comfortable sleep. Anything less forfeits the chief sexual joy of living and sleeping together – the fact that you can take one another at any hour of the night when both want it, and relax together immediately afterwards. If you have room, have a single bed as well, in case either partner is sick and feels more comfortable solo – twin beds have no place in a full sexual relationship.

Beside the bed itself you need four pillows – two very hard to go under the buttocks, and two soft, to sleep on. The room must be warm at all times of the year – warm enough to sleep without getting chilled and without bedclothes if you wish. Electric blankets shouldn't therefore be necessary – the sort you lie upon will in any case not stand up to sexual intercourse. Unless you are very prosperous and it excites you to set up a special 'sex room,' bedroom chairs and stools can be chosen without too much ostentation to complete the necessary equipment for all eventualities (see *Equipment*), together with a soft rug, soft enough to be really comfortable for the underneath party, and mirrors. You also need enough bedside drawers to hold extras which you may need on impulse without having to get up and find them – lubricants, contraceptives, vibrators and so on. A well-designed bedroom can be a sexual gymnasium without it being embarrassing to let elderly relatives leave their coats there.

Water-beds are a relative innovation. They can indeed produce extraordinary sensations, and they have a natural period of resonance which tends to take over – one has to move in their rhythm, but this itself is a stimulating constraint. Expensive – best kept for the odd extramural occasion when you re-honeymoon in a hotel room that's fitted with one. With the spread of inflatables we may see a whole range of new sexual furniture-surfaces in the next few years.

birdsong at morning

What your partner says in orgasm should never be quoted at him or her – it can be played back when you are both in a suitable mood, but only then. It is the one time when people are spiritually most naked. There is a striking consistency, over ages and continents, in what women say in orgasm. Japanese, Indian, French and English all babble about dying ('Some of them,' said Abbé Brantome, 'yell out "I'm dying," but I think they enjoy that sort of death'), about Mother (they often call for her at the critical moment) and about religion even if they are atheists. This is natural – orgasm is the most religious moment of our lives, of which all other mystical kicks are a mere translation. Men are apt to growl like bears, or utter aggressive monosyllables like 'In, In, In!' The wife of The Leopard in the novel used to yell out 'Gesumaria!' and there are an infinite variety of sounds short of speech. Why these are so charming in both sexes it's hard to say. The Indians classified them, compared them to bird-cries, and warned how easily parrots and mynahs pick them up, with bad social vibrations when they repeat the lesson – hence no parrots in the love chamber. It is important to learn to read them while enjoying the music, and in particular to know when 'Stop' means stop and when it means 'For God's sake go on.' This is an individual language. You need simply to be a sensitive field observer.

Some of the 'words' are common – a gasp when a touch registers right, a shuddering out-breath when you follow through. Women, and some men, talk continuously in a sort of baby-whisper, or repeat four-letter words of the most unlikely kind – some you can hear several blocks away, while others still are dead silent or laugh or sob disconcertingly. Of the really noisy performers, some like to be allowed to yell, while others like to be gagged, or stuff their hair in their mouths in the style of a Japanese print (Japanese houses have paper partitions). Men can be equally noisy but are not usually so continuously vocal.

BEDS *overleaf*
Still the most important piece of sexual equipment.

The important points are these – in mutual, let-go intercourse, make as much noise as you like. It is curious that we need to write this down, but house and hotel designers haven't yet realized it – they all seem to be married to noiseless, childless partners, or they'd avoid plasterboard. Totally silent intercourse, with each partner's hand firmly over the other's mouth, can be fun if you simply can't risk being overheard. Another variation is to have two kinds of intercourse at once – straight, gentle coitus, while each partner describes some other much wilder proceeding in fantasy, perhaps for next time. The fantasy can be as wild as you like. This is the place to experience things you can't possibly act out, and to learn your partner's fantasy needs. These fantasies can be heterosexual, homosexual, incestuous, tender, wild or bloodthirsty – don't block, and don't be afraid of your partner's fantasy; this is a dream you are in. But be careful about recording such dreams, as they can be disturbing at the daylight level. Let them go with the release of orgasm.

Lovers who really know one another won't be frightened, nor take advantage. If you do find this double nakedness disturbing, set rules – practicable or happy fantasies only; never, never refer to pillow-talk in anger later on ('I always knew you were a lesbian, etc.'). This is contemptible. Fantasy apart, the only really disturbing manifestation of love-music is when the woman laughs uncontrollably – some do. Don't be up-tight about this. She isn't laughing at you.

birth control

This is the discovery which more than any other makes carefree sex possible. Before that one had to be infertile to enjoy the kind of extended sexual play which is now available to everyone who is reasonably housed (and which will eventually be available to everyone, together with control over their fertility). No other method being wholly reliable, women who have once experienced the security of the Pill and discovered the play-function of sex are not going to return to the old insecurity. The Pill is still the safest and best method, and a safer drug than aspirin. The loop, and similar indwelling appliances, which prevent implantation, don't suit everyone but work well for some. If you can't use these, it is back to the cap plus a good chemical spermicide. Some women find capping themselves before sex offputting and complain that half the sensation is lost and they get consumer resistance from their man (though if it is the only method she can use, don't make a song and dance about it; that won't change anything and will make her apprehensive); other women, given privacy and washing facilities, don't mind, though both caps and spermicides can spoil both the feel of the

BIRTH CONTROL *opposite*
The discovery which more than any other makes carefree sex possible.

vagina and the genital odor, but usually not seriously. The man should check with his finger that the cap really is over the cervix as part of loveplay. One point about the Pill is that by turning off the normal acid vaginal secretion, it makes it far easier to catch VD or thrush, even from very slight genital or oral contact.

Condoms are a useful protection – moreover the very

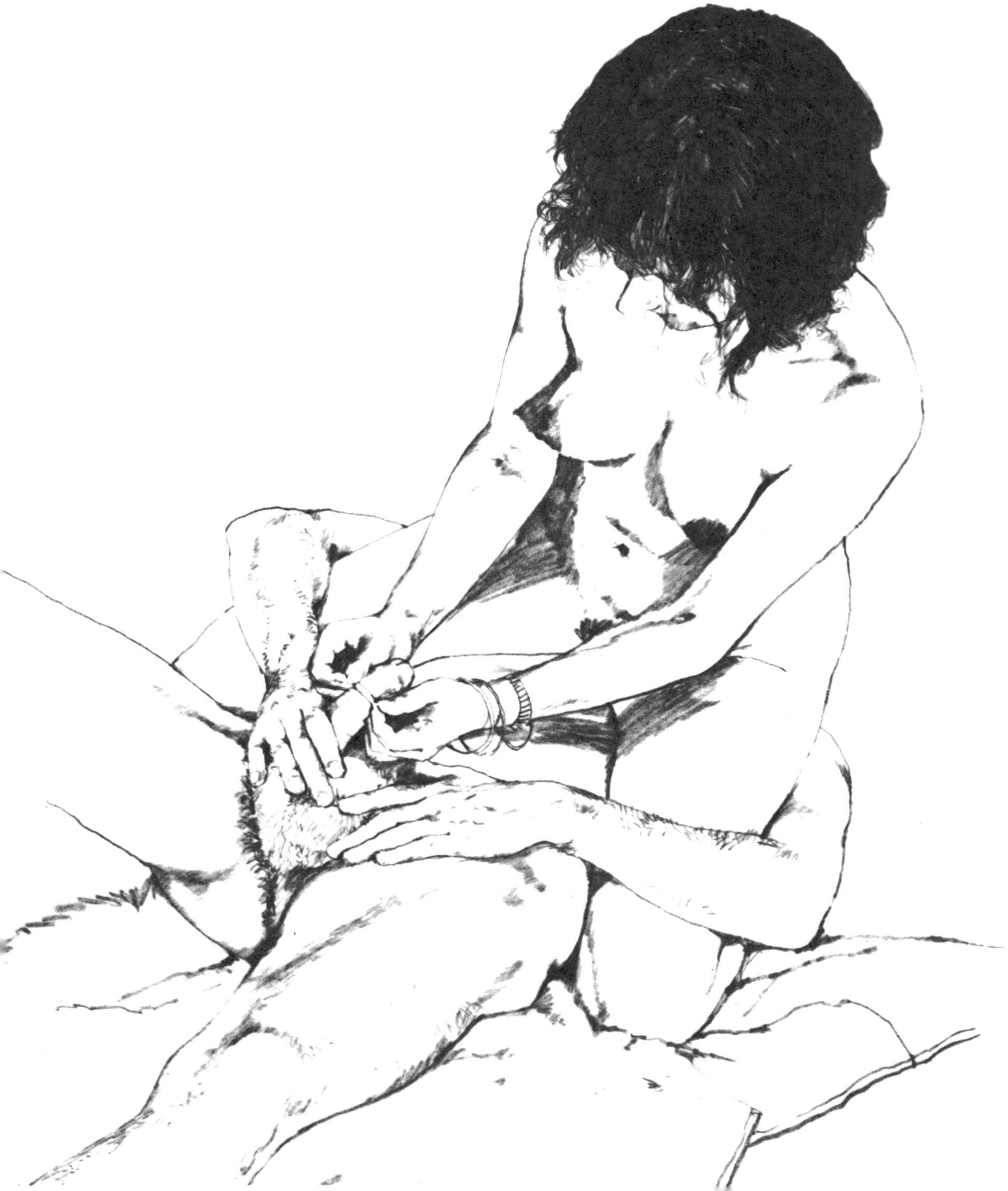

manipulation involved in letting the woman put one on her man excites some people: thin or 'gossamer' condoms can slow down some over-quick ejaculators. Uncircumcised men, and men with a pointed rather than round-ended glans, can't usually use the teat-ended kind – in this case ask for the round-ended variety. The various knobbed or otherwise decorated sheaths sold to vary vaginal sensation are not reliable or leakproof as contraceptives (see *Gadgets and Gimmicks*), so don't trust them. See *Rubber*. Many people dislike the feeling of no contact.

Finally, never take a risk. Wanted children can limit the sex play of adults by being around; this is a small price to pay if one does want them, and privacy can usually be arranged. Unwanted children are the one moral and ecological offense which nothing today can excuse. In an emergency douche thoroughly at once with soapy water, put spermicidal foam or jelly well into the vagina, rubbing it over the cervix, and see a sympathetic doctor next day – implantation can usually be prevented. But such emergencies shouldn't arise.

The so-called rhythm method ('Vatican Roulette') doesn't merit serious consideration. Not only is it highly unreliable, but it may well account for the slightly higher incidence of abnormal babies among Catholic users through stale eggs getting fertilized.

clothes

It is part of the recovery from puritanism that most people now make love naked and most lovers sleep naked. Clothes, when they are worn, are there to be taken off – making love can very well start by undressing one another, or by one partner stripping for the other. Womens' magazines and phonograph records now give what amount to courses on burlesk-type stripping as a conventional turn-on for the man, but this use of clothing *is* a conventional routine – for a start, it need not be the woman who strips. Each partner, moreover, should practice removing the clothes of the other sex without clumsiness or hold-ups, and preferably with one hand.

Clothes and their removal as a kick have, if one wants to be serious about it, a whole biology in terms of 'releasers,' a releaser being what turns somebody on. The releasers for the male are garments which emphasize breasts and buttocks or, like tight panties, 'simplify the outline' of the female. Women are not so dependent on this sort of concrete signalling – having the right man is their chief releaser, a social and emotional one – but many of them have preferences. A well-filled jockstrap, or a man naked from the waist down, can act as part of the preliminary scenery, and habitual nudity in bed and about the house doesn't blunt these natural reactions.

Quite apart from this, some people react very strongly to particular clothing-situations on a lock and key basis – usually these are men, occasionally women. This is the

CLOTHES *above*
If your man has a physical turn-on he will love you more the more skillfully you sense and use it.

basis of kinky fashions. Exactly what works on a particular person is highly individual; in this case he often knows and will ask for it. These clothing turn-ons work exactly as a salmon-fly works for the salmon. A bunch of feathers doesn't look like anything the salmon eats (and when one fishes for them at salmon run they aren't feeding in any case) but it combines a whole range of unrelated stimuli which excite curiosity, aggression, and enough other fishy emotions to provoke a strike. Human turn-ons are equally complicated. How they become programmed in a given individual isn't known, but there is an identifiable repertoire of components, like the repertoire of feathers one can use in a lure from which most of these stimuli are made. Super-skin is one – tightness, shininess and texture: super-genitalness – firm pubis, space between the thighs, extra pubic hair; mild threat – blackness, leatheriness, sadistic-looking buckles; submission – tied-upness, slave-bangles; and the suggestion of genitals elsewhere – red lips, emphasis on the feet, which have 'some symmetry with that which thou dost crave;' shininess and tinkling – earrings, chains: woman-ness – tiny waist, big breasts and buttocks, long hair. And so on. Humans love to fool around with the body-image and alter it.

Others are textures – wetness, fur, rubber, plastic, leather. Most males, but fewer females, respond slightly to all of these, and this is another basis of sexual fashion. Some respond so strongly to a few that they don't hit full sexual function without them, but the selection is highly individual, far more so than taste in food, and to tie your fly you have to know your salmon. Every such lure has at least three layers – tight, shiny, black leather is a superskin with a womany smell – it also suggests acceptance of the aggression of sex. Tiny, tight g-strings stress but hide her pussy, hold her perfume so she can be kissed through them, and suggest wicked, sexy girls rather than chaste sister-figures. Corsets make her hourglass-shaped and suggest tightness and helplessness. And so on. A horse, seen from behind, is a male 'releaser'– it has long hair, big buttocks and a teetering walk. A cow isn't.

Prostitutes, who know all this elementary biology, use all these lures, or dress one of them and catch fish who respond to it. Women in love, unless they happen to have similar turn-ons themselves, have long tended to be a bit scared of them as kinky, and, in particular, to feel 'he's in love with gloves or black lingerie, not with me.' This is the wrong approach. If your man has a physical turn-on, it has nothing to do with his valuation of you, and he will love you more the more skillfully you sense and use it. Turn-ons are not choosable – he has them or he hasn't. If he has them, you can catch your favorite fish at every cast. If he likes long hair you'd grow it – you might even

CLOTHES *opposite and overleaf*
If he likes you to look like a cross between a snake and a seal, wear what he gives you. If you like him a particular way, see he knows it.

try to make yourself slim, or blonde, to attract him. You can't make yourself tall, or beautiful, unless you are that way already. But if he has a preference you *can* meet you are unstoppable. The 'you' part is in letting him see you sense it and meet it. If you too have turn-ons, tell him, and use them.

Accordingly, the same tactic applies here as for sexual fantasies generally. Uninhibited partners will tell each other about them (try free-associating just before orgasm if you are shy). Really communicating partners look for them and put them on the menu unannounced – there is no more complete communication. As with other fantasies, if the thing itself doesn't turn you on equally, the response will. Infantile, symbolic, fetishistic and generally wild fantasies are part of love, and only a problem if they take up too much time and start spoiling the full reciprocity of sex (see *Fetishes*). For most people they don't, and a great many people of both sexes have them. No matter how odd, they are usually rewarding – more so than ties or candy as anniversary presents. People are still rightly shy about their innermost mind-life; if your partner seems preoccupied and is blocked over this, ask him or her to give you the thing he or she would most like to see you wearing when you come to lovemaking, and wear it. If you really can't share these essential kids' games or communicate such turn-ons for fear of each other's reactions you shouldn't be in bed together at all. Noncommunication, not normal human fantasy, lands people in the divorce court for incompatibility; a fantasy which really turns you off is subject for discussion and adjustment through make-believe, and just as men tend to be programmed for concrete signals, women are programmed to pick up the kind of signal which turns their partner on – after a few big orgasms together all but the oddest fantasies get to be shared.

So, if he likes you to look like a cross between a snake and a seal, wear what he gives you. If you like him a particular way, see he knows it. Some women are bothered that a man who occasionally likes them to dress him in their clothes is unvirile (it causes less anxiety the other way round). But all of us have a person of the opposite sex inside us – Queen Omphale dressed the hero Hercules in her clothes, and he wasn't exactly unvirile. This is a common game or ceremony in other cultures. We accept sex as pleasure and are starting to accept it as play. Now we need to accept it as ceremony, plus the fact that we are all bisexual and that sex includes fantasy, self-image, psychodrama, and the other things which our society still finds worrying. Bed is the place to act these things out – that is one of the things human sex is for.

Special preferences apart, it's worth knowing at least

as much as a pro about the common turn-ons, because for most couples they have stunning surprise value as unscheduled extras on special occasions. If a particular one doesn't work you needn't repeat it, and clothes are easy to take off.

Makers of sexy lingerie cater for honeymoon trousseaux but don't seem to produce a sexually practicable female g-string. This should tightly cover the whole pussy and pubic hair, nothing else. It should undo from the sides with hooks, or better with ribbons, so that it can be taken off when astride without kicking your man. The traditional 'leaf' worn by Japanese prostitutes is made of silk, not nylon, because it holds your perfume better. See *G-string*. This isn't street wear – you wear it only for sex: the first direct genital kiss is given, or taken, through it. Later you can surprise him by suddenly taking the two ends and putting it hard over his nose and mouth. Men are better catered for, with what are called in Europe 'posing pouches' worn by wouldbe strong-men for near-nude photos. Use these in the same way. Two such minimum g-strings make the ideal nightwear, if you want nightwear.

come again

Not all can, but we are sure that far more could than actually do, men especially.

Multiple orgasm comes easily to many if not all women if they are responsive enough and care to go on, either with intercourse or afterplay, after one orgasm; that is, really responsive women who definitely fall in the once-and-it's-over category like men are fairly rare. Some women get one continuous series of orgasms with no single, big peak. Responsiveness is an unanalyzably subtle mixture of physiology, mood, culture, upbringing and having the man she wants. Therefore, if you can get one really intense climax you could probably get more if you went on. The chief exceptions are those who are fragile and tire easily, or who want to savor the period of intense relaxation after each orgasm rather than switch to a new kind of stimulation.

With men it is more complicated still. Some can get six or more full orgasms in a few hours provided they aren't timestressed and don't attempt it daily. Some can do it daily. Others can't get a second erection for a set time. It pays to establish this time early on – it may be shorter than you think. Whether it is alterable nobody knows – nor yet whether individual differences depend on physical or mental factors, though certainly a great many men have been hocussed by talk about sex being exhausting into a performance below what they could manage.

Since exercise and practice improve almost all performances it would be odd if they didn't improve this one.

In any case it's not, for the man, the number of orgasms that matter – most men can get a second by slow handwork and a third from self-stimulation within an hour of full intercourse – it is rather the ability either to hold off your own orgasm as long as you want, or to go on after, or soon after it, even if you don't come a second time. Failing this one can't take a woman the whole way in unsupplemented intercourse. Many lovers don't try but switch their techniques to economize – yet even so it's not the same unless you manage to finish, if not together, at least fairly close together.

Ability to hold and to repeat is particularly important to the many (usually over-continent) males who have hair-trigger trouble. Don't let it become a self-aggravating worry. It matters not a jot provided you can get another erection inside half an hour – there are plenty of other things to do while you are waiting. Avoid performance anxiety: instead, find out by trial just how soon you can

COME AGAIN *below and opposite*
If he can't, doesn't or is worried, it is no use reasoning with him. You, Madam, must take over.

get a serviceable erection again – usually this will be long-lasting and won't end in a full climax, but will enable you to give her ten, twenty or more minutes of full intercourse while you concentrate on her.

If he can't, doesn't, or is worried about it, it is no use reasoning with him. You, Madam, must take over. Full technical details are given under *Hairtrigger trouble*. If you look disappointed you'll have had it for the night and possibly for keeps. Suggest some diversionary entertainment, give him half an hour, then stiffen him yourself by hand and mouth-work. Tell him out of hours what you intend doing; you want to see how soon he can get stiff again (otherwise it looks as though you were unsatisfied and he'll feel guilty and switch himself off). Bring this off neatly and you'll have added a new dimension to both your lives. Two important points – one, *immediately* after a full orgasm some men can't stand any genital stimulation – they feel it as intense pain. If he is like this, give him a half hour or more. Two, if he really is up-tight about it, quite a few women can be perfectly well penetrated with the merest half-erection if taken from behind on their side. Once started like this, full erection usually follows.

Some men when tired can't get an erection but can ejaculate on hand or mouth-work: others get an erection which lasts indefinitely but can't reach orgasm. This last sort, who are actually slow, not fast, responders, make sexual athletes. Whether it can be cultivated as a choice isn't clear, but abundant sex and a certain amount of masturbatory training in holding back a climax will help. Most over-fast responders are having sex far too rarely.

Corpse revivers: the best are skillful manual and oral work and direct suction. A woman can carefully take not only the penis but the whole scrotum as well into her mouth and hold them with her lips, then suck firmly on the penis itself while pressing with a finger at its root behind. Then, when she feels stiffening, she can switch to in and out movements. Vigorous masturbation will always produce a second ejaculation in time, even if it doesn't produce a serviceable erection. Some couples, all passion spent, but still wanting one more orgasm before finishing, like to lie facing and watch one another as they bring themselves to climax. This is an added experience, not a confession of defeat, and can be immensely and unexpectedly exciting.

deodorant

Banned absolutely, the only permitted deodorant is soap and water although the unfortunates who sweat profusely may well have problems. A mouthful of aluminium chloride in a girl's armpit is one of the biggest disappointments bed can afford, and a truly deodorized woman would be

opposite A game of skill, from Jodhpur Rajasthan, circa 1820

opposite A painting from the Punjab Hills of Kangra State, circa 1825

another – like a deodorized carnation. Cleanliness is another matter. Accordingly, don't give in to sales talk, unless you find that a so-called 'intimate deodorant' enhances a natural note which pleases you. Wash, and leave it at that. She says: 'Some men *should* use deodorants if they can't learn to wash.' See *Cassolette, Mouth music.*

foreskin

Cutting off this structure is possibly the oldest human sexual ritual. It still persists – on the ground, now, either that cancer of the penis and cervix is rarer when it is done (washing probably works as well) or that it slows down orgasm (for which there is no evidence). We're against it, though for some it is already too late. 'To cut off the uppermost skin of the secret parts,' said Dr. Bulwer, 'is directly against the honesty of nature, and an injurious insufferable trick put upon her.' The point is that if you have a foreskin, you conserve your options. It probably doesn't make very much difference, either to masturbation or to intercourse, but it makes some, and nobody wants to lose a sensitive structure. Normally one retracts it anyway for all these purposes, but if you haven't one there is a whole range of covered-glans nuances you can't recapture. Women who have experienced both are divided – and over which looks sexier. Some find the circumcised glans 'neater' and are even turned off by an unretracted prepuce as looking 'feminine' (this can be an insight into the symbolic wilderness behind the original Stone Age custom), while others love the sense of discovery which goes with retraction. If you are uncircumcised and she prefers the other, retract it – if vice versa, you've had it. In function it's probably a scent-diffusing organ – nothing to do with sensitivity.

Holding the skin back hard with the hand (her hand) during intercourse works for both circumcised and uncircumcised as an accelerator and a sensation of its own (see *Florentine*). Much of the action of various fancy penile rings is in holding back the skin of the shaft and/or the prepuce and giving extra tightness, which is why some men get extra feeling from them. If you think your glans is oversensitive, try keeping it constantly exposed. You can always have the exposure made permanent when you've tried it. In sum, the circumcised man isn't at any important disadvantage (or advantage), but we prefer to be able to choose our egg with or without salt and let our children do likewise.

frequency

The right frequency for sex is as often as you both enjoy it. You can no more 'have too much' sex than you can over-empty a toilet cistern (see *Excesses*) though you can

cut your fertility by having too many ejaculations, and you don't want to make intercourse such an anxious business that you have to stick to a daily schedule. Two or three times a week is a common rate. Many people have it much oftener Some people do stick to a pretty regular schedule – others like intensive weekends at intervals. Much under twice a week suggests you could be getting more out of it, unless you know by experience that the lower frequency is optimal for what you want. People who stick strictly to coital orgasm usually are opting for fewer climaxes than people who mix coitus with oral, manual and other plays, because these increase the number of climaxes most men can get. You should devise your own mix, in the light of your own responses: if one partner needs more, the accessory methods are useful to supply their needs and match them to yours. Frequency falls off normally with age, but there is no age when you won't on some special occasion, surprise yourself. Don't be compulsive about frequency (or worried if your friends say yours is lower than theirs). You aren't being scored. Realize there will be times when one of you just doesn't feel like it – through fatigue, preoccupation, etc.– and don't enforce a timetable on them or yourself.

love

We use the same word for man-woman, mother-child, child-parent, and I-mankind relations – rightly, because they are a continuous spectrum. In talking about sexual relations, it seems right to apply it to any relationship in which there is mutual tenderness, respect and consideration – from a total interdependence where the death of one maims the other for years, to an agreeable night together. The intergrades are all love, all worthy, all part of human experience. Some meet the needs of one person, some of another – or of the same person at different times. That's really the big problem of sexual ethics, and it's basically a problem of self-understanding and of communication. You can't assume that your 'conditions of love' are applicable to, or accepted by, any other party; you can't assume that these won't be changed quite unpredictably in both of you by the experience of loving; you can't necessarily know your own mind. If you are going to love, these are risks you have to take, and don't depend simply on whether or not you have sex together – though that is such a potentially overwhelming experience that tradition is right in pinpointing it. Sometimes two people know each other very well, or think they've worked things out by discussion, and they may be right. But even so if it's dignifiable by the name of love it's potentially an open-ended experience. Tradition has tried to cut the casualties by laying down all kinds of schedules of morality, but these

LOVE *opposite and overleaf*
Sexual love can give us our best and our worst moments.

MEN *opposite*
Male sex response is triggered easily by things, like putting a quarter in a vending machine.

never work 100 per cent. Nor are they of much use in classifying the merits of different kinds of relationship. Romantic sentimentalism made a whole generation see 'love' as a kind of take-over bid by one individual for another. Some moderns in revolt from this are, like Casanova, so hung up on no hangups that they won't accept the essential open-endedness of a real relationship between people.

If sexual love can be – and it is – the supreme human experience it must be also a bit hazardous. It can give us our best and our worst moments. In this respect it's like mountain climbing – over-timid people miss the whole experience; reasonably balanced and hardy people accept the risks for the rewards, but realize that there's a difference between this and being foolhardy. Love, moreover, involves someone else's neck beside your own. At least you can make as sure as maybe that you don't exploit or injure someone – you don't take a novice climbing and abandon them halfway up when things get difficult. Getting them to sign a form of consent before they start isn't an answer either. There was a hell of a lot to be said for the English Victorian idea of not being a cad ('person devoid of finer or gentlemanly feelings'). A cad can be of either sex.

Marriage between two rival actor-managers, each trying to produce the other regardless, isn't love. The relationship between a prostitute and a casual client where, for reasons they don't quite get, real tenderness and respect occur, is.

men (by him for her)

Prof. Higgins was right – men wish that women's sexuality was like theirs, which it isn't. Male sexual response is far brisker and more automatic: it is triggered easily by things, like putting a quarter in a vending machine. Consequently, at a certain level and for all men girls, and parts of girls, are at this stimulus level unpeople. That isn't incompatible with their being people too. Your clothes, breasts, odor, etc., aren't what he loves instead of you – simply the things he needs in order to set sex in motion to express love. Women seem to find this hard to understand.

Second, most though not all male feeling is ultimately centered in the last inch of the penis (though you can, if you start intelligently, teach him female-type sensitivity all over his skin surface). And unlike yours his sexuality depends on a positive performance – he has to be turned on to erection, and not turned off, in order to function; he can't be passively 'taken' in a neutral way. This matters intensely to men at a biological and personal level. It explains why men are emphatically penis centered and tend to start with genital play, probably before you are ready, and when you would rather wait to get in the mood.

Genital approach is how men get into the mood.

You need to understand these reactions, as he needs to understand yours. The Women's Lib bit about sex objects misses the point – sure the woman and the various parts of her are sex objects, but most men ideally would wish to be treated piecemeal in the same way. Accordingly, the most valued thing, from you, in actual love-making is intuition of these object reactions and direct initiative – *starting* the plays, taking hold of the penis, giving genital kisses ahead of being asked – being an initiator, a user of your stimulatory equipment. This is hard to put into simple terms; it is what John Wilkes meant by the divine gift of lechery – the art of sensing turn-ons and going along with them for the partner's response. It isn't the same for the two sexes because male turn-ons are concrete, while many female turn-ons are situational and atmospheric. Personal folklore apart, what the male turn-on equipment requires is the exact reverse of a virgin or a passively recipient instrument – not a demand situation, because that in itself can threaten a turn-off from inadequacy-feelings, but a skill situation; I can turn you on and turn myself on in doing so, and from that point we play it both ways and together. You can't of course control your turn-ons any more than he can, but it helps if a woman has some male-type object reactions, like being excited by the sight of a penis, or hairy skin, or by the man stripping, or by physical kinds of play (just as it helps if the man has some sense of atmosphere). It's the active woman who understands his reactions while keeping her own who is the ideal lover.

naked apes

We put a lot of biology into this book; too much exposition has been devoted to symbolisms in human sex behavior, highly important as these are, from a psychoanalytic standpoint which assumes, like old-style morality, that there is only one way of making love and only one thing it ought to express. Work on monkeys suggests that for man the possibility of prolonged and sensuous sex is something special, i.e. a 'displacement activity,' which enables all kinds of aggressions and anxieties as well as infant deprivation of skin sensation, to be worked out play-fashion in the context of mutual affection. Most people have at least one preferred sex behavior which a judge would find odd. If we saw these behaviors in fish or birds we wouldn't ask whether they were normal, but what they were for. No writer who has watched apes should say, as one did recently, that any voluntary movement in sexual intercourse is evidence of latent sadism – if it is, then 'latent sadism' means using sex to dissipate natural aggression in play. Problems only arise when the natural play-function isn't able to dissipate deeper anxieties.

Man's chief differences from most apes are pair-formation, the extensive use of sex as social bonding and play, shift of interest from brightly-colored buttocks to breasts (one baboon has this too) and imagination. Well-known ape residues are blushing – all that is left of the mandril's red facial sex-skin (it happens all over to many women in orgasm, as a spotty-looking rash), and persisting buttock interest, which may include reddening them by smacking. Worth knowing only because sex is more fun, and preferences less alarming, if they make sense as natural history. Apes, like men, masturbate and play bi-sexual games.

nakedness

The normal state for lovers who take their work at all seriously, at least as a basic requisite – subject to the reservations under *Clothes*. They don't so much start clothed and shed what they must, as start naked and add any extras they need.

Nakedness doesn't mean lack of ornament. The oriental lady takes off all her clothes but puts on all her jewels – the only practical need, as with wrist watches, is to see they don't catch or scratch. This is for daylight; it is difficult to sleep in them. For night, probably increase in the value of lovemaking is the main reason that most people now sleep naked. The only exception may be after; warm bodies tend to stick, and a blotter worn by one or other can add to comfort. We find we spend more and more of our time together naked or wearing the enhancing minimum. It affects our choice of clothes and of, for example, nonclammy chairs.

Nudists, incidentally, used to be a dead loss – there are no pants like invisible pants. Now, thank goodness, the uninhibited young are moving in, for whom nudity is natural not a ritual and lovemaking is included, instead of eurhythmics or basketball – or as well.

Organized 'nudism' in most countries is a family affair. This is probably a good idea. For biological reasons which we've hinted at elsewhere (see *Penis, Vulva, Children*) the nudity of one's own parents can be worrying to children, and shouldn't be overdone. Children of militant progressives often develop disconcerting modesty, which should be respected even if nakedness at home comes naturally. There is accordingly a lot to be said for the opportunity to look at men and women in general under unforced conditions and without programmed incest and dominance anxieties: not 'father is bigger than I am' but 'all men are bigger than I am, and one day I shall be a man.' It is the discharge of residual adult anxiety of this sort about our acceptability and competitive status which

NAKEDNESS *overleaf*
The normal state for lovers who take their work at all seriously.

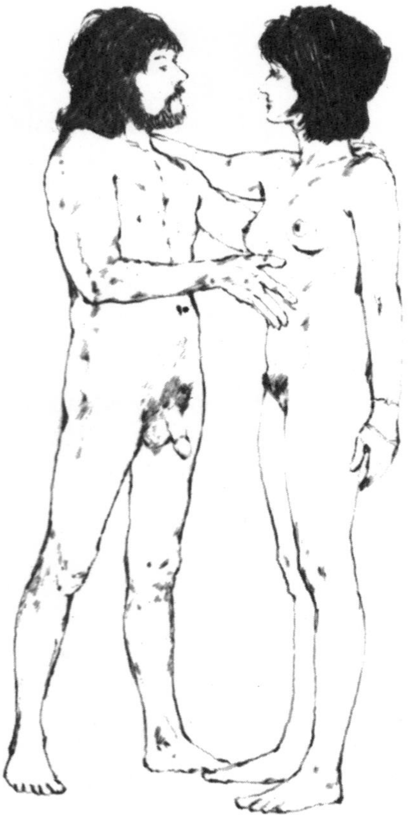

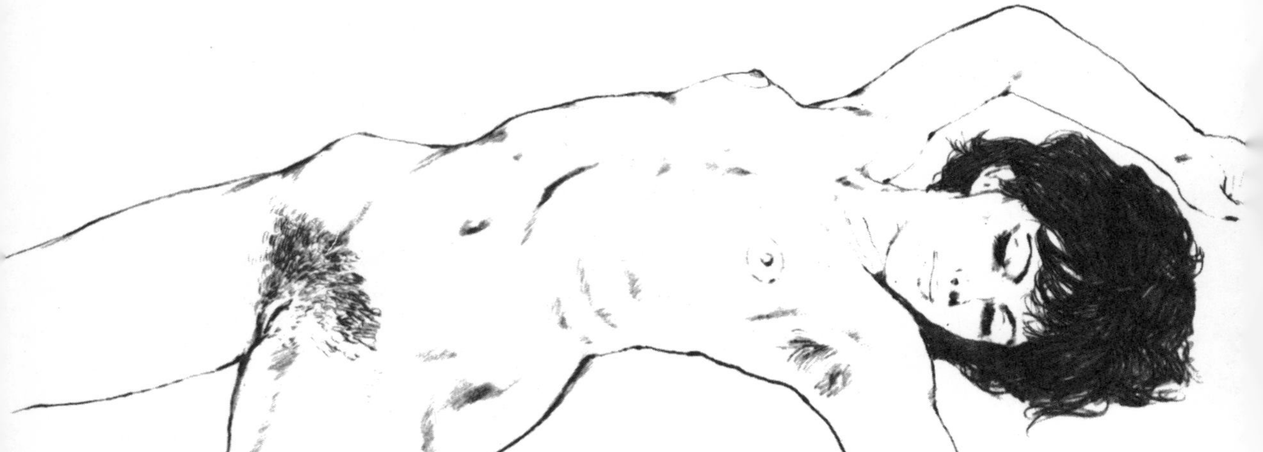

probably makes group nudity so relaxing, rather than the opportunity of getting sunburned, and explains why it acts as a lay sacrament. Career nudists at a first meeting do have the openness of hippies or Quakers, though they quarrel a fair amount over dogma. You should be able to pick a naturist club to taste – they at least give facilities for open-air nakedness which are hard to organize at home.

normal

A nineteenth-century book about sex, unless it was meant for the (then rich) underground would have started with at least a genuflection to what was and wasn't sinful. The next generation of medical books, and much counseling literature, switched to laying down rules about what is and isn't normal.

Tack 'abnormal' onto a sexual taste and it becomes worrying. 'Normal' implies that there is something which sex ought to be. There is. It ought to be a wholly satisfying link between two affectionate people, from which both emerge unanxious, rewarded and ready for more. That definition includes the awareness that people differ wildly in what they need and in their capacity to be satisfied; more, statistically, than in almost any other measurable. Since sex is cooperative you can cater to one another alternately to bridge gaps. Add to this that sex, for reasons built into the species, makes us uniquely anxious compared with other divergences of need or taste and our culture is coming out of a period of moral panic into a re-awareness that there is nothing to fear. Accordingly, a lot of people are, in their sexual assumptions, like the generation of Victorian children brought up to believe that green sweets were poisonous and rice pudding was good for you because it was unpalatable: they need reassuring.

One trouble with the last generation was that because of censorship by Auntie, many good sex techniques were simply unfamiliar, and worrying or disgusting for that reason. It is not much over a lifetime ago that Krafft-Ebing wrote a textbook in which he described every sexual routine he didn't himself enjoy as a named 'disease,' salting the narrative with examples drawn from very disturbed people. Even Freud, who recognized that all of us have not one but a whole sheaf of sexually important drives – so much so that nearly all our interests have *some* sexual overtone – regarded maturity in terms of a pretty rigid highway code. There was practically an examination in 'maturity' to take at the end.

'Abnormal' accordingly means (1) unusual for the time and place – having intercourse ten times a day on a regular basis is unusual but it happens. If you can, fine. Leonardo and Newton were statistically unusual. (2) Un-

PENIS *opposite*
Lovers treat the penis as something very like a third party.

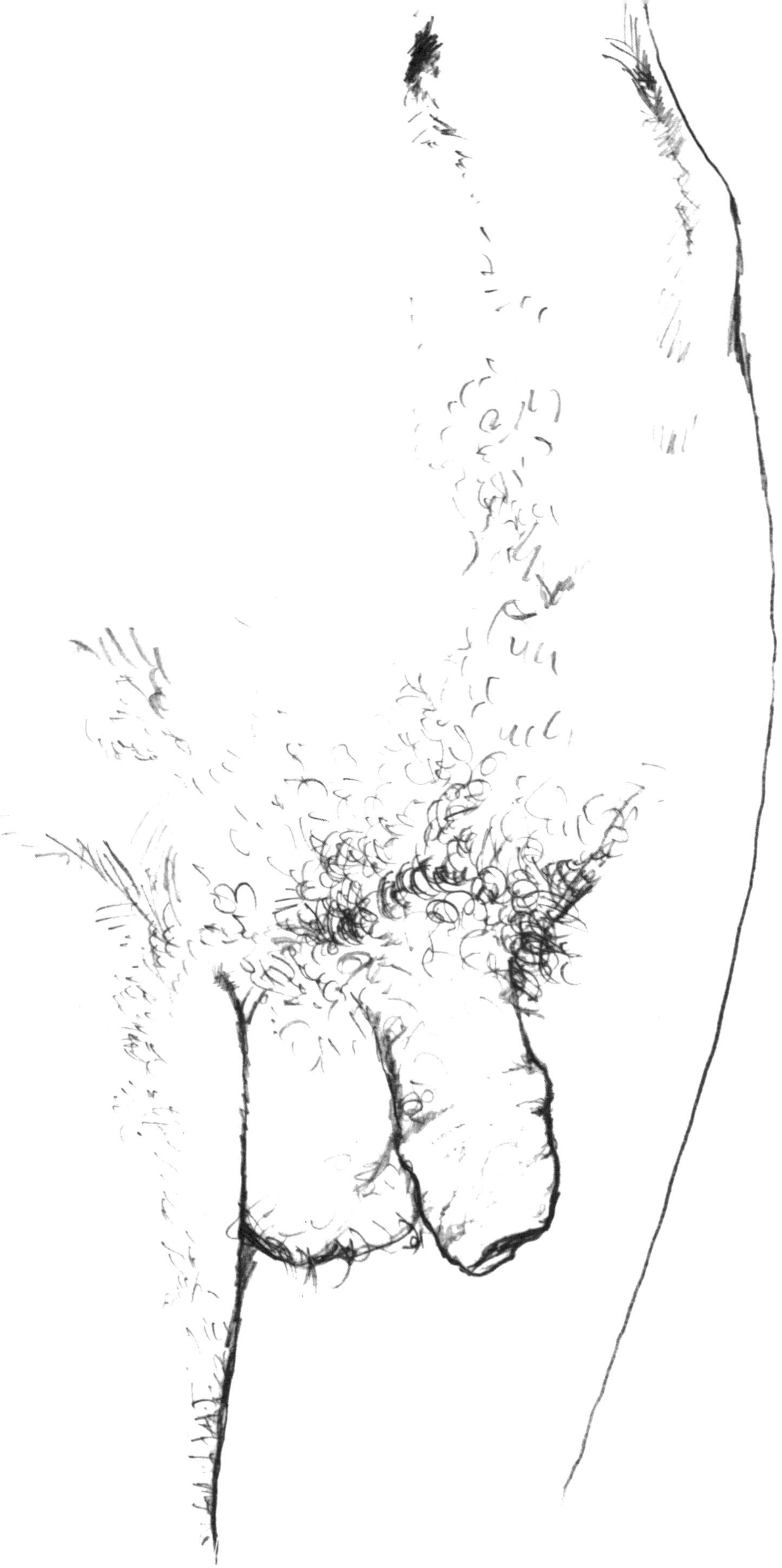

usual and disapproved. It's abnormal in Papua to bury dead relatives, and abnormal in California to eat them. Yet lovers all over the world would like 'to eat' one another, and the same idea underlies our most beautiful and moving religious rite. At the same time an Englishman or an American who actually ate a dead relative would have to be pretty sick. On a less extreme level, our society is scared of same-sex affection. In classical Greece it was a fashionable pose – everyone did it who could. In our culture the people who show exclusively this sort of response are those who must. (3) Unusual and handicapping. A slipped disk or a really worrying sexual obsession are abnormalities because they spoil life, for the owner and his or her associates.

Some sex behaviors are obviously odd, and restrict the range of enjoyment – like the man who could only get orgasm by getting into a bath of cooked spaghetti. He, however, liked it that way. Psychologists now do not usually ask 'Is this normal?' but 'Why does this particular person need this particular emphasis?' and 'Is this behavior, (a) spoiling his chances of being a full person, (b) tolerable for society?' Some, like rape or seducing children, obviously aren't tolerable.

In sum, we don't have a single 'normal' pattern of sex behavior, but a bunch of responses, like the fingers of a hand. In most people in a given culture fingers are of roughly the same lengths. Some people have one finger longer than usual – a few are unlucky enough to have one long finger and the others stunted. The difference here is that finger lengths are much more tightly programmed and vary much less than sex behaviors. Accordingly, if you must talk about 'normality,' any sex behavior is normal which (1) you both enjoy, (2) hurts nobody, (3) isn't associated with anxiety, (4) doesn't cut down your scope. Insisting on having intercourse only in the dark, in one position, and with as little pleasure as possible, which used to be the moralists' stereotype of normality, is a very anxious and limiting routine. Good, unworried lovers use all five fingers of all four hands.

penis

More than the essential piece of male equipment, even if it is often and expressively described as a 'tool,' the penis has more symbolic importance than any other human organ, as a dominance signal and, by reason of having a will of its own, generally a 'personality.' No point in reading all this symbolism back here, except to say that lovers will experience it, and find themselves treating the penis as something very like a third party. At one moment it is a weapon or a threat, at another something they share, like a child. Without going into psychoanalysis or biology it's

not a bad test of a love-relationship that while the penis is emphatically his, it also belongs to both of them. This particular set of programmed feelings in man is in fact the fine adjustment for all manner of experiences and feelings connected with sex-roles, identity and development. Freud's formulation, that the man is programmed to fear that the woman, or a jealous parent, will confiscate his penis, while the woman feels it is something she has lost, is biologically true but over-simple. What is true is that in a good sex scene it becomes 'their' penis. In any case its texture, erectility and so on are fascinating to both sexes, and its apparent autonomy a little alarming. This is programmed, and the fact that the human penis is much bigger relatively than in other primates is probably due to these complex psychological functions: it's an aesthetic as well as a functional object.

For precisely the same reasons it collects anxieties and folklore, and is a focus for all sorts of magical manipulations. Male self-esteem and sense of identity tend to be located in it, as Samson's energy was in his hair. If it won't work, or worse, if you as a woman send it up, or down, the results will be disastrous. This explains the irrational male preoccupation with penile size. Size has absolutely nothing to do with their physical serviceability in inter-

PLAYTIME *above*
The rules are only those of childplay–if it gets nasty or spiteful, stop the game.

course, or – since female orgasm doesn't depend on getting deeply into the pelvis – with capacity to satisfy a partner, though many women are turned on by the idea of a large one, and a few say that they feel more. The unstretched vagina is only 4 inches long anyway. If anything, thickness matters more. Nor has flaccid size anything to do with erect size – a penis which is large when at rest simply enlarges less with erection. There is no way of 'enlarging' a penis. Size doesn't differ appreciably between 'races,' nor correlate with big muscles elsewhere. Nor, except in very rare cases, is a penis too big for a woman – the vagina will take a full-term baby. If your penis, whatever its length, hits an ovary and hurts her, don't go in so far. A woman who says she is 'too small' or 'too tight' is making a statement about her worries, exactly as the man who is obsessed with being too small. They need reassurance and a different attitude to sex, not gadgets or exercises. Shape also varies – the glans can be blunt or conical. This matters only in that the conical shape can make teat-ended condoms uncomfortable through getting jammed in the teat. As to circumcision and uncircumcision, its effects are religious rather than sexual, see *Foreskin*. If you have anxious preconceptions, get rid of them. All the preceding statements are true.

Women who have really learned to enjoy sex are usually as fascinated by their lover's penis, size included, as men are by women's breasts, shape, odor and feel, and learn to play with it fully and skillfully. Circumcised or not, it's a fascinating toy quite apart from experiencing its main use. There is a whole play scene connected with uncapping, stiffening, and handling it, making it pulsate or ejaculate, which is a major part of togetherness. This is equally important for the man – not only is it ego-boosting, but good hand and mouth work practically guarantee a good partner.

Care and maintenance: if you aren't circumcised, you need to retract the foreskin fully for cleaning purposes, and if it won't retract beyond the corona all round the glans except at the front, get it seen to (this is a trifling operation with a blunt probe and doesn't necessarily mean you need circumcising). If it won't retract properly or is over-tight and gets stuck, get that seen to also. These are about the only things that are commonly wrong with a penis. Slight asymmetry often develops with time – this does no harm. On the other hand don't bend an erect penis, or use a position in which it could get violently bent by accident. (This usually happens with the woman on top if she is careless near orgasm, or in putting him in, and he is just short of fully stiff – keep a little control here.) It is possible, though difficult, to fracture one of the two hydraulics con-

opposite and overleaf
Two paintings from a collection from Bundi State, circa 1800–20

PLAYTIME *overleaf*
Sex is the most important sort of adult play. If you can't relax here you never will.

tained in the shaft. This is very painful and can lead to pain or kinking on subsequent erection. For the same reason avoid silly tricks with tubes, suction or 'enlarging' devices. The normal organ will stand up to extremely hard use, but not to these. Sores, discharge, etc., are illnesses and need treatment. Venereal disease apart, don't have oral intercourse with someone who has a herpes on the mouth – you can get recurrent herpes of the penis or the vulva which is a nuisance. If the foreskin is dry from masturbation or long retraction, saliva is the best lubricant unless you have a herpes yourself. Penile cosmetics are now sold – some are deodorants, others local anaesthetics to slow down response, and yet others ticklers. We don't recommend them.

playtime

We have said this before, but we repeat: sex is the most important sort of adult play. If you can't relax here you never will. Don't be scared of psychodrama. It works far better in bed than in an encounter group – be the Sultan and his favorite concubine, the burglar and the maiden, even a dog and a currant bun, anything you fancy for the hell of it. Take off your shell along with your clothes.

A few people are immensely excited by having sex with the assistance of the oldest human dramatic expedient, a mask – which suppresses you and makes you someone else (see *Masks*). Most of us can learn to do the same change without it, and when this comes the complete mental nakedness between you is the most exhilarating sort of nudism – so complete that one is healthily scared of it at first. Getting unscared is probably the most important lesson of sex. Don't use alcohol for this – it's a neutering drug. Real sex release when one achieves it is what alcohol, pot, etc., are substitutes for.

So let him be a Roman or a dog or a woman or a gangster, and let her be a virgin, or a slave, or a Sultana, or Lolita, or someone you're trying to rape, or indeed anything which turns either of you on. You weren't self-conscious about this when you were three – grow backwards again in an adult context. The rules are only those of childplay – if it gets nasty or spiteful or unhappy, stop the game: while it stays wild and exciting, it has a climax childrens' games lack; that is the privilege of adult play.

pubic hair

Shave it off if you prefer: we don't, but some people do. If you do once shave it, you're committed to a prickly interregnum while it regrows. Some prefer it off in the interest of total nudity or prefer the hardness of the bare pubis – most find it decorative. Most lovers regard pubic hair as a resource. Try brushing it lightly and learn to caress with it.

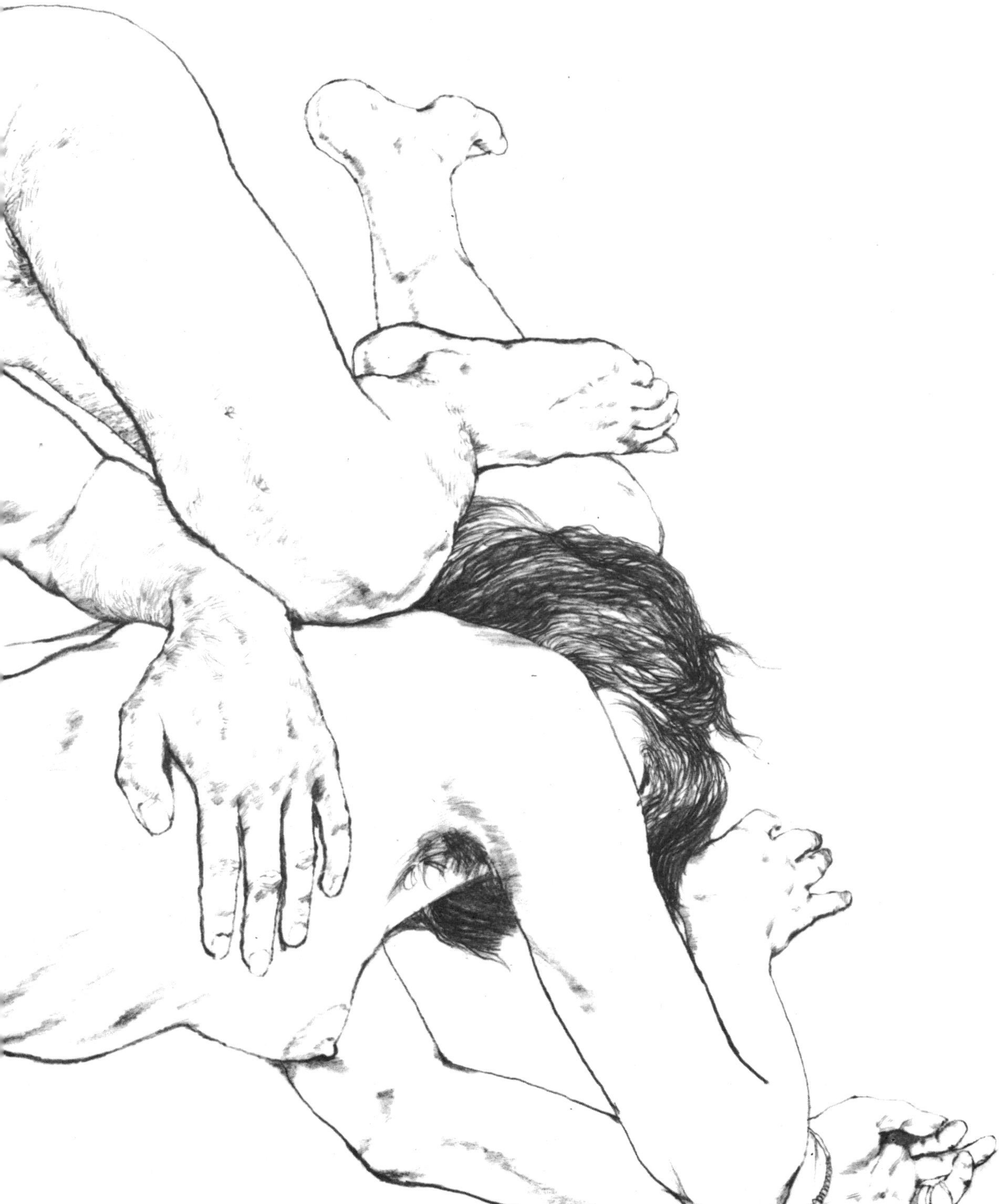

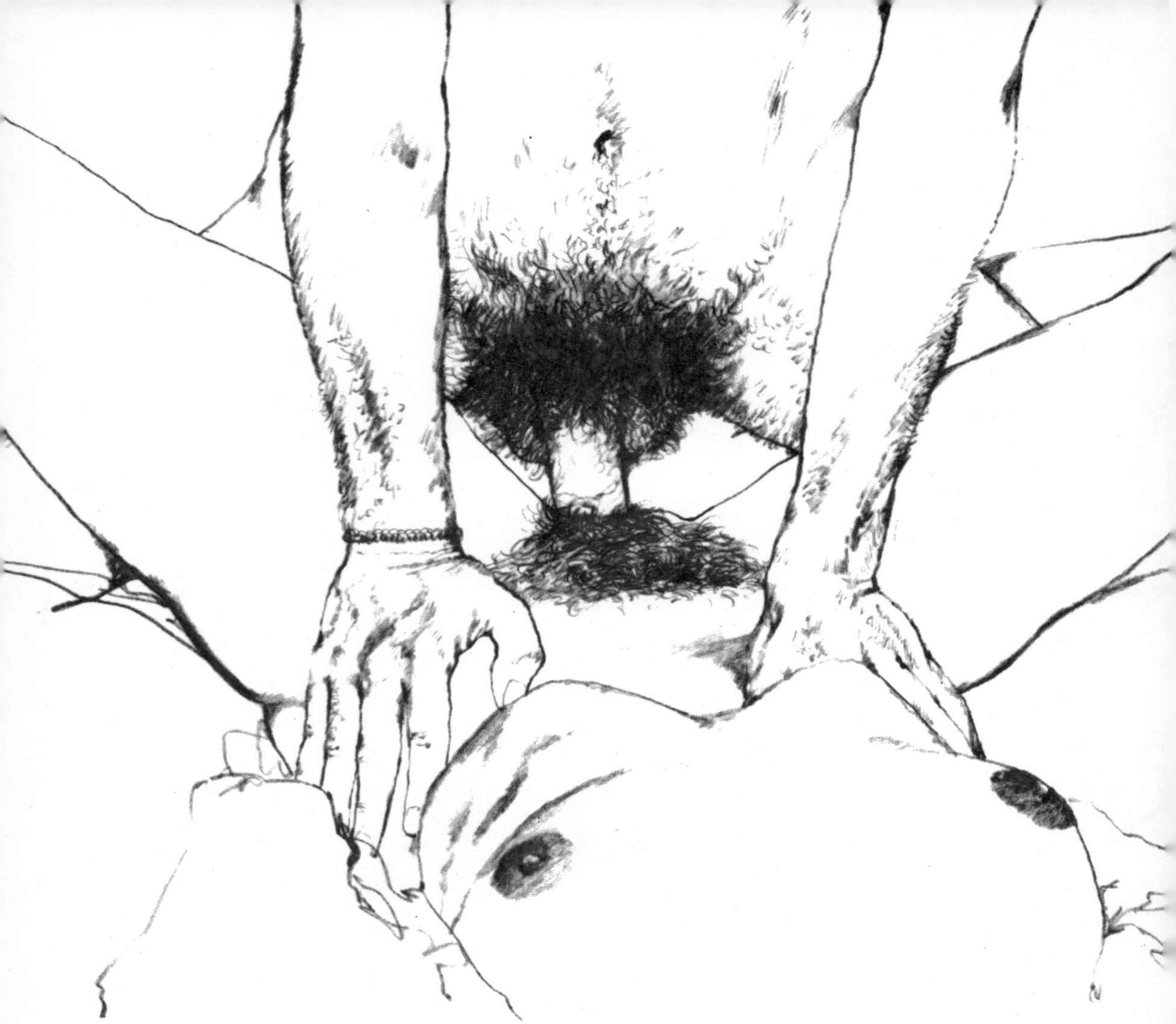

It can be combed, twirled, kissed, held, even pulled. In the woman it can move the whole pubis, skillfully handled, to the point of orgasm. For the woman, it's often best not to shave but to trim, confining the triangle to the middle of the pubis with a bare strip each side – the pattern of youth – removing hair which comes outside a g-string or bathing slip, and trimming enough to make the vulva fully visible. Better not try to dye it to match head hair – it never looks right – still less to bleach it. *M.A.S.H.* is quite wrong – you can't tell whether a blonde is natural by her pubic hair color. It is often shades darker than head hair – in black-haired women it can be nearly blue. Men can shave if they like, or their partners like, but it's difficult to shave the scrotum. Don't use depilatories around the genitals – they can burn. You may need to shave the penile shaft and root if you use a condom – otherwise the hairs can get rolled into it.

real sex

The sort our culture and most admass propaganda don't recognize: not that intercourse or masturbation or genital kisses aren't real sex, but some other things are real sex too, which people need, but which don't excite our time and age. We can list some: being together in a situation of pleasure, or of danger, or just of rest (if we admitted these as sexual we'd run the risk of having to love other people as people, and that would be worrying or inconvenient, to us or society): touching: oldfashioned expedients like holding hands (permissiveness makes more orgasms, but we miss out on old-style restricted courtship, kisses and looks that vagina-bent, with-it males now think of as schmalz): sleeping together even without, or especially after, intercourse.

Most women don't need telling this, but are as shy about telling it to males, for fear of seeming square, as males are about object-preferences or aggressive needs. Don't get stuck with the view that only those things which Auntie calls sexual are sexual. In a book on sexual elaboration, this needs saying, if you are concerned with love rather than an Olympic pentathlon. People in our culture who are hung up on the Olympic bit don't get much from it unless it helps them to learn this.

relaxation

It is probably the general experience, and we have been assuming here, that maximum feeling in orgasm goes with maximum muscular tension. A great many techniques (postures, bondage and so on) are designed to boost this tension. On the other hand, it is by no means universally true. The orgasm of total relaxation is rather harder to manage, largely because it cannot be boosted artificially, but is both different and, when it works, overwhelming. There are also some people, chiefly women, for whom tension seems actively to interfere with full response.

We've seen ideological writings about this which infer, for example, that tension-orgasms represent fear of full release, latent sadism and so on. One writer opined that yells, grimaces and convulsions indicate fear and pain rather than love and pleasure – presumably he had never seen himself making love, or had never had a wild orgasm. In fact, the only universal generalization about sex seems to be that no one pattern fits everyone. How far these differences between people depend on physiology and how far on latent aggression and the like is probably not a practically important question – some need one and some the other. Our point is that with practice most people can widen their repertoire by learning to use both, and sense the needs of the moment so as to alternate them, thereby doubling their range of physical sensation and making sex still more communicative. Certainly some tension represents fear of letting-go, and some people prefer to be 'forced,' voluntarily, to accept orgasms – in this case,

PUBIC HAIR *opposite*
Better not try to dye it to match head hair – it never looks right.

initially at least, it's probably sensible to make use of the responses you have. If you recognize this kind of reaction, however, don't omit to try the other mode. Mammals seem to vary, according to species, between fight-and-rape-type mating and a version in which the female appears near-indifferent, so there isn't much to be learned from zoology.

The straight, sleepy, non-special intercourse, on your side or in the matrimonial position, is relaxed, but this isn't what we mean. In going for a fully relaxed orgasm, either one partner is totally passive and the other a soloist, or both achieve a state of non-effort in which wholly automatic movements – internal, for the woman – take over. Try both kinds – it is easier initially to work up both modes together.

Probably the easiest initial method is for the less-active partner in ordinary intercourse (this usually but not always means the one underneath) to try stopping all movement just as the orgasmic buildup begins and go completely limp (warn your partner first). Some people do this naturally: if you have had any of the fashionable relaxation training, starting by letting one finger get heavy and so on, use the same technique here. You may find that on the first few occasions the fact of trying produces a different sort of tension, but after a few attempts most easily-stimulated people can learn to let their orgasm happen, and will find that this feels different from the equally pleasant orgasm one produces, either by trying or by struggling and postponing. Don't postpone – don't, in fact, be active at all. Then practice the same kind of relaxation while your partner masturbates or sucks you. The movements he or she makes will be physically the same as for 'slow masturbation' as we've described it, but the operator is looking for quite different feedback – in the 'hard' version, whether the partner is tied or free, you are deliberately holding back or forcing them on, keeping just that much out of step with their reactions. In the 'soft' version you need to be a fraction ahead of those reactions so that they don't need to move or struggle. The difference can't be described, only felt. Practically, it means a quicker, steadier rhythm of stimulation – no slow teasing and no sudden bursts – you are making it and they are letting it happen.

Once you have got this right in intercourse and in other kinds of stimulation, including all the extras we've mentioned, you can go on to complete 'motionless' coitus. It won't of course initially be entirely motionless, but try, after the first round of gentle movement, what happens if you stop thinking. Movements of a sort will continue, but in time and with practice get less and less voluntary, especially if the woman has good vaginal

REAL SEX *opposite*
Permissiveness makes more orgasms, but we miss out on old-style courtship.

RELAXATION *above*
Essential if you hope to go as far in making love communicate as you are physically and mentally able.

muscle control. Ultimately, some people learn to insert and do nothing, but still reach an orgasm in which they totally fuse, giving a sensation of being a single person – not describable, again, and probably not always realizable, but fantastic when it happens. We should stress that this doesn't involve going slow, holding back, or any other voluntary intervention. If you find it not working, switch back to ordinary movements, but without taking too much thought – sometimes you will both sense that the moment has come to shift position and go all out for a big one; complete fusion isn't biddable, and ordinary, athletic sex is fine. If, on the other hand, it does happen you will want to repeat it.

Reliable relaxation, and the almost frightening self-loss that goes with it, are what most sexual yogis have aimed at, except that they usually tried not to ejaculate. Some of these sexual mystics recommend a special relaxed posture (man on his left side, girl on her back at right-angles, knees drawn up, legs bridging his hips, feet flat on the bed). Whether this helps may well depend on your build. What is worth suggesting, even for people who can't totally relax, is that they play through all the techniques we have described, aiming at relaxation instead of maximum tension, and adjusting their feedback accordingly. Similarly people who naturally relax in intercourse should try occasionally to play it for full tension – just as women who like to thrash around should sometimes try being forcibly held still, and vice versa. This sort of experimentation against one's built-in response is better value in widening one's range of lovemaking than mechanical variations of posture or trying out gadgets and stunts. It is one part of lovemaking which requires effort beyond mere curiosity, but it's essential if you hope to go as far in making sex communicate as you are physically and mentally able.

semen

There is no lovemaking without spilling this, on occasions at least. You can get it out of clothing or furnishings either with a stiff brush, when the stain has dried, or with a diluted solution of sodium bicarbonate. If you spill it over each other, massage it gently in – the pollen-odor of fresh semen is itself an aphrodisiac, which is why the smell of fresh grass or thalictrum flowers turns most people on. If you want a very copious ejaculate, he can masturbate nearly, but not quite, to orgasm about an hour beforehand to increase prostate secretion.

size

Preoccupation with the size of their genitals is as built-in biologically to men (it is a 'dominance signal,' like a deer's antlers) as sensitivity about their breasts and figure is to women. That, however, is its only importance. The 'average' penis is about 6 inches overall when erect and about $3\frac{1}{2}$ inches round, but penises come in all sizes – larger ones are spectacular but no more effective except as visual stimuli. Smaller ones work equally well in most positions. Accordingly, excessive preoccupation with size is an irrational anxiety, on which quacks batten – one can't increase it, any more than one can increase stature. Girls should learn not to comment on it except favorably, for fear of creating a lasting hang-up – men should learn not to give it a second thought. The few cases where male genitalia are really infantile go with major gland disturbances and are treatable but rare.

The same applies to vaginal size. No woman is too small – if she is, it is due to inability to relax, or a tough hymen. The normal vagina stretches to accommodate a full-term baby – and a tight woman gives the man extra intense feelings. Nor is any vagina too large – if it seems a loose fit, switch to a posture in which her thighs are pressed together. Genital anatomy probably fixes which postures work best for a given couple, but not more than that. With rare exceptions, men and women are universally adapted.

Non-erect size in the male is equally unimportant – some men before erection show no penile shaft at all, but

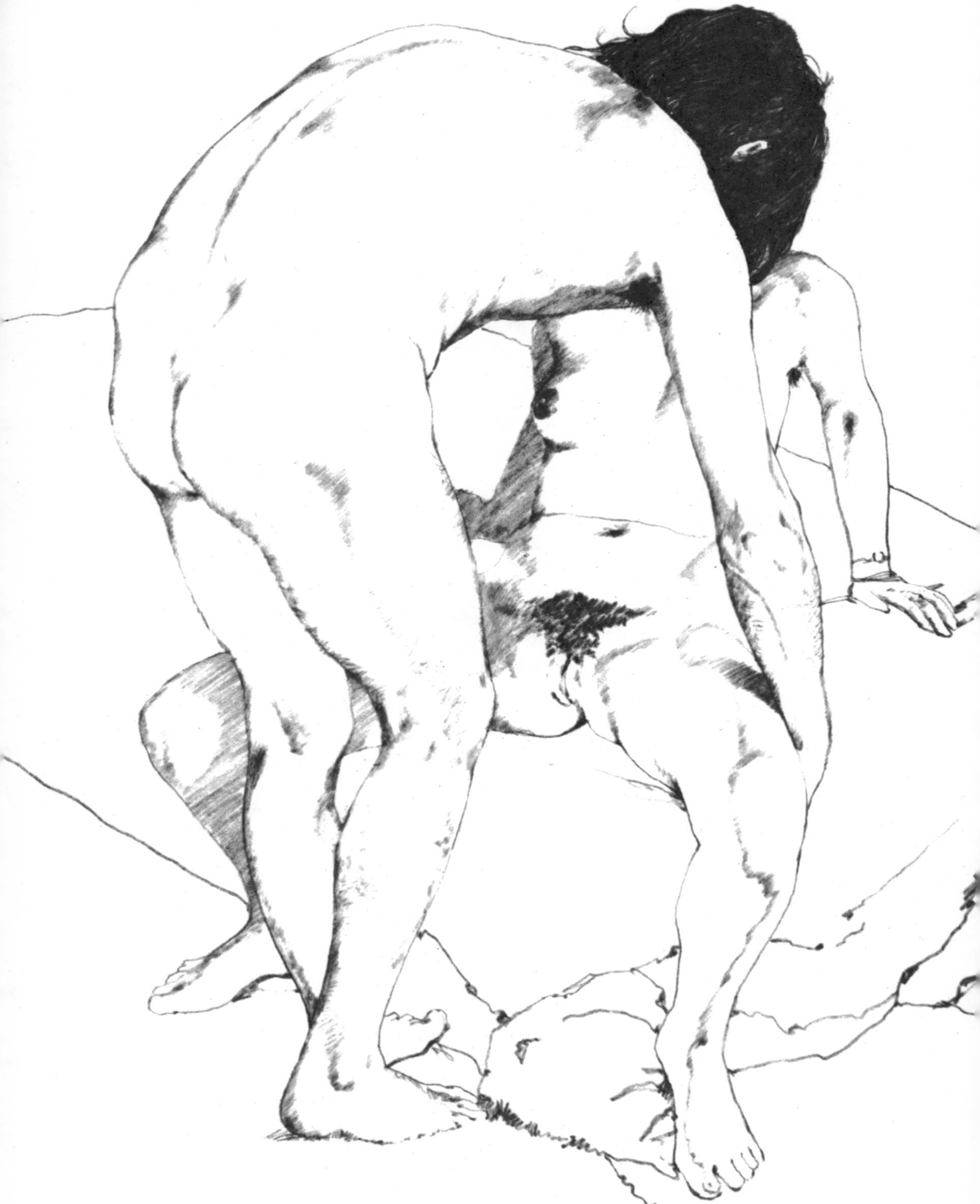

extend to full size easily. The same applies to testicle weight – it varies, as does nose or mouth size, but has little to do with function. Small genitals are usually due to active muscles in the under-skin layer – a cold bath will shrink the best-endowed male down to Greek statue proportions. The only practical exception is that with a very big penis and a very small woman she should be careful on top, or she will knock an ovary (which feels as a man feels if you knock a testicle) and he shouldn't thrust too hard until he knows he won't hurt her. As to the size of other structures, such as breasts, these may be individual turn-ons, but every build has its sexual opportunities built-in: use them.

tenderness

This, in fact, is what the whole book is about. It doesn't exclude extremely violent games (though many people neither need nor want these), but it does exclude clumsiness, heavyhandedness, lack of feedback, spitefulness and non-rapport generally. Shown fully in the way you touch each other. What it implies at root is a constant awareness of what your partner is feeling, plus the knowledge of how to heighten that feeling, gently, toughly, slowly or fast, and this only comes from an inner state of mind between you. No really tender person can just turn over and go to sleep. Many if not most inexperienced men, and some women, are just naturally clumsy – either through haste, through anxiety, or through lack of sensing how the other sex feels. Men in general are harder-skinned than women – don't grab breasts, stick fingers into the vagina, handle female skin as if it was your own, or (and this goes for both sexes) misplace bony parts of your anatomy. More girls respond to very light than to very heavy stimulation – just brushing pubic or skin hairs will usually do far more than a whole-hand grab. At the same time don't be frightened – neither of you is made of glass. Women by contrast often fail to use enough pressure, especially in handwork, though the light, light variety is a sensation on its own. Start very gently, making full use of the skin surface, and work up. Stimulus toleration in any case increases with sexual excitement until even hard blows can become excitants (though not for everyone). This loss of pain sense disappears almost instantly with orgasm, so don't go on too long, and be extra gentle as soon as he or she has come.

If we could *teach* tenderness most of this book would be superseded by intuition. If you are really heavy-handed, we agree with a recent book which suggests a little practice with inanimate surfaces, dress fastenings and so on. Male strength is a turn-on in sex, but it isn't expressed in clumsy handwork, bear-hugs and brute force – at least not as starters. If there is a problem here, remember you

TENDERNESS *opposite*
Shown fully in the way you touch each other.

both can talk. Few people want to be in bed on any terms with a person who isn't basically tender, and most people are delighted to be in bed with the right person who is.

The ultimate test is whether you can bear to find the person there when you wake up. If you are actually pleased, then you're onto the right thing.

variety

Plan your menus. Nobody wants a seven-course meal every time. At least seventy-five percent of really rewarding sex will be your absolutely straight, bedtime or morning, pattern. For longer sessions you need to be rested – weekends, holidays and special occasions on impulse. If you make up your mind that over the course of time you'll try everything and have sex everywhere, the occasions will arise: when you feel one coming on, or know you will have the opportunity, plan together with the book if you like, but don't expect necessarily to keep to what you outlined. Stick to it sometimes, however, so you don't miss things. Most couples will strike out perhaps a third of our suggestions as not turning them on, and pick up three or four headed 'We must try that,' if they haven't already.

Usually start with vaginal sex, move on to handwork, use mouth-work to get a further erection – maybe have a final orgasm by masturbating together. Prolonged spin-outs involving makebelieve, experiments and so on often go best on waking fresh – so do positions needing a very hard erection. Unlike a man, an untired and responsive woman can afford to take orgasms from any source in any order, unless her pattern is one overwhelming orgasm only – if so, keep it for last. See *Come again*. Varying times of day is well worthwhile but depends on your commitments and how far you can get privacy or clear your mind of other things, but try never to put it off if you both want it, except to 'save up' for something. Planning and thinking about sex to come is part of love. So is lying together in complete luxury afterwards.

virginity

Have a bit of respect for this. The first time doesn't so much 'matter more' to a woman than to a man, but it matters differently. If you find yourself getting into bed with a girl who is a virgin on only a few hours or minutes acquaintance, you're going too fast for both of you. For a start, she's unlikely to be baby-proof: stay with the non-coital extras until you're both quite sure you know what you are doing. Cutting notches is irresponsible. Whatever you do be gentle and slow, as she's bound to be tense and nervous – even if she doesn't look it.

Girls who are virgins will usually say (you can't tell reliably by inspection) and a loving man will ask – men don't

VULVA *opposite*
Lovers should learn early on to watch each other masturbate.

usually advertise the fact. However experienced he seems, the idea should be in the back of the woman's mind that this could be the first time and he may need help: if you're critical or disappointed you could do real mischief. If you're both virgins, you are starting from scratch – don't hurry it.

There's usually no physical problem over first intercourse if you're careful (see *Defloration*) – the commonest is simply male over-eagerness or nervousness (see *Impotence*). If there are problems, get them dealt with at once.

vulva

'The part of you,' as the advertisement says, 'that is most girl,' but also as magic as the penis, and to children, primi-

WOMEN *opposite*
It matters to them who is doing what, far more than it does to most men.

VULVA *below*
As magic as the penis, and to children, primitives and males generally, slightly scarey.

tives and males generally, slightly scarey: it looks like a castrating wound and bleeds regularly, it swallows the penis and regurgitates it limp, it can probably bite and so on. Luckily, few of these biologically programmed anxieties survive closer acquaintance, but they are the origins of most male hangups including homosexuality. Primitives and prudes treat it as if it was radioactive –'all magic,' said a Papuan wizard, 'radiates from it as fingers do from a hand,' and a lot of female put-downs throughout history grew from this kind of Freudian undergrowth.

Sensitive in all its parts – the phallic-minded male is inclined to make a reassuring rush for the clitoris. Lovers should learn early on to watch one another masturbate – few women enjoy excessive clitorial emphasis at the start. Length of labia, size and tightness of the opening make little difference to performance – position relative to the male pubic bone makes more: some lovers only get really good apposition in one or two postures, though usually the tension produced by movement and pulling on the labia in intercourse more than makes up for this. Normally slightly moist, or women would squeak when they walk, the vulva wets more or less copiously with sexual excitement. Any staining or offensive discharge indicates infection (usually with trichomonads or yeasts) in the vagina, and needs treating. The normal vulval odor varies greatly between women and between times, but should always be pleasant and sexually exciting.

Whether or not your lover has ever explored a woman's pussy in detail, with fingers, eyes and tongue, make sure he explores yours. Learn to kiss with it – you have two mouths to his one.

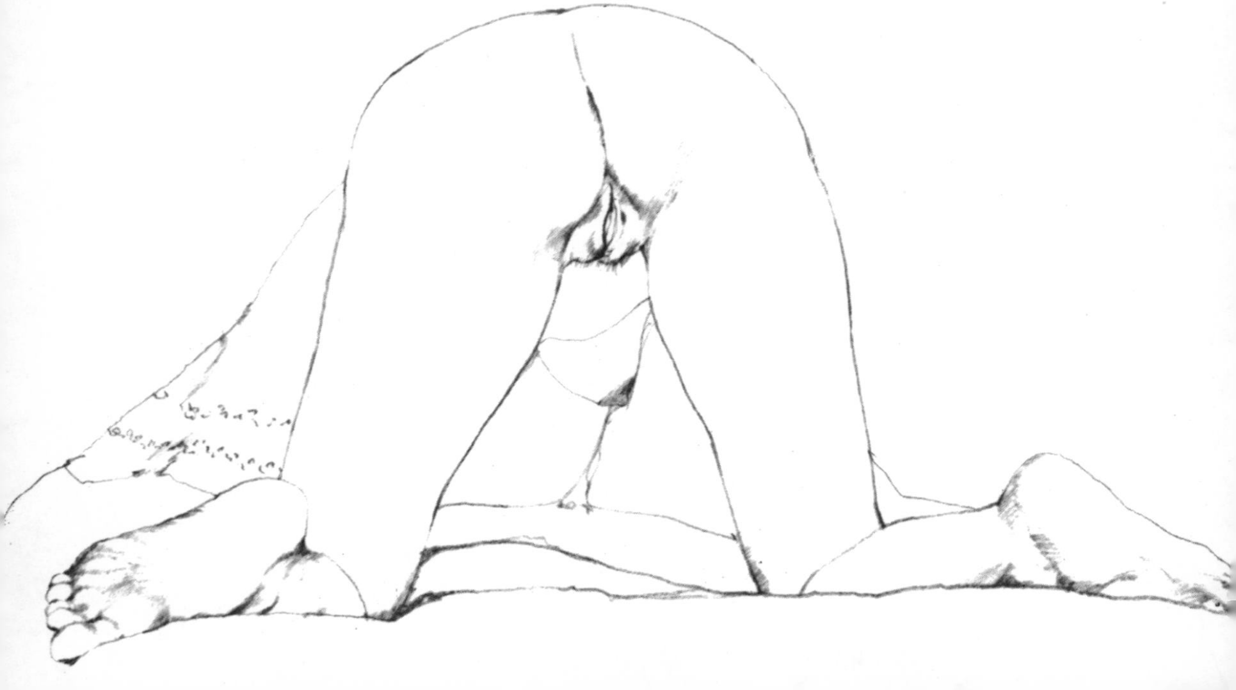

For care and maintenance see *Bidet, Cassolette, Menstruation*. Don't as a rule douche – wash.

Hide-and-seek with the woman's pubic triangle is one of the oldest human games. See *Clothing, Chastity belt*. Cultivate the cunning use of a really practical g-string.

waking

She says: 'Sleep patterns matter, and it's the man who wakes with an erection. While it's great to be woken with intercourse, this doesn't apply when one has had a ghastly day and has an interview coming up next morning; use some sense. It also doesn't apply in the middle of a dream one has to finish.' Some women take minutes or hours to wake up, and though they enjoy gentle intercourse waking – and it works far better than an alarm clock – don't expect athletics. The trouble is that this is the time when many males are ready for them and expect to be ridden, masturbated, sucked and what have you. Keep these early waking workouts for Sundays and holidays and preferably make coffee first, erection or no erection. Some people are lucky in having roughly the same sleeping hours, but if one were early and the other a night person that too could well give rise to real problems. If you have these, talk about them; some people do use sleep as an excuse for avoiding intercourse, but between lovers who are on different clocks it can be real and doesn't imply rejection.

If you have children, you have to be ready to be woken by them, and restrict yourselves accordingly. Don't lock them out. Rearrange your sex life to get the necessary privacy at other times – if all else fails get a baby-sitter and stay at a motel once a month. The sound and fury of really ongoing sex would give primal scene problems to any small child, so don't take risks; the sort of sex we have, and are talking about here, almost excludes fertility – it's a choice one may have to make, while houses and family-structure are as they are.

women (by her for him)

Women, like men, have direct physical responses, sure, but these *are* different (breasts and skin first, please, not a direct grab at the clitoris) and can't be short-circuited. It matters to them who is doing what, far more than it does to most men. The fact that, unlike you, we can't be visibly turned off and lose erection often confuses men into hurrying things or missing major resources. It isn't true that nudity, erotica, etc., don't excite women – probably the difference is that they aren't overriding things. Is it fair, I wonder, to give a simple instance? You can make orgiastically satisfactory love with a near stranger in half an hour flat. But please don't think for that reason that you can do the same for a woman who loves you personally if at the

opposite Two miniatures painted on ivory from the Ganges Valley, circa 1840–80

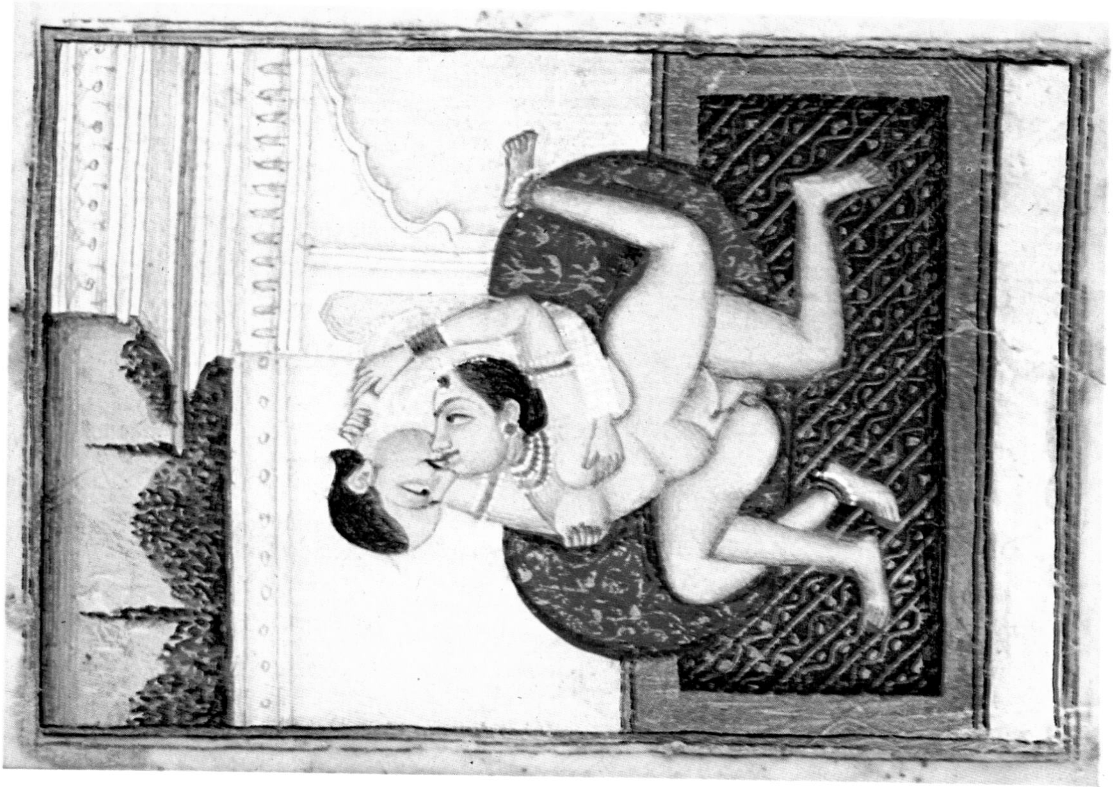

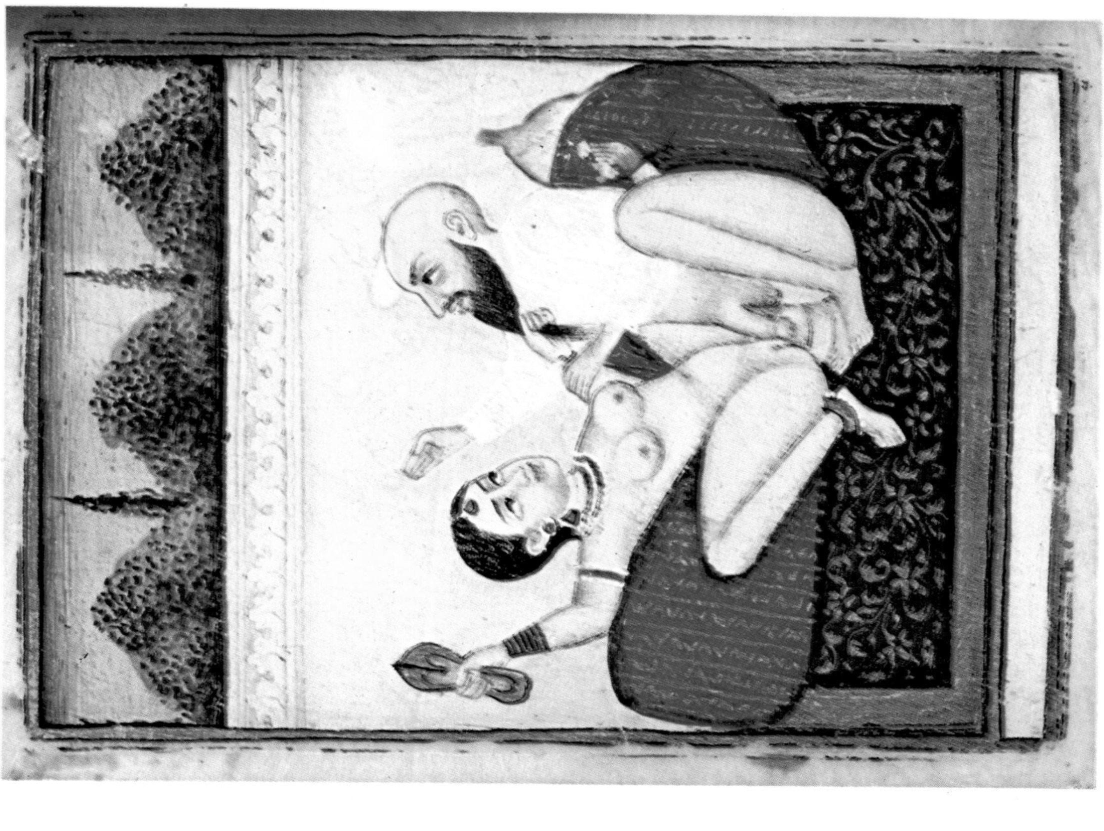

end of the half-hour you put her into a taxi with a bunch of roses and go off to a wife. Granted this, however, there are common reactions.

We seem to be less heavily programmed than you for specific turn-ons, but once we see one of these working on a man we care about, we soon program it into our own response, and can be less rigid and more experimental *because* of this ability. Often if women seem underactive it's because they're scared of doing the wrong thing with that particular man, like touching up his penis when in fact he's trying not to ejaculate – *tell* us if you see us at a loss. The penis isn't a 'weapon' for us so much as a shared possession, rather like a child – it's less the size than its personality, unpredictable movements, and moods which make up the turn-on (which is why rubber dummies are so sickening). Another important thing is the tough-tender mixture: obviously strength is a turn-on, but clumsiness (elbows in eyes, twisted fingers, etc.) is the dead opposite. You never get anywhere by clumsy brutality; however brutal good lovemaking sometimes *looks*, the turn-on is strength-skill-control, not large bruises: and the ability to be tender with it. Some people ask 'Tough or tender?' but the mood shifts so fast you've got to be able to sense it. Surely it's possible – because some lovers do it – to read this balance from the feel of the woman. No obsessive views about reciprocity – who comes on top, etc., does in fact even out during the passing of time: there can be long spells when one enjoys and is happy to let him do the work, and others when you need to control everything yourself and take an extra kick from seeing how you make him respond.

Women aren't 'masochistic' any more than men – if they've knuckled under in the past it's only through social pressures. If they're sadistic, they unfortunately don't reify it like a man and act it out in bed by wearing spurs and cracking a whip (any girl who does this is doing it as a male turn-on): they're more likely to express it as no-saying or nagging, which contributes to nobody's orgasm. Men have a real advantage here in the constructive use of play (and can help women to reify). Since we all have some aggressions, good sex can be wildly violent but still never cruel. A little frightening helps some people sometimes. Anyhow the old idea of man as raper and woman as rapee being built-in is contrary to all experience in a world where role-swapping is general.

As to the Women's Lib bit, nobody can possibly be a good lover – or a whole man – if he doesn't regard women as (a) people and (b) equals. That is really all there is to be said.

Our sense of smell is the keener – don't oversaturate early on with masculine odors; just before orgasm is prob-

opposite A painting from Rajasthan, Bindi State, circa 1790

ably the time for full odor contact. Our own smell excites us as well as yours.

The sort of hand and mouth-work which men like varies enormously. Some like it very rough, some hate it anything but extremely gentle, others in between. There is no way for a woman to tell except by asking and being told – so it's up to the man to say what he likes or he may get the opposite.

Some men are extraordinarily passive, or unimaginative, or inhibited, and – oddly – when they are any of these things, we do not become correspondingly aggressive. We may long to do things and feel thoroughly frustrated, but we won't dare show it in most case . So a woman's love-making will only be good with a good lover and, more important, she will resent any man who is unexciting, not only because it is unexciting but also because she will know she has been unexciting too.

Finally, just as all women are more alike to a man than all men are to a woman, women probably really do differ sexually rather more than men, because of the greater complexity of their sexual apparatus (breasts, skin and so on as well as pussy). Never assume you don't need to relearn for each person. This is true for women with a new man, but perhaps a little less so.

Main Courses

which everyone needs

bidet

This article of European bathroom furniture is beginning to be trendy in America. It used to be necessary when post-coital douching was the rule, but the Pill has altered that. For washing it can be useful, for example after anal intercourse or cleaning your feet, and less trouble than a shower, though a woman showering looks better than sitting on a bidet like a battery hen. Indiscriminate douching is medically a bad idea in any case – the vagina is self-cleansing and water merely upsets its natural hygiene. Keep the douche, and the bidet, for cleaning-up after menstrual periods.

breasts

'In our maturer years,' wrote Darwin, 'when an object of vision is presented to us which bears any similitude to the form of the female bosom . . . we feel a general glow of delight which seems to influence all our senses, and if the object be not too large we experience an attraction to embrace it with our lips as we did in early infancy the bosom of our mothers.' Alfred Perlès greeted a socialite who was seated next him at dinner with the words 'Those aren't bad – fish them out and let's have a look at them!' Breasts are the natural second target, but often the first one we reach. Just how sensitive they are, in men as well as in women, varies enormously – size is unimportant, as with other sexual organs. Some don't answer at all, even in the emphatically non-frigid; some answer to extremely gentle touches, some to very rough handling (but they are sensitive structures – don't let your residual anger at having been weaned get the better of your commonsense).

Round and round the nipple with the tongue tip or the glans, soft kneading with both hands, gentle biting and sucking gently like a baby are the best gambits. She can use these on the man, plus very gentle fingertip friction – men's nipples easily get sore, however. If her breasts are big enough to meet, one can get a surprising degree of mutuality from intermammary intercourse. This is a good expedient on occasions when she is closed to the public. Lay her half flat on pillows, kneel astride (big toe to her clitoris if she needs helping) and your foreskin fully retracted. Either you or she can hold the breasts together – wrap them around the shaft rather than rub the glans with them. It should protrude clear, just below her chin. An orgasm from this position, if she gets one, is 'round' like a full coital orgasm, and she feels it inside. Breast orgasms from licking and handling are 'in between' in feel. Rub the semen well into her breasts when you have finished (see *Semen*).

Breasts, vagina and clitoris all at once make the most concentrated and fastest buildup of sensation once intercourse has begun, for some women at least. Few men can

BREASTS *opposite*
Just how sensitive the breasts are, in men as well as women, varies enormously.

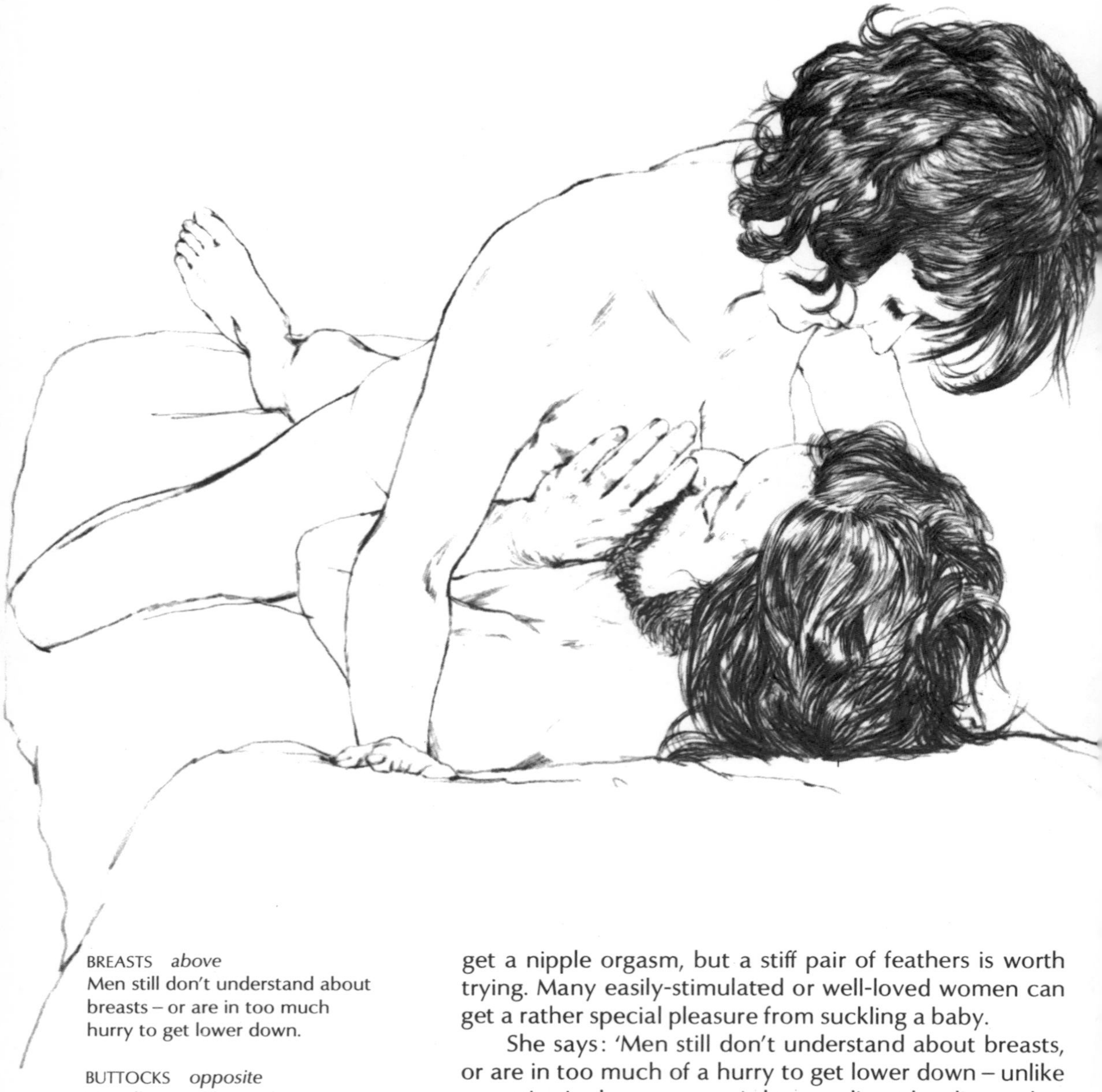

BREASTS *above*
Men still don't understand about breasts – or are in too much hurry to get lower down.

BUTTOCKS *opposite*
Visually, good buttocks are a turn-on almost equally for both sexes.

get a nipple orgasm, but a stiff pair of feathers is worth trying. Many easily-stimulated or well-loved women can get a rather special pleasure from suckling a baby.

She says: 'Men still don't understand about breasts, or are in too much of a hurry to get lower down – unlike a man's nipples, a woman's have a direct hot line to her clitoris. A man who can dial this correctly and will only take the time can do anything. Palm-brushing, eyelid-brushing, licking, and loud sucking like a baby can work wonders; the orgasms one gets from these are mind-blowing, without detracting a jot from intercourse to come after. *Please take time.*'

Intercourse between the breasts is equally good in other positions – head to tail, or with her on top (especially if she has small breasts), or man sitting, woman kneeling: experiment, accordingly.

buttocks

Next in line after breasts, and alternate with them as visual sex stimuli for different cultures and individuals. Actually the original primate focus, being brightly colored in most

apes: apparently equally fancied by the Mousterian culture which produced some of the best Stone Age figurines, while more recent primitives 'made their selection by ranging their women in a line and picking her out who projects furthest *a tergo*' (Darwin). Major erogenous zone in both sexes, less sensitive than breasts because they contain muscle as well as fat, and needing stronger stimulation (holding, kneading, slapping or even harder beating – see *Discipline*). Intercourse from behind is a pleasure in itself but be careful if she has a weak back. In any position the muscular movements of coitus stimulate the buttocks in both sexes, particularly if each holds the partner's rear fairly tightly, one cheek in each hand. These extra sensations are well worth cultivating deliberately. Visually, good buttocks are a turn-on almost equally for both sexes.

cassolette

French for perfume box. The natural perfume of a clean woman: her greatest sexual asset after her beauty (some would say greater than that). It comes from the whole of her – hair, skin, breasts, armpits, genitals, and the clothing she has worn: its note depends on her hair color, but no two women are the same. Men have a natural perfume too, which women are aware of, but while a man can be infatuated with a woman's personal perfume, women on the whole tend to notice if a man smells right or wrong. Wrong means not so much unpleasant as intangibly not for them. Often their awareness of a man includes conditioned extras like tobacco.

Because it is so important, a woman needs to guard her own personal perfume as carefully as her looks and learn to use it in courtship and intercourse as skillfully as she uses the rest of her body. Smoking doesn't help this. It can be a long-range weapon (nothing seduces a man more reliably, and this can happen subliminally without his knowing it) but at the same time a skillful man can read it, if he is an olfactory type, and if he knows her, to tell when she is excited.

Susceptibility and consciousness of human clean perfumes vary in both sexes. Whether these are inborn differences, like inability to smell cyanide, or whether they are due to unconscious blocking-out we don't know. Some children can't understand the point of blind man's buff because they know by smell who is touching them: some women can smell when they are pregnant. Men can't smell some chemicals related to musk unless they have a shot of female sex hormone. There is probably a whole biological signal mechanism here which we are only just starting to unravel. Far more human loves and antipathies are based on smell than our deodorant-and-aftershave culture admits. Many people, especially women, say that

CASSOLETTE *opposite*
Far more human loves and antipathies are based on smell than our soap-and-aftershave culture admits.

when it's a question of bed or not-bed they let their noses lead them.

Women have the keener sense of smell, but men respond to it more as an attractant. In lovemaking, the note changes in regular order, from the totality of skin and *gousset* to her 'excited' note, then to her full genital odor, then, when intercourse has begun, to a different scent. Finally the seminal odor will appear in her breath and trigger the next bout.

Some benighted savages still cut off the clitoris. It's said that women themselves are the most insistent about the necessity of mutilating their daughters. Ours don't go that far, but do still chop off their armpit hair, or did until a new generation started to realize that it was sexy. This might be forgiveable in a hot climate with no plumbing. Now it is simply ignorant vandalism. Some of the nicest of them still do it, and even the wouldbe sexiest are ineducable in the face of fashion. This could be played as an argument for lifeboat whiskers or Sikhism, but men's facial hair doesn't have the day-to-day importance of a woman's little tufts. These are antennae and powderpuffs to introduce herself in a room, or in lovemaking. They are there to brush the man's lips with; he can do the same more circumspectly. Kissing deeply in the armpit leaves a partner's perfume with you. In the genital kiss, start with the lips covered, then brush the closed lips, then open her: when she gives the kiss to a man, she proceeds in the same order. It's the fullest way to become aware of her as a presence, even before you start to touch.

croupade

Any position in which he takes her squarely from behind, i.e. all rear-entry positions except those where she has one leg between his or is half-turned on her side (see *Cuissade*).

cuissade

The half-rear entry positions, where she turns her back to him and he enters with one of her legs between his and the other more or less drawn up: in some versions she lies half-turned on her side for him, still facing away.

earlobes

Underrated erogenous zone, together with the adjacent neck skin – the small area behind the ear has a 'hot line' to the visceral nerves via the vagus – and the nape of the neck. As with all extragenital sites, more effective in women than men. Once established (gentle fingering, sucking, etc., during buildup and before orgasm, to condition the response) earlobes can trigger full climax from manipulation alone. Some women find the noise of heavy breathing excruciating and a definite turn-off, so be careful. Heavy

CROUPADE *opposite*

earrings help, and can actually maintain subliminal erotic excitement, especially if long enough to brush the neck when she turns her head—this is the function of the large oriental and Spanish candelabra-type earrings. The sex difference in response probably accounts for their relative rarity worldwide in male fashions.

Swinging weights as erotic stimuli to condition a particular area aren't confined to the ears. If earrings are the screw-on type, take them off and try them gently on her nipples, labia or clitoris – ask first!

equipment

The Austrian gymnastic professor van Weck Erlen wrote a book in which, along with over 500 postures you draw lots to carry out, he advised a 'sexuarium' complete with gymnastic mat and trapezes. For his sort of sex you'd need

them. The idea of a 'sexuarium' complete with mirrors, red light and black decor turns some people on – there are a good few 1930's palaces in Beverly Hills which have one. On a smaller scale one can fit out the basement. Our preference is for the bedroom, however, and the result needn't be embarrassing.

The bed we've discussed already. The gymnastic-mat idea isn't a bad one at all – a really thick carpet (or carpet piece if you can't afford it wall to wall) is as good, with plenty of room to roll around. Some people favor stools for the bent-over positions, front and back: as one needs a bedroom stool, this can be chosen the right height. A pile of hard square cushions is more suited for diversification. Two of the bed pillows will be hard, for use in bed – the cushions are for floor work. If you like big mirrors these can be inside closet doors, or turn over to show a chaste decoration. The best chair for intercourse is a fully-upholstered one without arms. If you want to tie each other

to it, check for size and convenience – if you only want it for straight intercourse it is best padded all over: or have separate chairs for each. A ceiling mirror is fun, but expensive and obvious if you mind that. You need an adjacent bathroom and shower. The ordinary motel bedroom layout is excellent for all these things, except that they don't pick the chairs with an eye to coition.

Naturally it is exciting to set up a fantasy place for fantasy experiences, complete with your own light show, if you have the money and energy. What we don't want to do here is to give the impression that you really need this – you don't, any more than you need a dream kitchen to be a first-class chef. You need the bare minimum – privacy, heating, washing space, a bed, one or two ordinary furniture surfaces, genitalia which work, love and imagination.

If you want extras, these will depend on what you want to do. Acrobatic position-merchants like to have a

CUISSADE *opposite*

EQUIPMENT *above*
You don't need any extras to have superlative sex, given the right person and the right attitude.

FLANQUETTE *opposite*

FRONTAL *above*
All the face-to-face positions where one partner has both thighs between those of the other.

step-stool (fixed down, so it isn't dangerous) or even a short ladder. Some people fancy a *Rocking chair*. Old-style bordels went in for all manner of stage sets, but these were either for the obsessed or once-in-a-while settings for an extra kick, not permanencies. If you are including other couples you need corresponding extra space, whether you go all together or alternate demonstrations. Colored room light is an extra which some people find rewarding – so are a Land camera and a tape-recorder. If you use extras of any sort, from cushions or vibrators to cameras, lubricants, ropes or g-strings, make sure they are at hand and don't have to be fetched. Have a cloth towel ready – paper tissues stick to the skin. But you don't *need* any of these things to have superlative sex, given the right person and the right attitude.

Probably the only advantage of a really private sex-room is that you can fill it with erotic pictures without erotising 'square' guest-space, and entertain Auntie without her asking what those rings in the wall are for. But a slide projector works fine on any white wall or ceiling, and you'd be surprised how unobservant the uninitiated are.

feet

Very attractive sexually to some people—he can get an orgasm, if wished, between their soles.

Their erotic sensitivity varies a lot. Sometimes, when they're the only part you can reach, they serve as channels of communication, and the big toe is a good penis substitute (see *Big toe*).

Tickling the soles excites some people out of their minds; for others it's agony but increases general arousal. You can try it as a stimulus, or, briefly, for testing bondage. Firm pressure on the sole at the instep, however administered, is erogenic to most people. But so can almost any touch be in a woman who's that way minded – one can get a full orgasm from a foot, a finger, or an earlobe. Men respond less far but equally easily if the handling is skillful.

flanquette

The half-facing group of sexual postures – she lies facing him with one of her legs between his, and consequently one of his legs between hers, the frontal equivalent of the *Cuissades*. These positions give extra clitoral pressure from the man's thigh if he presses hard with it.

food

Dinner is a traditional preface to sex. In old-time France or Austria one booked a restaurant room with no handle on the outside of the door. At the same time there is a French saying that love and digestion went to bed together and the offspring was apoplexy. This isn't quite true. On the other hand, immediately after a heavy meal is not an ideal moment – you can easily make your partner, especially the woman if she's underneath, sick.

A meal can be an erotic experience in itself – for a demonstration of how a woman can excite a man by eating a chicken-leg or a pear 'at' him, cannibal-style, see the lovely burlesque in the film of *Tom Jones*. A meal *à deux* is, quite certainly, a direct lead-in to love play (see *Big toe, Remote control*) but don't include alcohol. Recent work shows that even in small doses it's a powerful neutering drug, and it's quite the commonest cause of unexpected impotence – so forget the folklore and ignore the commercials. If you're serious about sex, stay with Perrier water. Love and food

opposite and overleaf Two scenes from the sixteenth-century Ming dynasty novel Chin P'ing Mei or *The Golden Lotus*

mixed well in Greek and Roman times when you reclined together on a couch, or fed one another (geishas do this still). Some people enjoy food-and-sex games (custard or icecream on the skin, grapes in the pussy, and so on) which are great for regressive orality but messy for an ordinary domestic setting. Most lovers with privacy like to eat naked together and take it from there according to taste.

History is littered with 'aphrodisiac' foods – these are either magic (eryngo roots, which look like testicles, phallic asparagus and so on), olfactory (fish, tomatoes straight off the plant, which smell sexy) or miscellaneous. One can't prove that onions, eels – phallic and otherwise – ginseng root and so on don't work on some people. The trouble is that any *reputed* aphrodisiac works if you think it will, while many true pharmacological responses can get overridden in particular individuals by other factors. Broad beans are a reputed aphrodisiac – not only do they look like testicles, but they contain dopamine. We both respond so quickly to one another that any effect of this sort is hard to gauge personally. Hot spices, which induce skin flushing, are another physiologically plausible line of attack. But none of them are lifesavers, or come up to the combined effect of 'the time and the place and the loved one together.' However, experiment by all means. Only very heavy meals and excessive drinking are specific turnoffs.

frontal

All the face-to-face positions where one partner has both thighs between those of the other – he astride both hers or between them. Includes all the varieties of the *Matrimonial* plus most of the more complicated deep facing positions. Gives more depth (usually) but less clitoral pressure than the *Flanquettes*. To unscramble a complicated posture for purposes of classification, turn the partners round mentally and see if they can finish up face-to-face in a matrimonial without crossing legs. If so, it's frontal. If not, and they finish face-to-face astride one leg, it's a flanquette: square from behind (croupade): or from behind, astride a leg (cuissade). It's as simple as that.

This isn't an intellectual classificatory exercise. Postures are to be used in sequence, and one needs to make as few radical shifts, such as climbing over legs or turning a partner over, as possible – consider, in dancing, the difference between an impetus turn and a natural spin turn. This is important in planning sequences, though once you get used to going through five, ten or twenty postures at a single session you'll do it automatically: at first, whichever partner leads, they need to envisage all the stages in getting where they are going to avoid clumsiness and breaks, other than natural and intended ones.

FRONTAL *overleaf*
Postures are used in sequence and one needs to make as few radical shifts as possible. Avoid clumsiness.

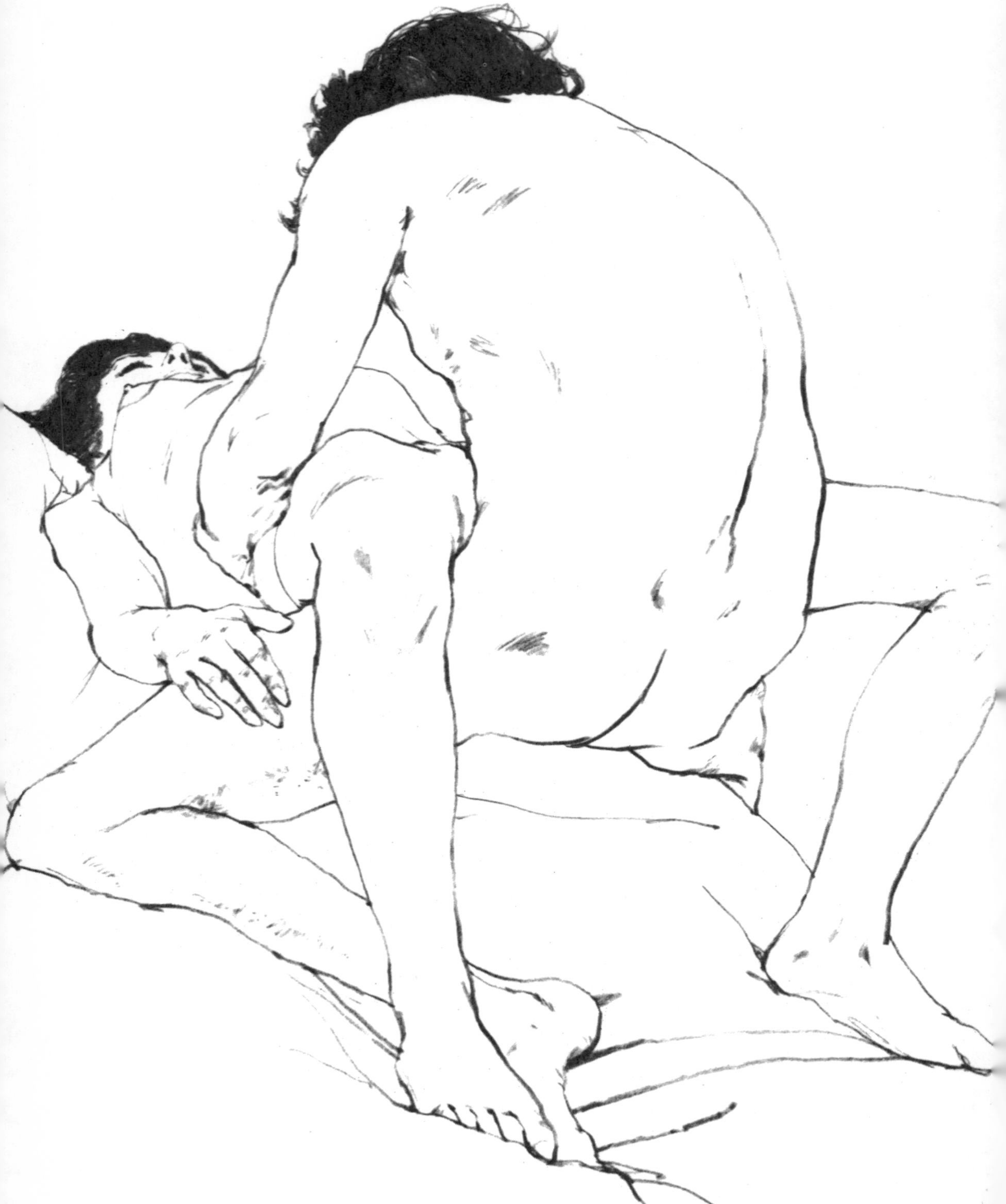

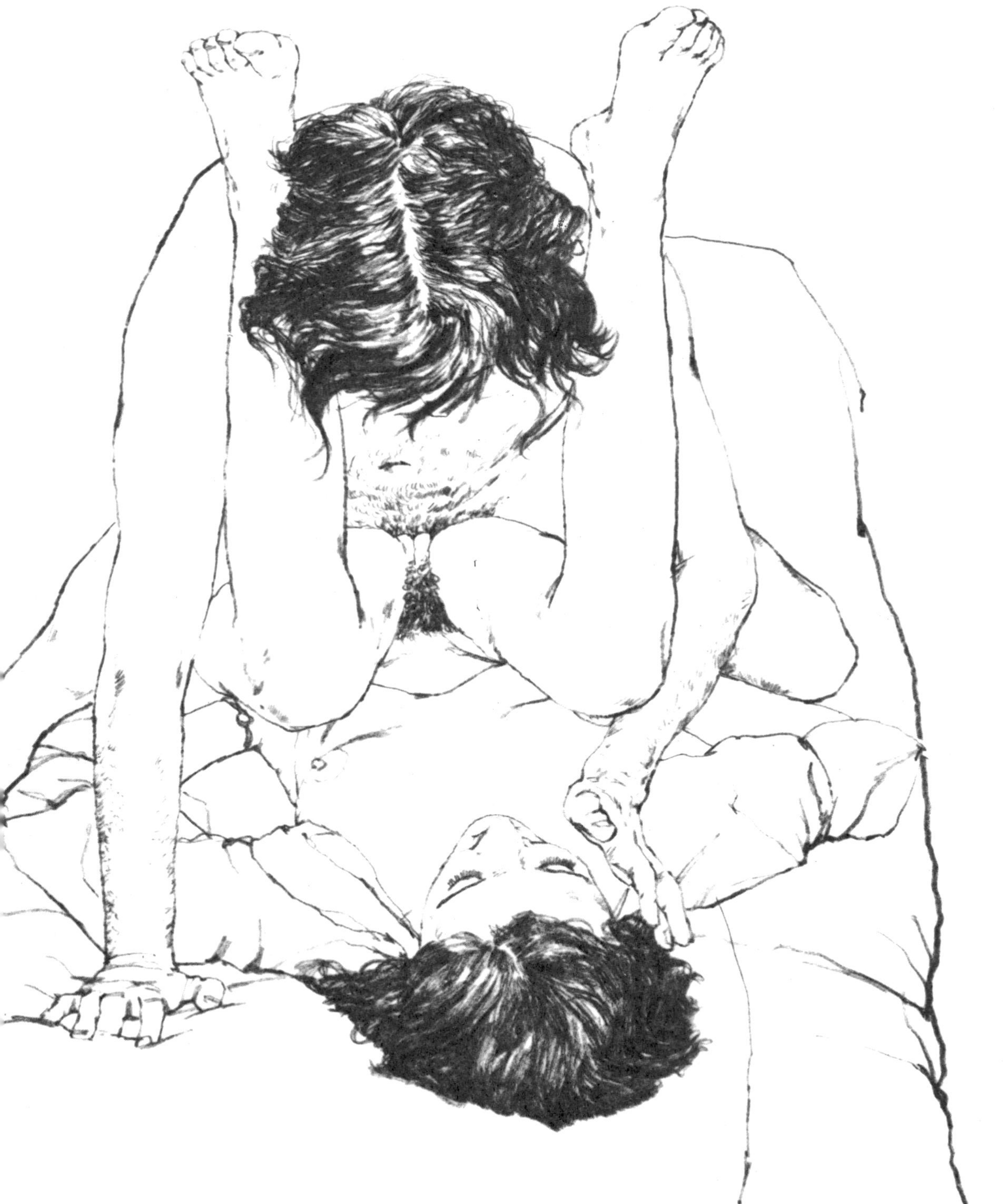

hair

Head hair has a lot of Freudian overtones – in mythology it's a sign of virility, witness Samson or Hercules. Our culture having learned in the last generation to associate long hair with women and short hair with manly conformity is occasionally excited to frenzy when young males now prefer to reject the stereotype and wear their hair, in the words of the seventeenth-century Harvard MS. 'in the manner of ruffians and barbarous Indians' – or of George Washington. Freud thought that long female hair acted as reassurance to the male by being a substitute for the phallus women don't have. Be that as it may, long male hair stirs all kinds of hostility in up-tight people who are upset by anything which looks intersexual in terms of their conventions. This is temporary – in many ages it has been as fashionable as now, and tends to go with a less anxious idea of maleness.

Sex play with long hair is great because of its texture – you can handle it, touch each other with it, and generally use it as one more resource. Some women are turned on by a fair amount of masculine body hair because it looks virile, others turned off by it because it looks animal – this seems to be a matter of attitude. Male face hair is another focus of convention – sometimes everyone has it as a social necessity, at other times it is persecuted, or confined to sailors, pioneers, and exotic people such as artists and chefs. Schopenhauer thought that it covered the parts of the face 'which express the moral feelings,' and disapproved, on the grounds that it was immodest to wear a sex signal in the middle of one's face. Today you can please yourself, or better, your partner.

handwork

Sex for all males and many females begins in the handwork class – both when we start to discover our own bodies and when we start to have access to each other's. For both sexes it is basic training – in mutual sex good handwork is never superseded. A couple who can masturbate each other really skillfully can do anything else they like. Handwork is not a 'substitute' for vaginal intercourse but something quite different, giving a different type of orgasm, and the orgasm one induces oneself is different again from orgasm induced by a partner. In full intercourse it is a preparation – to stiffen the man, or to give the woman one or more preliminary peaks before insertion. After intercourse, it is the natural lead-in to a further round. Moreover most men can get a second orgasm sooner from partner-stimulation than from the vagina, and a third after that if they masturbate themselves.

A woman who has the divine gift of lechery and loves her partner will masturbate him well, and a woman who knows how to masturbate a man – subtly, unhurriedly and

HAIR *opposite*
Sex play with long hair is great because of its texture – you can handle it, touch each other with it and generally use it as one more resource.

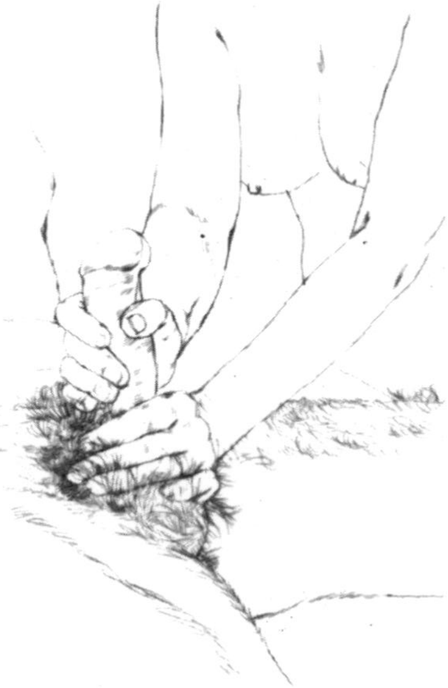

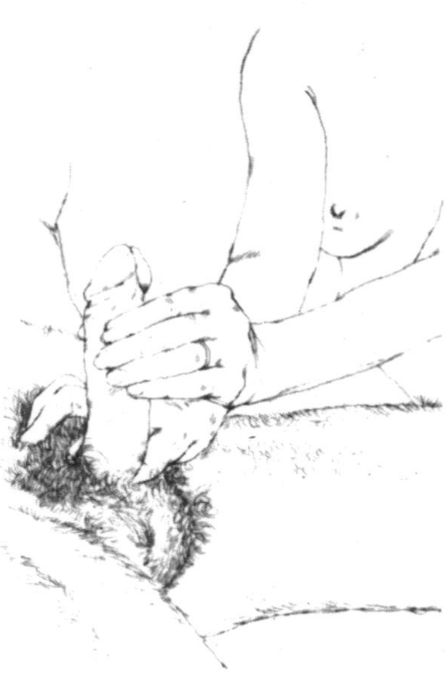

mercilessly – will almost always make a superlative partner. She needs intuitive empathy and real enjoyment of a penis, holding it in just the right place, with just the right amount of pressure and movement, and timing her action in bursts to coincide with his feeling – stopping or slowing to keep him in suspense, speeding up to control his climax. Some men can't stand really proficient masturbation to climax unless they are securely tied (see *Bondage*), and virtually none can hold still for slow masturbation.

The variation can be endless, even if she hasn't the choice of foreskin back, foreskin not back, which again yield two quite distinct nuances. If he isn't circumcised she will probably need to avoid rubbing the glans itself, except in pursuit of very special effects. Her best grip is just below the groove, with the skin back as far as it will go, and using two hands – one pressing hard near the root, holding the penis steady, or fondling the scrotum, the other making a thumb-and-first finger ring, or a whole hand grip. She should vary this, and, in prolonged masturbation, change hands often. For a full orgasm she sits comfortably on his chest or kneels astride him. During every extended sexual session one orgasm – usually the second or third – is well worth giving in this way: the French professionals who used no other method and called themselves 'les filles de la veuve Poignet' didn't only stay in business through fear of infection. It is well worth devoting time to perfecting this technique – it fully expresses love, and can be domesticated in any bedroom. Rolling the penis like pastry between the palms of two hands is another technique, best used for producing an erection. Firm pressure with one finger at the midpoint between penis and anus is another. For some occasions she can try to copy his own favorite method of self-masturbation; using her own rhythm has a different and sometimes more startling effect.

He needs to notice how she masturbates herself. Most men neglect the labia in favor of the clitoris. Clitoral rubbing can be as mind-blowing for her as slow masturbation is for him, but it can be painful if it is unskillful, repeated too often or straight after an orgasm achieved in this way. She says: 'The main difficulty from the man's point of view is that the ideal pressure point varies from hour to hour so he should allow her to guide him to the right place. Most men think they know automatically, having succeeded once – they are often wrong.'

For preparation as well as orgasm, the flat of the hand on the vulva with the middle finger between the lips, and its tip moving in and out of the vagina, while the ball of the palm presses hard just above the pubis, is probably the best method. Steady rhythm is the most important thing, taking it from her hip movements, and alternating with

gentle lip stretching – then a full attack on the clitoris and its hood with the forefinger or little finger, thumb deeply in the vagina (keep your nails short). For faster response, hold her open with one hand and work gently with all the fingers of the other (in this case she may need to be fixed down). Switch to the tongue occasionally if she becomes dry, because she won't realize until afterwards how sore you have made her.

In mutual masturbation to orgasm you take out your need to move on your partner. It works better than sixty-nine because under these circumstances you can let go without losing your partner or hurting them. Side by side on your backs is probably the best position.

When she masturbates him, she may get extra pleasure from seeing his ejaculation – if you want to avoid spilling semen in a strange bed, use one of the short glans-condoms called American tips (this is their only use – they are dangerous contraceptives, as they come off during intercourse).

However much sex you have, you will still need simple, own-hand masturbation – not only during periods of separation, but simply when you feel like another orgasm. Some women feel left out if they find their partner mastur-

HANDWORK *opposite and above*
In mutual sex good handwork is never superseded.

bating; but if you feel vibrations when he thinks you are asleep and want to get in on the act, tackle him there and then and finish him yourself at full speed – or better, start on him slow-style then stop, tie him, and make him watch you masturbate yourself, slowly and with style, before you put him out of his misery. The unexpected sight of a woman giving herself an orgasm when he cannot move is unbearably exciting for most men. Make sure he can't get loose. Finally, watching each other take the last orgasm separately but together makes a wonderful end to any afternoon in bed.

kisses

These, at one level, don't require teaching, but it's easy to be so set on insertion that one overlooks them. (See *Real sex*). Lip and tongue kisses add immensely to intercourse in all face-to-face positions: breast kisses are essential if the woman isn't to miss a whole range of feeling; genital kisses (see *Mouth music*) are a tender resource on their own. Kisses can be put anywhere on the body, they can be given with lips, tongue, penis, labia or eyelashes – mouth kisses range from a mere touch to the kiss *à la cannibale* which leaves a bruise.

A lot of people maintain mouth contact continuously throughout intercourse, and prefer face-to-face positions for this reason. The deep tongue kiss can either be a second penetration, the man's tongue imitating exactly the rhythm of what is going on elsewhere, or she can give it, penetrating him, to call the rhythm. Even without any penetration, some people favor a tongue-battle which can last minutes or hours, with several orgasms for the girl, a form of non-genital heavy petting called *maraichignage*. If you are in private, move on to breasts, and go from there. Another pleasure is to make her a carpet of flowers, by covering every inch of her body with small, close kisses: then she can reply, using lipstick to mark where she's been. From there it is only a little way to doing the same with a tongue-tip (see *Tongue bath*): moreover, unlike a man, she has two mouths to kiss with, and some women use them beautifully. Eyelids too can be used for nipple, lip, glans and skin kisses.

If you haven't at least kissed her mouth, shoulders, neck, breasts, armpits, fingers, palms, toes, soles, navel, genitals and earlobes, you haven't really kissed her: it is no trouble to fill in the gaps for completeness and makes a touching compliment.

A good mouth kiss should leave its recipient breathless but not asphyxiated (leave an airway open), and nobody likes their nose squashed into their face. Clean your teeth before making love, and if you are having whisky, garlic, etc., both of you have it.

HANDWORK *opposite*
A woman with the divine gift of lechery will almost always make a superlative partner.

KISSES *overleaf*
Make her a carpet of flowers by covering every inch of her body with small, close kisses.

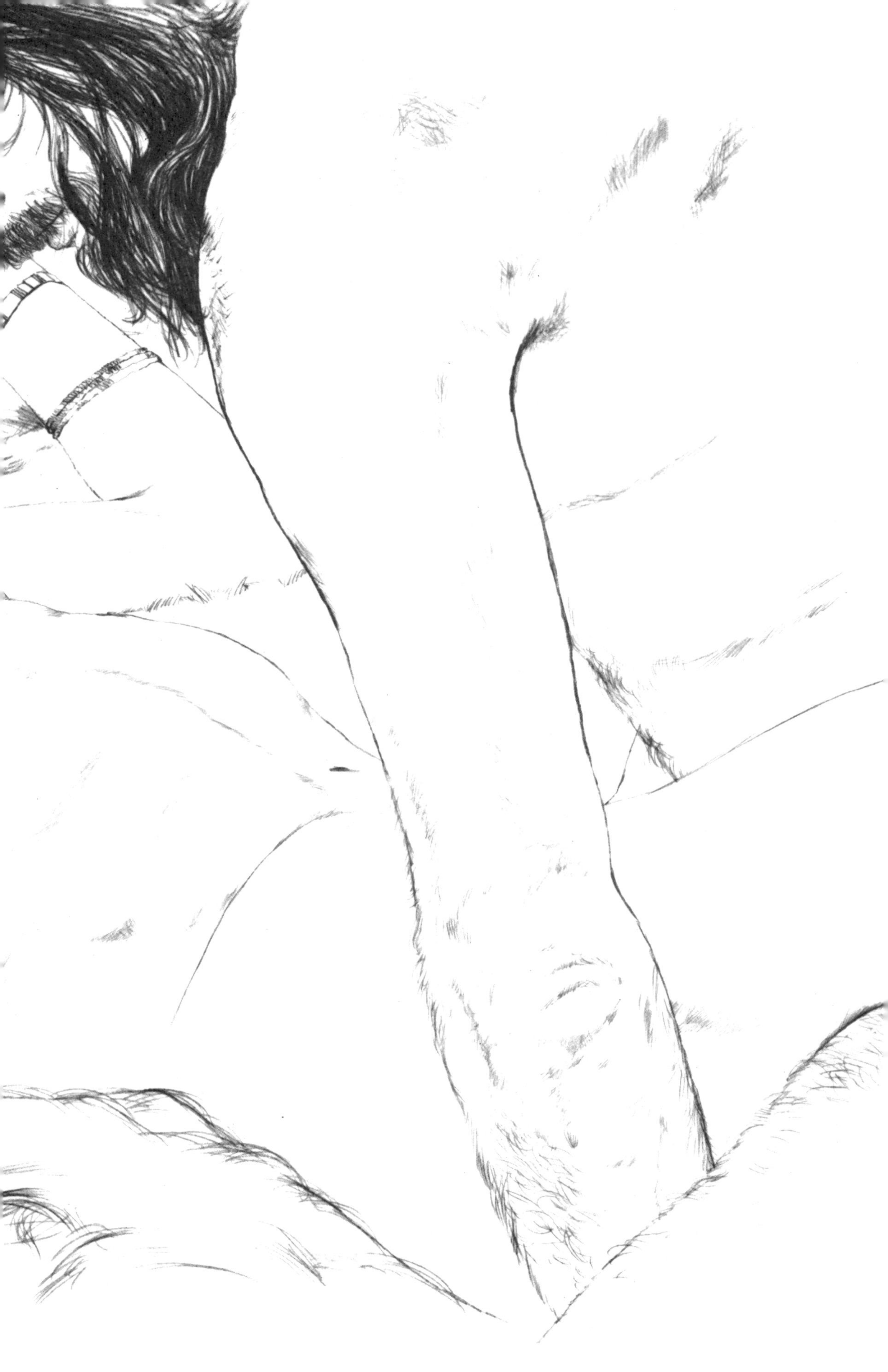

little death

La petite mort: some women do indeed pass right out, the 'little death' of French poetry. Men occasionally do the same. The experience is not unpleasant, but it can scare an inexperienced partner cold. A friend of ours had this happen with the first girl he ever slept with. On recovery she explained, 'I'm awfully sorry, but I always do that.' By then he had called the police and the ambulance. So there is no cause for alarm, any more than over the yells, convulsions, hysterical laughter or sobbing, or any of the other quite unexpected reactions which go with complete orgasm in some people. By contrast others simply shut their eyes, but enjoy it no less. Sound and fury can be a flattering testimonial to a partner's skills, but a fallacious one, because they don't depend on the intensity of feeling, nor it upon them.

Men don't very often pass right out – that's *her* privilege, though they can give a splendid impersonation of a fit. In any case you'll soon get to know your partner's pattern.

lubrication

The best sexual lubricant is saliva. For most sexual purposes, greasy materials, such as petroleum jelly, are too greasy and being unwettable they leave an unpleasant feel. Jellies tend to cut sensation too much. The normal excited vagina is correctly set for friction; if she is too wet, as may happen on the Pill, dry gently with a handkerchief-wrapped finger (not tissues – you'll never stop finding the bits). To increase friction, try honey – it washes off easily and is harmless.

Interference with friction is the main drawback of contraceptive creams, foams and so on, making them unpopular with some couples, but see our comment on protection against AIDS.

matrimonial

Every culture has its own fads about best positions, and experiment is essential. If we come back to the good old Adam and Eve missionary position, with him on top, astride or between, and her underneath facing – and we do come back to it – that is because it's uniquely satisfying. Chiefly it's unique in its adaptability to mood; it can be wildly tough or very tender, long or quick, deep or shallow. It is the starting point for nearly every sequence, second only to the side positions, and the most reliably mutual finishing-point for orgasm. If you start in it you can deepen it by raising her legs, move to the clitoris by putting one leg between hers, roll about or right over finishing with her on top, kneel and lie back into the Letter X with each partner lying between the other's legs (see *X position*), move into back, side or standing positions, then come back for the finish. It is also, together with the deeper versions, the ideal

MATRIMONIAL
opposite and overleaf
The good old Adam and Eve missionary position.

quick-orgasm position for both sexes. The only equally quick position for him is from behind if she is very tight, and the only quicker for her is astride on top. In fact, the chief reason for using the other 600 positions is to delay his final orgasm while multiplying hers. Experimentation will show you which suit you best.

Even excluding the leg-raising variants this position has won more medals at international expositions than any other. On the other hand, there is no one surefire sex

position which suits everyone. There are nonfrigid women who never come in this position, or only rarely: whether this is due to unconscious forces or position of the vulva, which can be a problem, doesn't matter a damn – try another position, especially if the man is overweight. The matrimonial and all deep or weightbearing positions are now known to be a bad idea in pregnancy: a few non-pregnant non-responders have had their lives changed by one or two hard pillows under the buttocks. There are non-matrimoniable women who have to be taken sitting, face to face, or from behind, finger to clitoris, or who need to ride. If the man needs her flat to finish, give her several orgasms in her preferred position first, then turn her. A gentleman is defined as one who takes his weight on his hands. There are great advantages anyway in ending in a position where you can settle in each other's arms without exertion.

The tuning adjustments for matrimonials can be highly important – hard enough bed, use of pillows if she is slim or built that way. Bed, cushion and flesh should between them give the consistency of buttocks which would be esthetically a bit too big. Tough or tender, how high you ride, pinned down (fold her arms gently up behind her and hold each of her thumbs in one of your hands) or not pinned down, astride her legs (holding them open by putting a foot under each of her insteps) or between them, spreading her with your legs – all make subtle differences. If your pubis isn't very hard and she needs a touch more clitoris, try a leg-between position or add finger contact. She can for her part hold your foreskin or penile shaft skin forcibly back with her hand (see *Florentine*).

menstruation

Primitives avoid menstrual intercourse because it is bad magic, and many moderns because it is messy. At the same time, the height of a period may be the girl's randiest time. If so, intercourse is harmless unless the male is liable to attacks of urethritis. You can ignore the flow and wash after, or she can douche, put in a cap, and flush afterwards (this is inclined to make her too dry, however). But periods are the natural time to concentrate on learning the full, mutual use of other, replacement techniques. Nature programmed them to encourage your versatility. Shallow, labial penetration is effective with a tampon in place – or you can try having sex under a running shower instead of in bed. The magical hazards can now be discounted, whatever grandmother taught. But menstrual blood is a potential source of the AIDS virus if the woman is a carrier, and greatly increases the risk of heterosexual transmission.

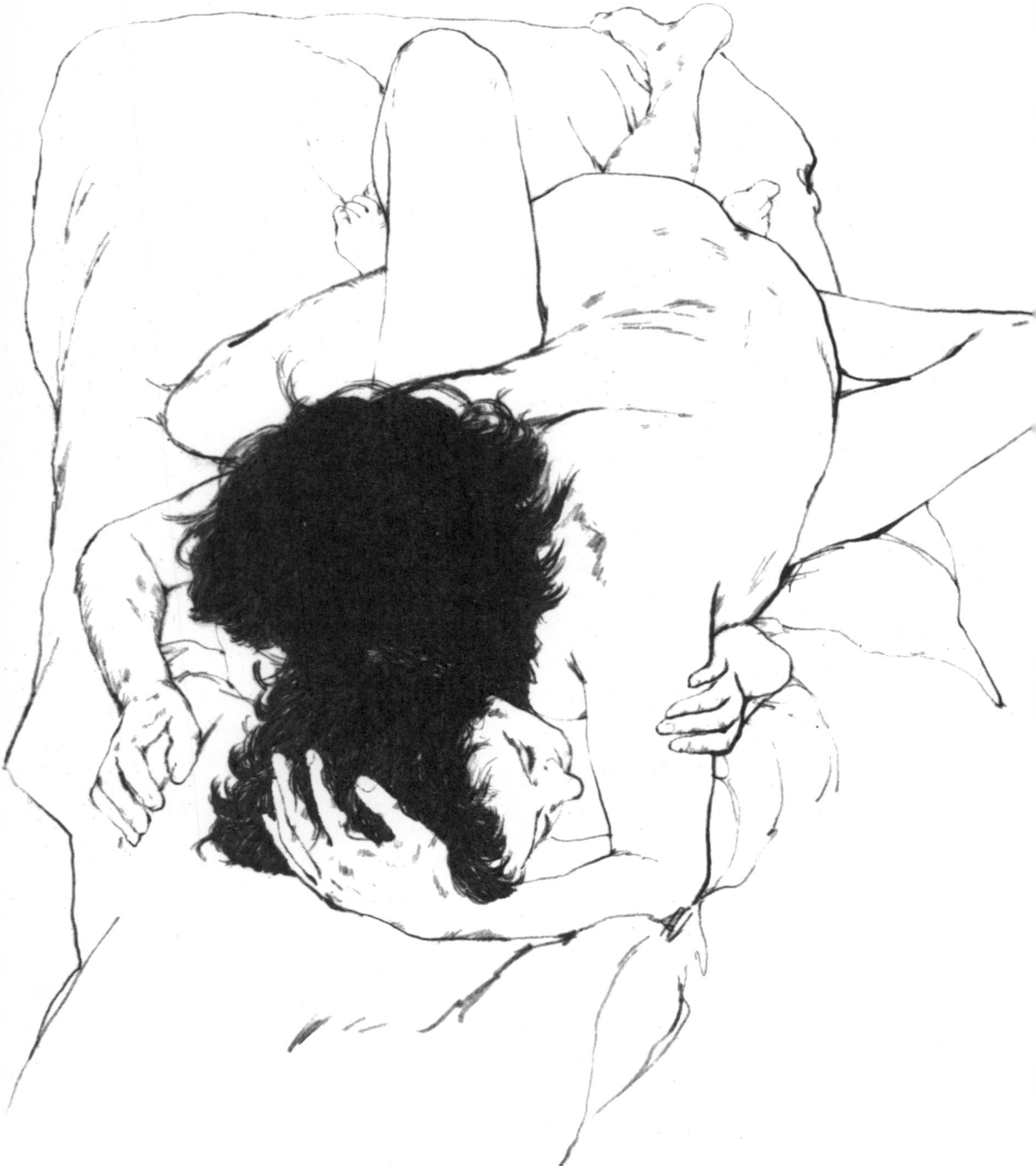

missionary position

Name given by amused Polynesians, who preferred squatting intercourse, to the European matrimonial. Libel on one of the most rewarding sex positions.

mons pubis

The decorative fat-pad over the female pubic bone which acts as a buffer in face-to-face intercourse and (more important) serves to transmit sensation to the rest of the area when it moves. Many men are not aware, if they are oversold on direct clitoris stimulation, that most women can be brought to orgasm simply by holding this gently in

MISSIONARY POSITION *above*

the cupped hand and kneading or shaking it, before, without, or as well as putting a finger in the vulva (see *Pubic hair*). You can either grasp it (it exactly fits the palm) or rest the heel of your hand on it while using the fingers on the labia, or you can cup the whole area, mons and closed labia, in your palm and fingers. Practice seeing how much sensation you can produce with your partner lying completely closed.

mouth music

It wasn't many years ago that genital kisses, or rather the taboos on them, were a king pretext for divorce on grounds of perversity, cruelty and so on. We've come some way since then – now there are textbooks, and they figure in movies. Personal preferences and unpreferences apart, most people now know that they are one of the best things in sexual intimacy. In regard to AIDS, the omnipresent preoccupation, there seems to be no clearcut case of its being transmitted by oral sex, but if you don't know your partner it would be wise to avoid it – in particular to avoid contact with semen.

Soixante-neuf is fine but has some drawbacks. It needs attention and care to give your partner your best, and consequently you can't go beserk over it, as you can over a mutual genital orgasm: impending orgasm, especially in the woman, just isn't compatible with careful technique, and the man can even be bitten. Another slight, but in some men, real defect is that in soixante-neuf the woman is the wrong way around for tongue work on the most sensitive surface of the glans (this explains the acrobatics in some Indian temple statues, which aim to get both mutuality and a better approach for the woman). Our own experience is that mutual genital kisses are wonderful, but if you are going to orgasm it's usually better to take turns.

Who goes first is clearly a matter of preference, but one can give the woman dozens of purely preliminary orgasms in this way, as many as she can take, and she will still want to go on from there, so the man had better save himself for later. A few men can't take even the shortest genital kiss before ejaculating – these should save it until they need a new erection, when it is a uniquely effective way of raising the dead.

Some girls do and some don't like the man to go all the way and ejaculate (if they love him very much, that may make all the difference, but not always). Those who don't can easily stop just short of getting him there, shift to another *foyer* (between the breasts, for example) or they can compress with both hands to gain time – this needs alertness and doesn't always work. It's also apt to wreck his orgasm. Others once they are used to it don't find the experience complete unless their lover does ejaculate. John Hunter wrote, 'The semen would appear both by smell and taste to be a mawkish kind of substance: but when held in the mouth it produced a warmth similar to spices.' If the slight bitterness, rather than the whole idea, is what they dislike, it can easily be avoided by taking him really deeply. With experienced women we guess it is about fifty-fifty, come or not come; in any case you can always ask, and partners soon learn each others' tastes. She says: 'A couple of important points to remember here are the retching is a reflex action if something large is poked down your throat; so if she does retch it may well not be because she hates it but because she can't help herself. A large penis will also stretch the mouth quite a lot and if she is covering her teeth with her lips to protect you, violent movements may lacerate them. Be considerate.'

Normal genital odor is a big part of the genital kiss for both partners, which means that the parties should wash often, but not immediately beforehand: they ought to know each other well enough to say, if it is ever disagreeable, and switch or wait. A few minutes' vigorous intercourse will often put this right, though the woman's odor changes in character. Contraceptives can upset it too. The marketers of intimate deodorants and flavored vaginal douches show evidence only of sexual inexperience – nobody wants peach sauce on, say, scampi. Seaweed odors or musk would be more in key. The woman's *Cassolette* is her secret weapon to an extent that women in America don't seem to realize – French women know better. Some men respond violently to it without realizing the fact; it's also the ideal perfume fixative, and a touch behind the ears at a dance, in advance of, or instead of, bottle perfume can be deadly. His, by contrast, will please her more the longer she loves him. Wash with white soap, and here as everywhere treat deodorants the way a chef would treat deflavorants. How the hippie generation thinks you can live the good sex life without washing defeats explanation.

For some couples the simultaneous, 69-type kiss really does represent the ultimate in sensation. For them, since loss of control will be complete, the woman can't be the beserk type, nor want him to stop short of ejaculating. The woman-on-top position in most books is all right, especially if she combines mouth with handwork, but it gives the man a stiff neck. We favor the no-cushions position, i.e. head to tail on their sides, each with the under thigh drawn up as a cushion for the partner's head. The man can open her widely by slipping his arm in the crook of her upper knee.

The mutual kiss can be long or short; the short is just

in passing – the long can last minutes or hours according to taste and speed. Both fit nicely between rounds of intercourse, as well as acting as hors d'oeuvres or a corpse reviver.

If, on the other hand, they are going alternately, let him start, preferably in this same no-cushions position, while she does very little. Then it can be her turn; or they can go on to intercourse, putting off fellatio until he has had one orgasm and a rest and is due for his next erection. In this way she can abandon herself, and watch her technique when she sucks him. She will probably get the best results with what the Chinese call the 'jade flute' position – an instrument which is self-explanatory, and is played like a recorder, facing him, thumbs underneath, fingers on top. Her technique depends on her man – for instance, on whether or not he is circumcised. Not all men find tongue or lip contact with the glans pleasurable. For some it's ecstasy, while others prefer foreskin movement over the covered glans with the shaft held tight. The various sorts of nibbling, etc., described in sex books come naturally to most people. One finds them out on a basis of learn and teach. For a more active male position and a fast orgasm, she lies back, and he has oral coitus as fully and deeply as she can stand it. She must keep her teeth well open, making him a vagina with her lips and tongue. He needs to keep a little control, to avoid being involuntarily bitten.

The reverse equivalent is when she kneels astride and gives herself, exactly as in a passionate mouth-to-mouth kiss, brushing first, then open and deeply, while he uses long tongue strokes, from the vagina to the clitoris, with an extra twitch to her glans as he reaches it each time.

When it's his initiative, he can do worse than try the cascade position, if she is portable. This is really only 69 standing up, but it gives her the unique sensation of an orgasm head-downward. To get her there he lays her face-up across the bed, head over the edge, stands astride her face, then bends over and picks her up, legs round his neck. She can return his kiss, but near orgasm she had far better slip him between her breasts or into her hand, and abandon herself to full orgasm.

The first genital kiss, to an inexperienced girl, is another 'situation.' Kneeling before her, 'vers le buisson ardent des femmes' looks fine, but one can't reach to do more than nuzzle. We suggest this: with the lady face-up along the bed, sit on the edge half-facing her feet. Kiss her all over; then reach over and pick up her farther leg and kiss her foot. Quickly slip your nearer elbow through her raised knee, open her, and kiss gently on the closed labia until she is ready for deeper and deeper tongue strokes. Fewer and fewer women are now inhibited about being kissed, though rather more can't get pleasure from kissing the man. A surprising number of girls cannot initially be got there at all *without* prolonged genital kissing, a fact which Indian love books recognize. For a very shy girl (or man), try it in the dark – but certainly try it. In the other direction, good mouth work is perhaps one of the most valued gifts a girl can give to her man, and well worth practicing. A spontaneous genital kiss to a man is one of the most moving gestures in the whole sexual experience.

navel

Fascinating to lovers, like all the details of the human body. It's not only decorative but has a lot of cultivable sexual sensation; it fits the finger, tongue, glans or big toe, and merits careful attention when you kiss or touch. Intercourse in the navel is practicable (there are stories of naive couples who thought that was the usual way, and it's a common childhood fantasy about how sex is conducted). If she is plump she can hold up the skin on each side to make labia. In any case, the finger or tongue tip slip into it naturally in both sexes.

négresse

A la Négresse – from behind. She kneels, hands clasped behind her neck, breasts and face on the bed. He kneels behind – she hooks her legs over his and pulls him to her with them – he puts a hand on each of her shoulder-blades and presses down. Very deep position – apt to pump her full of air which escapes later in a disconcerting manner – otherwise excellent.

postures

Endless time has been spent throughout history, chiefly by nonplaying coaches, in describing and giving fancy names to upwards of six hundred of these – collecting them is obviously a human classificatory hobby. Most people now know the obvious ones and have learned which make for quick and slow orgasm and how to use them in series. A few people, either for symbolic or anatomical reasons, can only get orgasm in one or two.

We haven't gone into postures here in this kind of detail. Most of the non-freak ones come naturally, and few of the freak postures merit more than a single visit out of curiosity.

The only part we regret is the loss of the fancy names, Arabic, Sanskrit or Chinese, which go with them. Inspection will indicate which fit special situations such as pregnancy, fat male with thin girl, height differences, etc.

NAVEL *opposite*
The finger and the tongue tip slip into it naturally.

POSTURES *overleaf*
Only trial will indicate which work best, or at all.

Only trial will indicate which work best, or at all, orgasm-wise. Couples often start by trying the lot, but nearly inevitably end up with one or two, going back to the book for special occasions. Some of the really wild fantasies in Oriental manuscripts do have a point – the girl astride in Mughal pictures who is balancing lighted lamps on her hands, head and shoulders or shooting at a target with a bow is only showing that she can bring the man off with her vaginal muscles alone while keeping the rest of her still (see *Pompoir*) and so on. Others are mystical or merely gymnastic. All the poses we show are practicable (we've tried them for fit, if not to orgasm) and more or less rewarding.

quickies

Short and sharp has a charm of its own, but it needs a rate of mutual turn-on and physical response in the woman which is learned as a rule *only* in much longer sessions. A really good couple can manage either at will – short and

POSTURES *above and opposite* Couples often start by trying the lot, but nearly inevitably end up with one or two, going back to the book for special occasions.

sweet, or indefinitely prolonged and differently sweet. In other words you can't fully appreciate the quickie without mastering the art of prolongation.

Once you've got this, the quickie is the equivalent of inspiration, and you should let it strike lightning fashion, any time and almost anywhere, from bed in the middle of the night to halfway up a spiral stair: anywhere that you're suddenly alone and the inspiration is bilateral. Not that one of other won't sometimes specifically ask, but the inspirational quickie is mutual, and half the fun is that the preliminary communication is wordless between real lovers. The rule is never to resist this linkup if it's at all possible – with quickness, wit and skill it usually is. This means proficiency in handling sitting, standing and other postures, and making love without undressing. The ideal quickie position, the nude matrimonial, will often be out. This may mean on a chair, against a tree, in a washroom. If you have to wait and can go straight home, it will keep up to half an hour. Longer than that and it's a new occasion. Around the house, try not to block, even if you *are* busy.

rear entry

The other human option – for most mammals it's the only one. Works admirably standing, lying, kneeling, sitting, or with the woman astride. The lack of face-to-faceness is

QUICKIES *opposite*
You should let it strike lightning fashion, any time and almost anywhere, from bed to half way up a spiral stair.

REAR ENTRY *below*
Works admirably standing, lying, kneeling, sitting or with the woman astride.

more than compensated for by extra depth and buttock stimulation, hand access to breasts and clitoris, and the sight of a pretty rear view. For the standing positions she needs something of the right height to support her – in the head-down kneeling positions you need to be careful

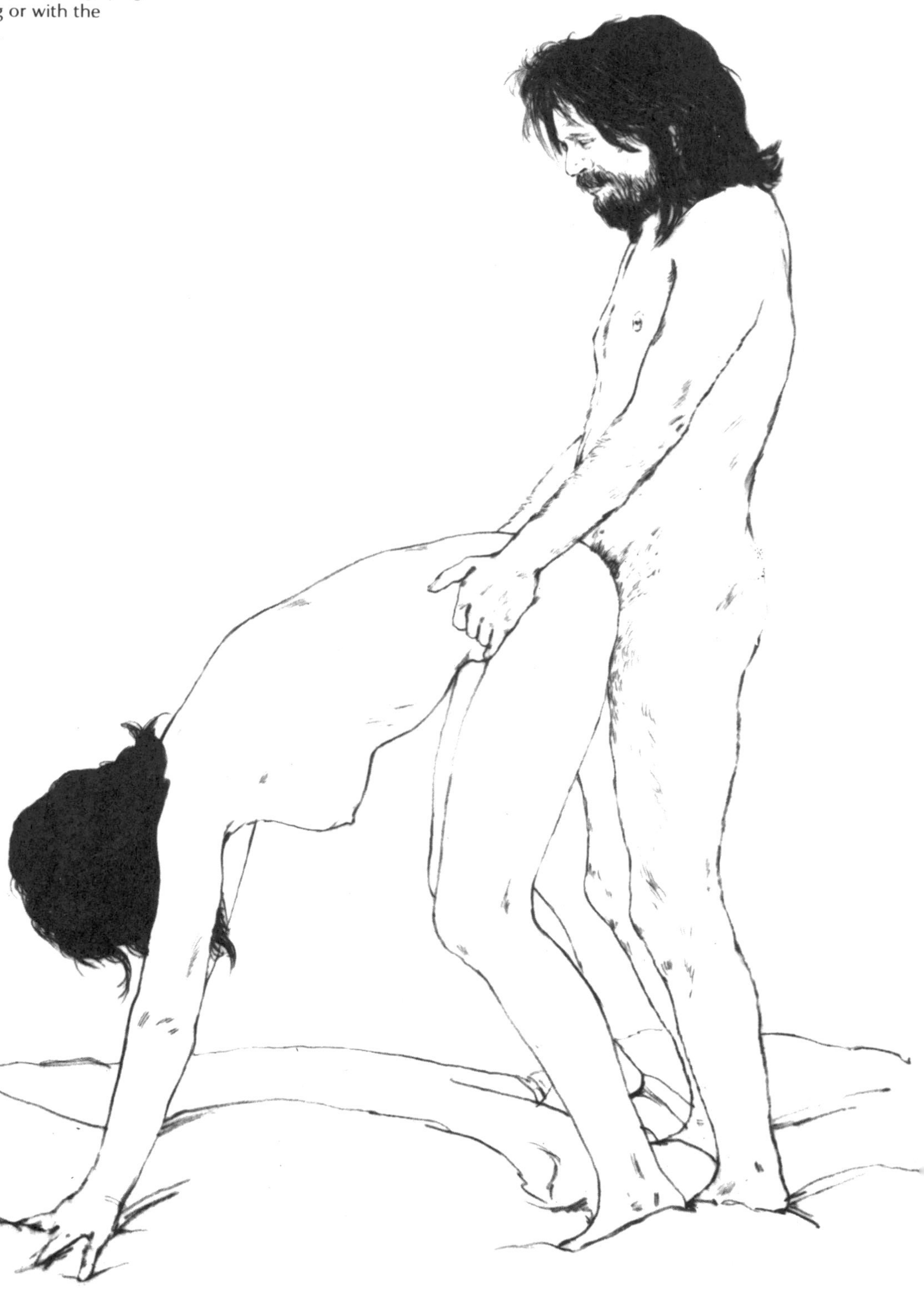

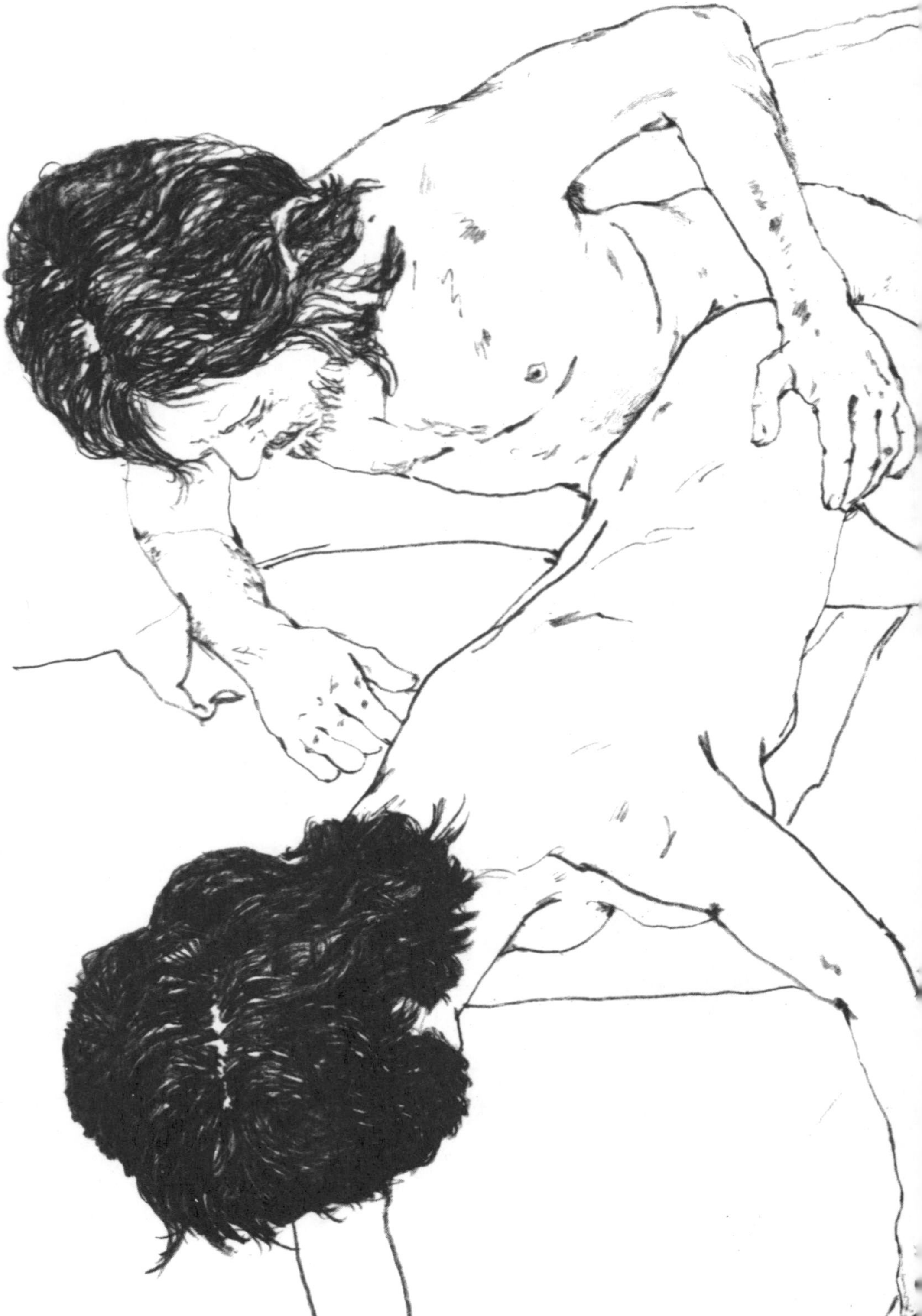

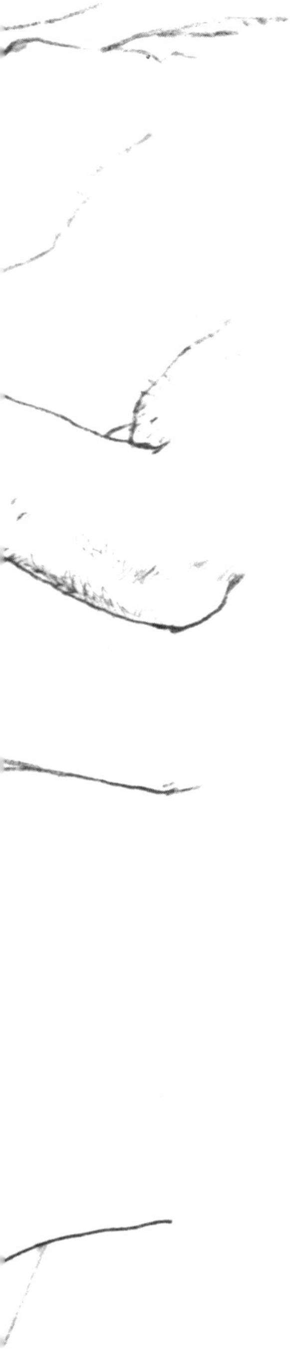

not to push her face into the mattress, and in all of the deep variants you need to avoid going too deep too hard, or you will hit an ovary, which is as painful as hitting a testicle. A few women are put off by the symbolism – 'doing it like animals,' 'not being valued if we aren't face to face' – but the physical payoff is so intense that they shouldn't allow these feelings to make them miss it. They could try it first with the man lying on his back and the girl lying faceup on top of him, or kneeling astride facing away, though these don't give the unique depth and total perineal stimulation of the rear kneeling positions (see *Négresse*). The man can hold her breasts or pubis, or, if she likes to be controlled, grasp her wrists behind her. A pile of hard pillows under her middle will help to prevent the position collapsing if she doesn't like being forcibly held, or she can kneel on the floor with her chest on the bed or a chair-seat. The head-down position is best for depth and total apposition – avoid it if it hurts her, or if she has a weak back, or if she is pregnant. Some women like a finger on the clitoris during intercourse, and this is easy in all rear positions. It's worth trying in any case, as it totally alters the range of sensation. Grasping the whole pussy in one hand gives a different sensation again and doesn't give the excessive sharpness which comes from strong clitoral stimulation. Or you can withdraw briefly and give a few clitoral strokes with the glans, guiding it with your hand.

While the deep kneeling position is, or can be, one of the toughest, from behind on your sides is about the gentlest (à *la paresseuse* – the lazy position) and can even be done in sleep – best if she draws her top thigh up a little and sticks her bottom out. This is one position which, in many women, can be managed with very little or even no erection; it can help to cure partial impotence or nervousness on the male side by restoring morale. It's also excellent if you want it gentle for health reasons, for fat or slightly disabled people, and so on.

It's well worth experimenting with the full range of rear positions at least as fully as with the face-to-face series, because there will be at least one you'll almost certainly use regularly along with the matrimonial and its variants and the woman-astride positions.

scrotum

Basically, a control device to keep the testes at the right temperature for sperm production – moves up when you are cold and down when you are warm. It is also a highly sensitive skin area, but needs careful handling, since pressure on a testis is highly painful to its proprietor. Gentle tongue and finger work or cupping in the hand is about right. You can take it right into your mouth.

REAR ENTRY *above*
It's well worth experimenting with the whole range of rear positions.

showerbath

Natural venue for sexual adventures – wash together, make love together: only convenient overhead point in most apartments or hotel rooms to attach a partner's hands. Don't pull down the fixture, however – it isn't weightbearing. See *Discipline*.

skin

Skin is our chief extragenital sexual organ – grossly underrated by most men, who tend to concentrate on the penis and clitoris; better understood by women.

She says: 'The smell and feel of a man's skin probably has more to do with sexual attraction (or the opposite)

SKIN *opposite*
Our chief extragenital sexual organ – grossly underrated by most men.

than any other single feature, even though you may not be conscious of it.'

Skin stimulation is a major component of all sex. Not only its feel when touched, but its coolness, texture and tightness are triggers for a whole range of sex feelings. These can be boosted in some people by emphasis, and by adding other textures, especially fur, rubber, leather or tight clothing. Much underrated part of human sexual response, to be played to the full if it turns you on. See *Clothes, Friction rub, Pattes d'araignée, Tongue bath.* Use these to educate your own and your partner's skin.

tanding positions

The traditional 'upright' is a quickie, and apt to produce stiff male muscles unless she is tall. Many women need to stand on two Manhattan phone directories with the yellow pages, or an equivalent. Best undertaken up against a solid object such as a wall or a tree (not a door, whichever way it opens). Alternatively, you can be free standing, legs apart for stability and arms clasped round each other's buttocks – looking down as you move can be really sensual.

There are two kinds of positions – this one, subject to a good match in height, and the Hindu versions where he picks her up: these are tremendous if she is light as an Oriya dancing girl, otherwise they need to be executed in water to make her weightless (see *Bathing*). For a tall girl, try with her arms round your neck, one of her feet on the ground, and the other over your elbow. She can then go legs around waist, both legs over your arms, and even both legs round your neck, lying back, if you are strong enough, into a head-down position. Try this over a bed in case you drop her, but stand on a firm floor, not a mattress. If you are back up to a wall she can swing herself with one foot. Not good orgasm positions – designed rather to spin out coition. Standing positions from behind need no special comment – she needs to lean over or hold onto something rigid. If you have real height problems, try the upright positions on a flight of stairs. The head-down genital kiss is a winner if you are strong enough to hold her up, and she takes a good leg grip.

tongue bath

Going systematically over every square inch of a partner, tied if they like, with long, slow, broad tongue strokes. Start behind, turn them and cover the front surface after, so as to be in position to go on to coition or hand and mouth work. If the woman gives this, she follows it by covering the whole available surface equally systematically with slow strokes of her open vulva. Mini-versions cover particular areas in the same way.

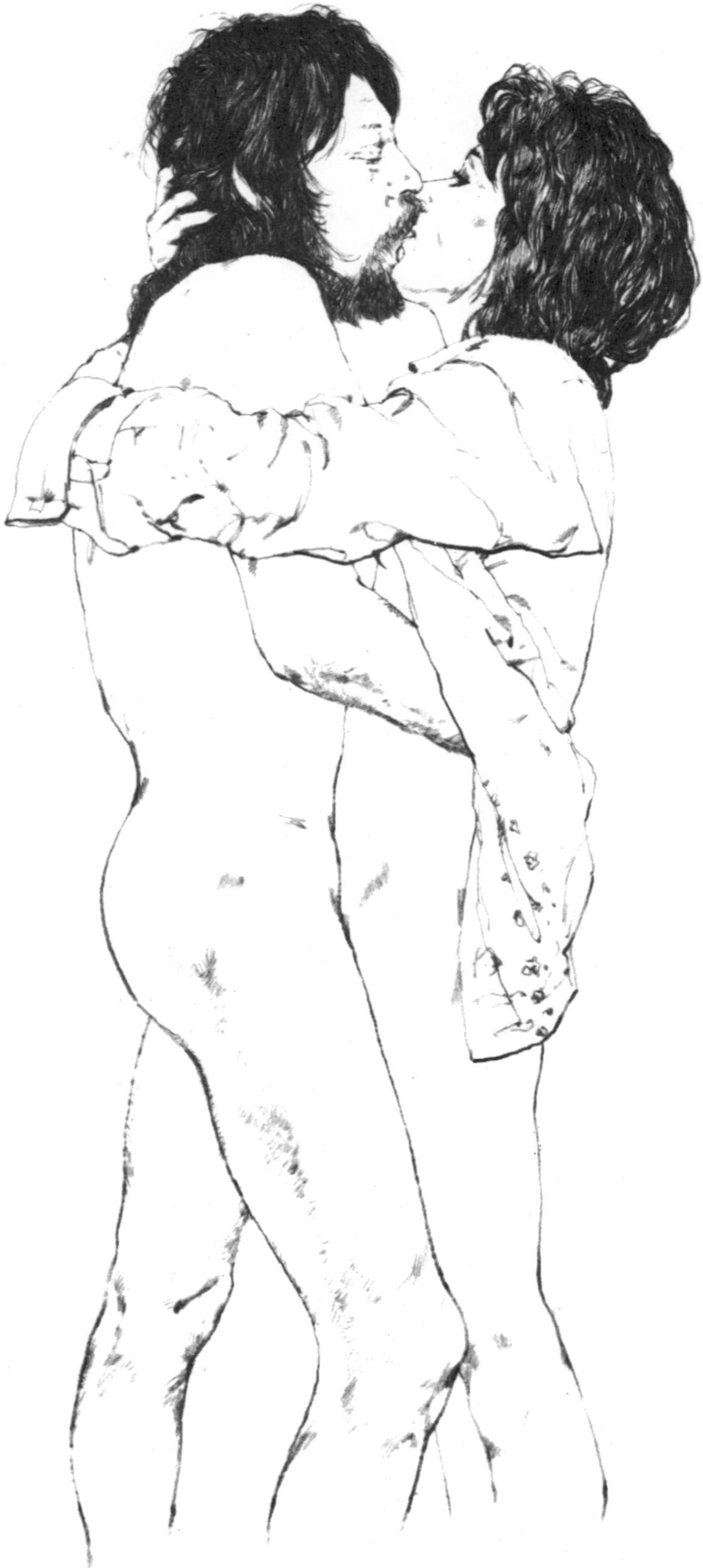

upper hands

If the matrimonial is the king of postures, the queen is her turn on top, 'riding St. George.' Indian erotology is the only ancient tradition devoid of stupid patriarchal hangups about the need for her to be underneath, and unashamed about accepting her fully aggressive role in reciprocal sex. With a woman who has good vaginal muscle control it can be fantastic for the man, but for her it is unique, giving her total freedom to control movement, depth and her partner. She can lean forward for breast or

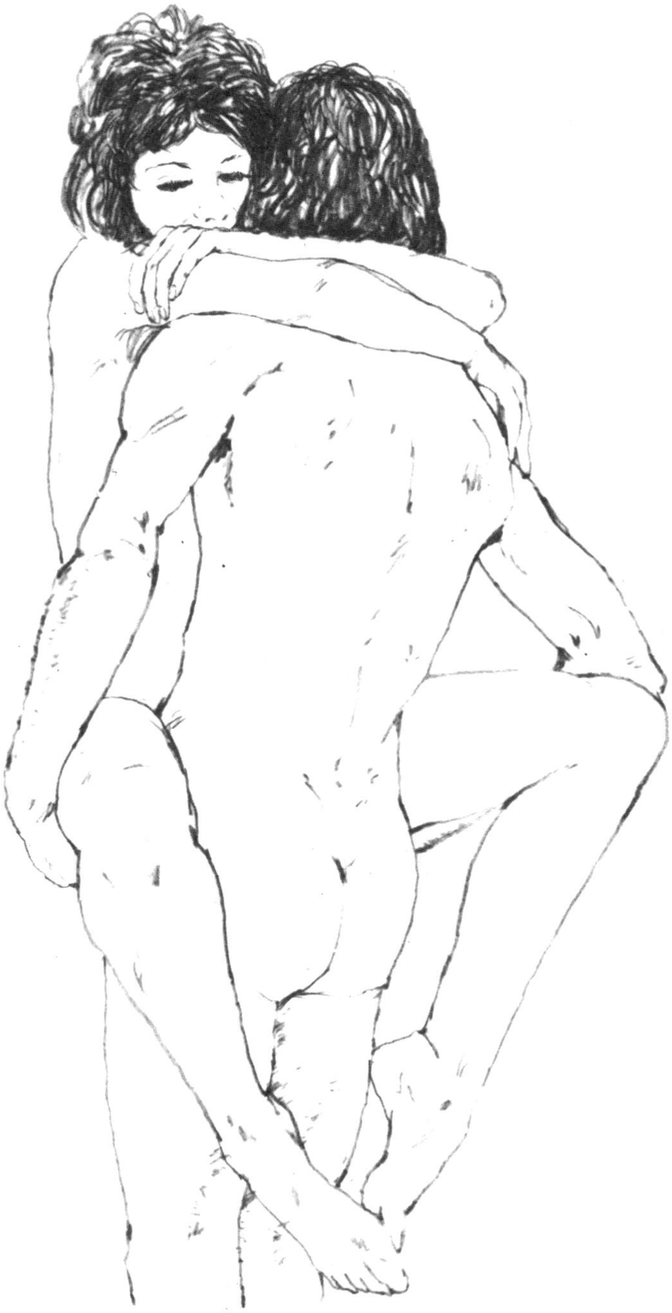

STANDING POSITIONS
above and opposite
Traditional upright is apt to produce stiff male muscles unless she is tall.

UPPER HANDS *above*
Riding St. George.

X POSITION *opposite*
A winner for prolonged slow intercourse.

mouth kisses, back to show herself to him, touch her own clitoris as she moves, delay if she wishes, for emphasis – the lot. She can also ride him facing or facing away, or turn from one into the other, once or often. Riding postures need a stiff erection (or she may bend him painfully with an over-hurried insertion). This is about the only kind of intercourse in which one or both can be injured by clumsiness or by slipping, so test yourselves gradually. Once in, she can go facing, backing, kneeling, sitting, crosslegged upon him. sideways or round and round, and make movements in three dimensions and circularly with her hips. She can also lie on him (reversed matrimonial), legs astride or between. When she has taken her main orgasm he can either turn her, or she can lie back astride him, head between his feet, without disconnecting, and go on in the letter X or the full matrimonial for his orgasm. Since it needs a stiff erection, and some women prefer to start from foreplay laterally or underneath, this makes a good second-figure of a series. If she wants to bring him to orgasm this way they should try it first, preferably on

waking and when he is fresh, with a hard waking erection. The round-and-round and cinder-sifting motions of the woman's hips – what the French call the Lyons mail-coach (*la diligence de Lyon*) – come easily with practice if you've got the right personality.

x position

A winner for prolonged slow intercourse. Start with her sitting facing astride him, penis fully inserted. She then lies right back until each partner's head and trunk are between the other's wide-open legs, and they clasp hands. Slow, coordinated wriggling movements will keep him erect and her close to orgasm for long periods. To switch back to other positions, either of them can sit up without disconnecting.

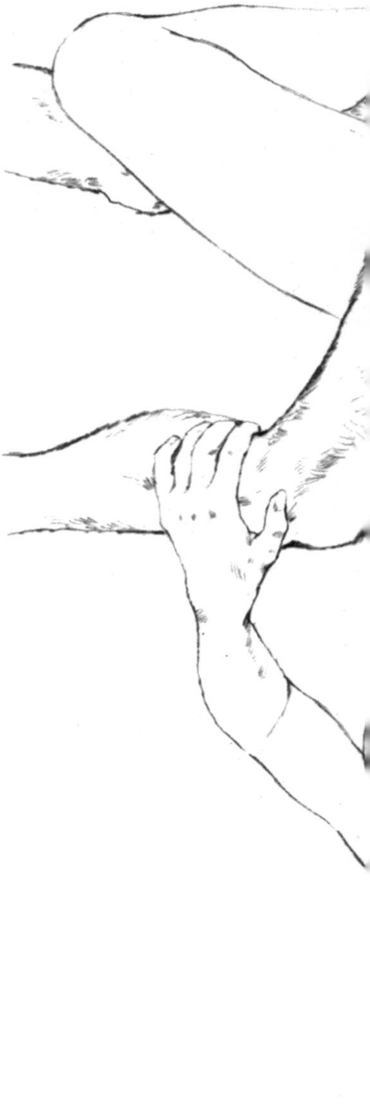

Sauces & Pickles

for special occasions

anal intercourse

In the light of present knowledge, this is best avoided altogether. It is something many couples try once, and a few stay with it, either because the woman finds it gives her intenser feelings than the normal route, or because it is pleasantly tight for the man. But it is also the preferred method of catching, or transmitting, the virus of AIDS, as well as hepatitis, cytomegalovirus and intestinal infections, and it can also cause mechanical damage.

Attempts, chiefly by male homosexuals, to render anal intercourse safer by using a condom have proved unreliable because the thin condoms designed for vaginal use tend to tear under the increased pressure and friction of a canal primarily engineered for other purposes. So long as AIDS remains incurable, it's too risky. This is one of the very few cases in which we have had to update the information originally given in this book in view of changed circumstances and new information.

The reason that AIDS is more easily transmitted anally than vaginally is that the rectal mucosa is not designed for friction and bleeds easily, so that semen can enter the bloodstream, and the rectum lacks the infection-resisting mechanisms of the vagina.

Anal sex has a chequered history. Regarded as an abomination because of its association in the public mind with homosexuality (though by no means all gays made use of it even before AIDS arrived), it has always been around. The Roman poet Martial threatened to divorce his wife for refusing, unlike other Roman matrons, to cooperate: in the nineteenth century anal intercourse was a popular working-class contraceptive. How far the hazard element is due to a new virus and how far it was always present we do not know. It is certainly present now. There are not many popular sexual practices that are physically dangerous, but recent circumstances and the most recent medical knowledge indicate that this is one of them. When a hazard as serious as AIDS appears there is plenty of scope to avoid it by altering your sexual repertoire.

armpit

Classical site for kisses. Should on no account be shaved (see *Cassolette*). Can be used instead of the palm to silence your partner at climax – if you use your palm, rub it over your own and your partner's armpit area first.

Axillary intercourse is an occasional variation. Handle it as for intermammary intercourse (see *Breasts*) but with your penis under her right arm – well under, so that friction is on the shaft, not the glans, as in any other unlubricated area. Put her left arm round your neck and hold her right hand behind her with your right hand. She will get her

sensations from the pressure against her breasts, helped by your big toe pressed to her clitoris if she wants it. Not an outstandingly rewarding trick but worth trying if you like the idea.

bathing

Bathing together is a natural concomitant of sex and a splendid overture or tailpiece. Taking an ordinary bath together has a charm of its own, though someone has to lean against the plumbing. Soaping one another all over, and, of course, drying one another, is a 'skin game' which leads on naturally to better things; after intercourse, a bath together is a natural come-back to domesticity or work. There are now large baths and conversation baths, but most of us see them only in expense account hotels.

Actual coitus is possible, and fun, in the shower if your heights match (see *Showerbath*) but no ordinary domestic or hotel bath is big enough for intercourse without punishing your elbows. Beside the novelty there isn't too much point anyway.

Sex while bathing is a different matter. The whole idea of intercourse in water is that it's like weightlessness or flying – the girl who is too big for all those Hindu climbing and standing postures becomes light enough to handle, and one can prop her at angles no acrobat could hold. All this has been rediscovered in the California swimming-

ARMPIT *above*
Classical site for kisses.

opposite and overleaf Three paintings by the great Japanese artist Hokusai (1760–1849) from the series *Loving Couples*, circa 1810

pool era; when we get to the design of the future, indoor equivalents will certainly spread among non-millionaires. Meanwhile there is the sea, after dark, when it is warm enough – on a gradually shelving beach one can have enough privacy even by day, and even re-emerge clothed: spectators will take it for callisthenics or life-saving. A pool has extras like steps and handholds, but is usually chlorinated. Water doesn't hinder friction, though its relative chill may mean that it takes some brisk rubbing to get an erection even in a very eager male. It might be a good idea to insert before going in, if possible, or for the girl to wear a diaphragm – we haven't heard of any harm coming from being pumped full of seawater, but chlorinated pool water might just possibly be irritant, as it is to the eyes. You can have excellent straight intercourse lying in the surf if you can get a beach to yourselves, but sand is a problem, and keeps appearing for days afterwards. A floating mattress is effectively a waterbed, but it is hard to stay on it without concentrating. We've heard of people combining coitus with swimming, and even scuba-diving, but they gave no practical details. Underwater coition, if more than a token contact, would use up vast amounts of air because of the overbreathing which goes with orgasm.

big toe

The pad of the male big toe applied to the clitoris or the vulva generally is a magnificent erotic instrument. The famous gentleman in erotic prints who is keeping six women occupied is using tongue, penis, both hands and both big toes. Use the toe in mammary or armpit intercourse or any time you are astride her, or sit facing as she lies or sits. Make sure the nail isn't sharp. In a restaurant, in these days of tights, one can surreptitiously remove a shoe and sock, reach over, and keep her in almost continuous orgasm with all four hands fully in view on the table top and no sign of contact – a party-trick which rates as really advanced sex. She has less scope, but can learn to masturbate him with her two big toes. The toes are definitely erogenic areas, and can be kissed, sucked, tickled, or tied with stimulating results.

bites

Hindu eroticians classified these at huge length. Gentle nibbling (of the penis, breasts, skin, fingers, ears, labia, clitoris, armpit hair) is part of the general excitatory repertoire. Hard bites at the moment of orgasm excite some people, but for most, like other painful stimuli, they are a turn-off. Women tend to bite more often than men, perhaps because they enjoy being bitten more than men do. (Remember that often your partner will do to you what

they really want done to them – being aware of this is the great secret of communicating sex.) Love-bruises, on the neck and elsewhere, which some lovers find act like a constant playback, setting off more lovemaking every time they are seen, aren't made by biting but by strong, continuous suction kisses. Sharp nips to the skin aren't as a rule erotic.

Be careful of biting at or near orgasm – the jaws go into spasm and you can bite really hard – in fact don't have an orgasm deliberately with a breast, penis or finger in your mouth. The need to bite can be taken out on something neutral like cloth or hair. This seems to be a case where the mammalian program of reflexes is over-tough for human enjoyment.

blowing

Not the slang sense (see *Mouth music*) but quite simply making a current of air on the (preferably pre-wetted) skin of any part of the body, either from the lips or from a hair-drier with the heat turned off. The best way to moisten an erogenous area is with the tongue, though for more extensive operations one can obviously use water or lotion. Air on a wet sensitive surface produces a sensation which can drive some people of either sex out of their minds – experiment on a small scale, using your natural equipment (saliva and breath). In the case of earlobes, breathe in, not out, or you'll deafen your partner. Elsewhere use steady continuous exhalation with the lips about an inch from the skin. The natural sequel to a tongue bath. For a bigger operation, use the hairdrier – the result is far wilder than the conventional routine with feathers, except for palms and soles – try mixing the two by hitching a couple of feathers to the drier nozzle on threads. Never (see *Hazards*) use a strong air source, and never blow into the vagina or any other body orifice (except the mouth – but mouth-to-mouth resuscitation isn't particularly erogenous).

bondage

Bondage, or as the French call it, ligottage, is the gentle art of tying up your sex partner – not to overcome reluctance but to boost orgasm. It's one unscheduled sex technique which a lot of people find extremely exciting but are scared to try, and a venerable human resource for increasing sexual feeling, partly because it's a harmless expression of sexual aggression – something we badly need, our culture being very up-tight about it – and still more because of its physical effects: a slow orgasm when unable to move is a mind-blowing experience for anyone not too frightened of their own aggressive self to try it.

'Any restraint upon muscular and emotional activity

BATHING *above*
Taking an ordinary bath together has a charm of its own, though someone has to lean against the plumbing.

generally,' wrote Havelock Ellis, 'tends to heighten the state of sexual excitement.' Men and women have always been excited anyhow by the idea of getting the better of each other, and 'erotic bondage' was always a popular turn-on – every self-respecting folk-heroine and most folk-heroes have to be bound hand and foot periodically so they can be rescued. The best man at a Berber wedding ties up the bride if she struggles, and she is expected to struggle so she can be tied up. Fantasies of the same sort have a big written and pornopicture literature (most of it wildly unpracticable and meant to be seen not felt) which act as a substitute for people who are hung up on aggression, or need an illusion of rape to be able to lie back and enjoy without guilt. Most of us have traces of these needs, and like to 'dominate' each other symbolically at times, or be dominated (no offence to Women's Lib, because this need is mutual). But bondage games are played by many straight lovers who want kicks, not substitutes, and fill a lot of important spaces. They take a little learning (first efforts are often painful, or come adrift, or waste an erection messing around) but with speed and skill many unlikely people swear by them as an occasional – if only because really professional slow masturbation isn't possible unless the subject is securely tied.

Many women enjoy the helplessness and the temporary exaggeration of male control, but bondage is an even better dodge for her to use on the over-macho male: he gets the mindblowing sensation of 'becoming one enormous penis', plus withdrawal of all performance anxiety – she gets the opportunity to be in total control of the pace and character of arousal, possibly for the first time in her life. Part of the current popularity of this kind of sexual play lies in exorcizing each partner's fear of control by the other by turning it into a source of increased physical sensation. Each enjoys the other's pretend fierceness. Porno bondage literature is good on technique but off-putting by playing up male hostility, which doesn't fit in the real enactment: psychiatric books, when aware of it, lump it with sadomasochism. It could, of course, be played in that way, as can sex in general: the best guarantee that it won't is strict insistence on equal turns.

In fact, really skillful bondage works like a bomb, sexually, on most non-timid males, both on the giving and the receiving end (as with any trick which involves both stimulation and symbolism, a well-tied sexual 'prisoner' both looks and feels sexy) – and on a fair proportion of girls once they get the idea; eventual responders of both sexes can require a lot of gentle preparation if they are scared by the aggressive symbolism, but this kind of fantasy only frightens people whose idea of tenderness is over-tender. Some women sense the need to be 'overpowered' sometimes. Others dig the domination symbol and like to be aggressors from the start. The idea is to tie your partner hand and foot, firmly but comfortably, so that they can struggle as hard as they like without getting loose, and then bring them to orgasm. Apart from being a wild sexual sensation, it enables many people who can't otherwise do so to let go to the last degree. They may yell blue murder at the critical moment but love it (one important skill here is to distinguish the noises which mean real distress – kinked wrists, cramp or the like – from the normal protests of ecstasy: the first mean 'Stop at once,' the second 'For God's sake go on and finish me off.')

Games of this sort are an occasional optional extra to all sorts of sex-play and intercourse, since the tied partner can be kissed, masturbated, ridden, or simply teased to orgasm, but they go extra-well in both sexes with the unbearably sharp sensations produced by slow, skillful handwork. 'Restraint' gives the receiving partner something muscular to do while remaining quite helpless to influence the march of events, or the rhythm and speed of stimulation (what Theodor Reik called the 'suspense factor'), and enables the active partner to push the woman, at least, to unbearable lengths (she, when her turn comes, can drive him frantic by spinning things out).

To make this work as a game it obviously needs to be effective but not painful or dangerous. Technique is worth a few words because this is a highly popular sex fantasy, which isn't included in square books, and some skill and care are called for. On any bed with four posts you can stake a partner out, supported by one or more pillows. This is the traditional bordel method, probably because it needs no skill. Extension like this inhibits orgasm in some people – many feel more with the legs open, but the wrists and elbows firmly behind the back, or by being tied to a chair, or upright to a post. The critical areas where compression boosts sex feeling are the wrists, ankles, elbows (don't try to make them meet behind by brute force), soles of the feet, thumbs and big toes (artful women break off halfway to tie these last two with a leather bootlace – if you doubt this, try it). There are divergences of taste over what to use for tying. Leaving aside kinks like straitjackets or boy-scout garters, different couples use leather or rubber straps, ribbons, cloth strips, pajama cords, or thick, soft rope. Straps are easiest for women who aren't very strong, or can't tie reef knots. They need holes at half-inch intervals. Triangular bandages are all right for quick hand-and-foot tying, but don't look very sexy – and it is the neatness and wriggling of the parcel which excite the active party. Old stockings are a favorite resource but murder to untie quickly in an emergency. Chains, handcuffs and so on are quick, but don't give any compression and hurt to lie on. If they lock you can't rely on releasing them quickly. The weird aparatus sold by adult-toy-makers is for the birds unless you only want to pose photographs. If you like it, make your own. For most straight couples a hank of clothesline is fine. Cut it into five or six four-foot and a couple of six-foot lengths, and use a lot of hand-tight turns – don't tie tight enough to bruise.

Some energetic people like to be gagged as well. As one lady put it, 'It keeps the bubbles in the champagne.' Gagging and being gagged turns most men on – most

BONDAGE *opposite*
The gentle art of tying your partner to boost orgasm.

women profess to hate it in prospect, but the expression of erotic astonishment on the face of a well-gagged woman when she finds she can only mew is irresistible to most men's rape instincts. Apart from the symbolism and the 'feeling of helplessness' it enables the subject to yell and bite during orgasm, which helps a total cut-loose, unless you have a rhinoceros hide and live in a soundproof room. It makes prompting impossible, so that your partner's initiatives are outside your control. Most men who are excited by this sort of game like to be silenced thoroughly. Untimid women often come to like it after a few tries if they're the biting kind or like the feeling of helplessness – others hate it and lose their orgasm if they try it. A few like to be blindfolded as well, or instead.

It's actually hard to gag anyone one hundred percent safely, except in movies, where a wisp of silk over the heroine's face enables the hero to walk past without hearing her. This is as well, as the prisoner must *never* be made incapable of signalling if anything is wrong. A long piece of cloth, with several turns well between the teeth, or a small rubber ball fixed in the middle of a one inch strap by a nut and bolt (the 'poire' of French bordel tradition) are quite fierce enough. Adhesive tape will silence someone but is torture to take off. Anything in the mouth must be firm, mustn't block breathing, and must be quick-release in case the subject signals danger – from choking, feeling sick, or any other source of discomfort. This signal (and this goes for *all* bondage games) must be agreed beforehand and never abused or ignored – penalty for illicit use, two further orgasms. A Morse-code grunt, 'shave and a haircut, two bits', is a safe choice. The Federal Safety Code must be observed and displayed in a prominent place on the premises. This is as follows:

1 Nothing may ever be tied round the front of anybody's neck, however loosely, and even if they ask for it.

2 Nothing loose or soft, which can get into the throat, or in general other than we've specified, may be put in anyone's mouth, or over their face, and all gags or knots must be quick-release.

3 Nobody helpless may ever be left alone, even briefly, especially face-down or on a soft surface like a bed. Don't leave a partner tied and go to sleep, especially if you have either of you been drinking. Don't keep anyone tied up for longer than half an hour.

4 Play bondage games only with people you know, not only socially but sexually, never with acquaintances, and avoid group scenes. This goes for couples as well as partners – some people are careless, and others are sadists.

BOOTS *above*
Good for dressing up games if you like them, but not very practical for serious sex unless you keep them for non-horizontal non-bed activities.

Apart from this, cruelty of any sort, tying someone who is really scared of the idea, tight cords, stuffing things in people's mouths, idiot tricks like hanging people up by any part of their anatomy, and the whole Sadie-Mae routine, which to straight couples is simply painful and a turn-off, belong to psychopathology not lovemaking. Bondage as a pleasurable sex game is never painful or dangerous. It can, of course, be played simply for the

CHINESE STYLE *opposite*
Wild geese flying on their backs.

symbolic aggression, but at least half the payoff in people (and there are many) who enjoy it is, for the person tied, directly physical, in struggling against restraint and in skin and muscle feeling, plus the release of any surviving childhood blocks which comes from having pleasure 'administered' willy nilly. It also helps get over our cultural taboo on intense extragenital sensations, which belongs in the same package.

Ropemarks usually go in a few hours if you've been gentle. Rope burns and bruises come from clumsy untying – don't saw through the skin, but be quick, so that the man doesn't get stiff through being left tied after orgasm, and the woman comes down to earth lying comfortably in your arms. You can be agreeably, adequately and symbolically fierce, whichever your sex, without being spiteful or clumsy and wrecking things. The right mix here, as in all sex games, is tough plus tender. If you can't sense how tough your partner likes it, ask, then subtract twenty percent to allow for the difference between fact and fantasy. Given these rules, any couple who enjoy violent lovemaking and like the idea could do worse than learn to make each other helpless occasionally – gently, quickly and efficiently. This is neither kinky nor frightening – just human. For the pièce de resistance which goes with bondage, namely *Slow masturbation*, see that section.

boots

Notorious sex turn-on for many people – the longer the better. Complicated symbolism here involving aggression (jackboots and so on), phallicism and the female lower extremity. Used to be the badge of the prostitute – now general wear for straight people: have changed places with corsets, which used to be general wear and are now chiefly a sex kick. Odd how the market in the respectability of sexually symbolic clothing swings over the years. One could learn a lot about human imprinting by plotting the prevalence of such preferences.

Good for dressing-up games if you like them. Not very practical for serious sex unless you keep them for non-horizontal non-bed activities. If your man likes them, try appearing suddenly in long, tight, black, shiny ones.

buttered bun

Woman who has recently had relations with another man: unexpected turn-on for some males. This seems to be a carry-over from a fairly general ape behavior, where sharing a partner is a form of bonding between males. Psychoanalysts have long since suspected that the motive in much wife-swapping (and also the attraction of the gang night out and of the prostitute, who is a 'shared' woman) was 'homosexual' in character – it's probably more accurate to say that it is an instance of the way in which primate bisexuality is used to cut down overt inter-male aggression. If the woman is your own wife, there is also a component of what psychiatrists have called masochism and biologists call 'stepping-down in the dominance hierarchy. Now a good way to catch AIDS.

chains

The tied-up, tinkling look – fashionable now, and they look well on naked skin. Some women like both the coldness and the symbolism, and some men spend hours locking and unlocking them – you could try them on him too for size. Uncomfortable and only symbolically effective if you want actually to hold a partner still, but they look fierce, and some people find them exciting. Bright tinkling objects turn on magpies as well as people. See *Earlobes*.

chastity belt

A turn-on for some people, they were sold in earnest until recently to 'prevent masturbation.' Like clothes, the real fun is in eventually taking them off. Many commercial ones don't even prevent intercourse. The kind with built-in stimulation, vibrators and so on sound more fun but cost a bomb. The genuine article, as used in the thirteenth century, wasn't meant to lock up the woman, but was worn by her as a deterrent against rape – the woman usually had the key, and some women were buried in them to prevent posthumous violation. The only worthwhile chastity-belt game is to try, when she has a period, how many ways you can circumvent a really tight g-string and both get orgasm. Male versions are sold and appeal to some people, presumably as a spinning-out technique. Expensive toys unless you want to make one.

chinese style

In the classical treatises, remarkably like uninhibited European sex, the best thing being the delightful names given to postures: 'Wailing Monkey Clasping a Tree,' 'Wild Geese Flying on their Backs,' for two quite ordinary positions (seated face to face; woman on top facing away). Main elaboration consists in various complicated mixtures of deep and shallow strokes, often in magical numbers – 5 deep 8 shallow, etc. Intercourse naked, on a Chinese bed, in the open air, or on the floor. Woman treated far less as an equal in sex than in Indian erotology. Mystical schools tried to avoid ejaculation (see *Karezza*).

clothed intercourse

Really a heavy-petting technique: she keeps her panties or g-string on, he carries out all the movements of straight intercourse as far as the cloth will allow. Favorite ethnologic variant, chiefly for premarital intercourse – called badana in Turkey, metsha in Xhosa, etc. etc. Odd we have no special word. Not reliable as a contraceptive unless the ejaculation-position is fully interfemoral, i.e. with the glans well clear of the vulva, cloth or no cloth. Some people who used this before marriage like to go back to it either as a starter or during menstrual periods. Inclined to be 'dry' and make the man sore if it goes on too long – many women can get a fair orgasm from it.

corsets

A turn-on for some people – luckily now confined to sex games; they used to be an obligatory article of fashion. Make a woman still more woman-shaped. Firm pressure on the waist and abdomen excites many women. Some men are turned on by being laced into them too. Probably work through tightness and skin pressure, but a lot of symbolisms are involved.

dancing

All ballroom dancing in pairs looks towards intercourse. In this respect the Puritans were dead right. The development of no-contact dances has come about because one doesn't now need a social excuse to embrace a girl, but as an excitant it need not involve contact at all – in fact dances like flamenco or the twist are far more erotic than a clinch because you aren't too close to see one another. At its best this sort of dance is simply intercourse by remote control.

Most good lovers dance well together. They can do it publicly or in private, clothed or naked. Stripping one another while dancing is a sensation on its own. Don't hurry to full intercourse – dance until his erection is unbearable and she is almost coming brought there by rhythm and the sight and perfume of each other alone.

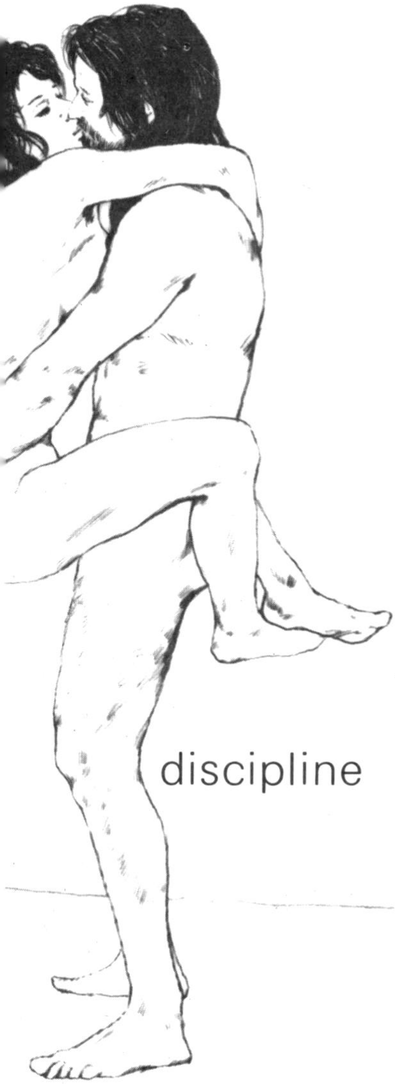

Even then you need not stop. Most couples can insert and continue dancing, either in each other's arms, or limbo-style, linked only by the penis, provided they are the right heights. Unfortunately this means that the woman needs to be at least as tall as the man, while as a rule she's shorter. Otherwise he has to bend his knees, which is tiring. If you can't dance inserted, and if she is small, pick her up into one of the Hindu standing positions, legs round waist, arms round neck, and continue like this. If she is too heavy, turn her and take her stooping from behind, still keeping the dance going.

This is a private game. Stripping at dances is getting commoner in some circles as a preliminary to group sex, but it usually is only a preliminary – after a few dances the floor empties and the couches fill up.

Seduction, or encouragement, while dancing is a natural. In the days of formal dancing one used to wish that the girl had her breasts on her back, where one could reach them, but that would have made it too easy. Gentle pressure, rhythm, sight and scent, and a knowledge of remote-control methods are all that are needed.

Most lovers are against Paul Joneses.

discipline

Codeword for beating each other as a sexual technique.

There is a venerable superstition, starting in English private-school scholars and backed by a vast literature from Meibom's *De Usu Flagrorum*, that beating is a sort of sexual Tabasco, the hottest erotic condiment, and no way-out party and no wide-scope porn is complete without it. Some of this is due to the fact that specialists in this field haven't suffered under the handicaps that affected, say, 69 or straight sex – beating is decent and can even be done in Church; sex isn't.

Beating is a kick which either works or doesn't. It doesn't work on either of us, so here we speak from inexperience. It's a violent skin stimulus, and Freud has been fully into the symbolism of punishment which goes with this – his conclusions go a long way to complicate Skinnerian arguments over what stimuli are 'aversive' and which act as rewards. Quite apart from fantasists and talkers who are far more excited by the idea in prospect and retrospect than the actual performance, some people are wildly turned on by it. For others, who have a real problem here, it may be necessary as a selfstarter. Skin stimulation and the occasional spank at the right moment fit well into most people's repertoire. Most find that anything more is disappointing in proportion to the scale of the performance (and possibly conducive to the thoroughly mischievous idea that women, in particular, enjoy being beaten up).

DANCING *above*
Stripping one another while dancing is a sensation on its own.

As we say, however, the idea of being beaten unquestionably turns some people on, and if it does you could try it. If you are lovers and one of you wants to be on the receiving end, the other need not be scared that they'll let out the beast in themselves by co-operating. If one of you wants to beat the other and he or she doesn't like it, or is turned off by the idea, that's harder – probably the loving answer is to settle for a lot of let's pretend and not much actual beating. This is a clear case where if you can't communicate fantasies, you shouldn't be lovers. Play it through a few times in words during straight intercourse (see *Birdsong at morning*). When you try it in practice, if it's the ritual which is the exciting part, make that big – don't be ashamed to ask for this, or give it: play matters. It can be a naughty-child or a mistress-and-slave routine or whatever – if your partner's fantasy doesn't turn you on naturally, play it as a game and enjoy his or her response. If it's the physical sensation, rhythm and style apparently matter far more than force, plus tantalization and the surprise element when the rhythm is suddenly broken.

Start gently at around one blow in one or two seconds, not more; gradually build up force until it is enough to make your subject want and not want you to stop. For two-way traffic the result, plus struggling, should both look and feel sexy, not cruel. The sauna twig level is nearly enough for most straight couples, but people who really go for beating like it hard enough to mark the skin. You can stick to the buttocks or cover the whole surface – back, belly, breasts, and even penis (careful!) and vulva (put her on her back with her feet attached to the bed-posts above her head, legs wide open; start on the buttocks, then give one light switch or two upon her thighs and vulva to finish her off.) Or tie the victim hands over head to the shower nozzle and work over them under running water. For a genuinely decadent European sensation you need real birch twigs. Canoe birch and gray birch, which are the nearest U.S. species, don't grow in the West, so if you live in California and want authenticity you may have to vacation with a chainsaw in the East or in Canada. You cut 2–3 foot straight branches with the twigs before the leaves come out, tie them into a bunch, and wet them before use. If you prefer all the trappings, one can buy ferocious-looking whips and paddles that make a great noise but do no mischief. People who want the physical stimulus usually prefer twigs. Don't use bamboo – it cuts like a knife. Don't play this game with strangers, ever. Lovers have enough feedback not to let the most violent play go sour. And never mix purely erotic beating with real anger or bad-temper – it could be dangerous. A game is a game is a game.

EXERCISES *opposite*
Any new trick you try needs a practice session in anticipation.

exercises

The Viennese Turnergesellschaft professors tried to make sex into a form of physical training. Good general tone certainly helps, but it's equally true that sexual exercise tones you up better than jogging. Adolescent masturbation, if it's guiltless and enjoyed, is one of the best specifically sexual exercises, and the man can use it at any age in learning to slow down his response to a level which gives the girl a chance. She, for her part, can learn to use her vaginal and pelvic muscles (see *Pompoir*) 'by throwing her mind into the part concerned,' says Richard Burton. This superlative knack can be learned, because girls in South India learn it. How exactly they learn has never been written down, unfortunately, and the first person to teach this properly to women who don't have the knack naturally will make a fortune. Whether the commercial device with a rubber cylinder and a pressure-gauge helps we simply don't know, since our female half has the trick naturally. The technique to try would involve having a bulb in the vagina and a light or pressure gauge to enable you to know when you were doing the right thing. Anyone can learn to waggle his ears in any direction in 30 minutes flat if he watches the ear on closed-circuit TV. This makes us think that the commercial gadget is well worth trying. If she 'throws her mind' with him in situ she should master

it, and he can tell her when she is succeeding. Sucking a large, strong Pyrex test-tube into the vulva without hands is another recommended exercise. Once learned it is wholly involuntary and needs no effort.

What we do suggest is that for any new trick you arrange a practice session in anticipation. The time to learn new figures isn't on the ice-rink or dance floor. The most common reason that an elaboration you both wanted disappoints, whether it's a fancy posture or some dodge such as bondage which needs to be quickly and efficiently set up, is the attempt to use it in actual, excited lovemaking 'from cold' – so that you mess about, lose the thread, and wish you hadn't bothered with it or blame whichever suggested it. The usual outcome is never to try again.

Not that rehearsal need be coldblooded or taken out of actual lovemaking. Anticipation being good in itself, you first fantasize about it, sit down together, plan, and rehearse. Then fit the actual trial-for-size into the waiting periods between bouts – when you're both excited enough not to feel silly, but not ready to go completely: try it while waiting for the next erection. Remember even Menuhin has to practice the violin daily, though in love once learned is never forgotten. If it works first time you should get the erection – in that case go where it takes you. This means you can rehearse something new for each special occasion, mastering every movement but quite deliberately holding back and not playing it live until the appointed time. The waiting will help when that arrives.

To practice things you must try in full erection, make the effort, and try the new posture when you have one – either without movement, if you are set on waiting till later, or switching after a few strokes to something else. Of course, if it takes over, as it may, you might as well carry on, and turn practice into performance there and then. For most postures you can try wearing g-strings, so as to get the motions without actual contact, and some people find this exciting in itself.

feathers

Recommended by some for skin stimulation (breasts, body surface generally, rather than the actual genitals, and palms and soles.) Try stiff wiry ones (heron or egret) or an oldfashioned feather mop.

femoral intercourse

Another dodge, like *Clothed intercourse*, to preserve virginity, avoid pregnancy, etc., in cultures which cared about virginity and had no contraceptives. Comes for us

FLORENTINE *below*
Greatly boosts intensity of male sensation if you get the tension right.

under the heading of substitutes. Used from before or behind, or in any other posture where she can press her thighs together. The penis goes between them, with the shaft between her labia, but the glans well clear of the vagina, and she presses hard. Gives the woman a special set of sensations – sometimes keener than on penetration,

so worth trying. One need not be so rigid about technique as were our forefathers, who had to try to keep sperm out of the vulva at any cost. With care one can do this from behind with the glans actually on the clitoris, with striking results. Good menstrual variant, or for at least a few strokes before you go in as usual.

feuille de rose

Tongue stimulation of the anus and perineum in either sex. Subject to the same warning as anal intercourse. See p.158.

florentine

Coitus *à la florentine*: intercourse with the woman holding the man's penile skin (and foreskin if he has one) forcibly back with finger and thumb at the root of the penis and keeping it stretched all the time, both in and out. Excellent way of speeding-up ejaculation, and greatly boosts intensity of male sensation if you get the tension right.

foursomes and moresomes

Uninhibited sex with multiple partners, often anonymous, which began to be popular at the height of the era of sexual experimentation is no longer possible because of the AIDS epidemic. There is no reason why stable couples should not make love in each other's company: whether or not they exchange partners is a matter of preference. That can be liberating or unpredictably disruptive, and in either case the motives and complications involved are not usually fully comprehensible to the parties involved. There is something to be said for anything which breaks down either the numbing convention of sexual privacy or the equally numbing convention of possessiveness, but the psychological hazards are considerable for any but very secure people.

Some experienced couples enthuse about exchanges. Others don't try them because they don't want to jeopardise the extraordinary mutuality which grows with real and total sex communication. This wouldn't affect the mere non-swap type of proximity. Since friends already swap hints on sex it seems natural to demonstrate, and one can learn a lot by watching, apart from the turn-on from other people's excitement. The famous one-way mirror scene is for real non-playing voyeurs or for bird-watchers who don't want to put their subject off. In fact it takes very little intercourse to make most people oblivious of their surroundings, although some might come down with a bump afterwards.

Both partner swapping and "orgies" involving large numbers did acquire both possibility and a degree of prevalence in the 1970s as a part of the experimentation released by the "new sexuality". In fact neither was new: sex with random partners or in a group setting has been a common human religious ritual, as it is a common (perhaps the commonest) human sexual fantasy. Of the positive claims made for what we might call "sociable sex", the most plausible is the reversal of the damaging effects of privacy: sex is the only important human skill which society decrees we must not learn by watching, and the sexual behaviour of others is of more than prurient interest. We tend to set out own norms from our own very limited experience.

The occasional, promiscuous sex which characterized Carnival and the Californian "open sexuality" cult was based on a structured, temporary suspension of social inhibitions. Predictably, in California, it was apt to become an addictive life style. It had observable psychological effects on participants, both beneficial and destructive. Since it would now be suicidal in places like Los Angeles, San Francisco and New York, where it was most prevalent, the argument is academic for the duration of the AIDS epidemic: the anonymous type of exchange cultivated by swingers and orgiasts of the early 1970s is much too dangerous. This applies to any sexual exchange with unknown quantities, dark horses or couples who have slept around extensively, particularly if it involves any male-male bisexual experiences, or people who have had such experiences. Bisexual men are the chief carriers, after drug addicts, of the HIV virus into the heterosexual community. It's hard enough to check the record of your own partner without checking than of another couple, emotional repercussions aside.

This doesn't apply to the sharing of sexual experience by enjoying it in company, particularly if we were able to approach this in the spirit of religious experience rather than of kicks. Religious promiscuity in the Tantrik and Vallabhacharya sects had a totally different object. Partners were assigned at random to remove any affectional element: the partners were to be not I and Thou but the God and the Goddess, and the object was not sensory or emotional kicks but the prolongation of the phase of pre-orgasm, normally brief, to use it as a launch pad for mystical experience, the putting together of Adam and Eve to form the Paradisal apple. It's perhaps more relevant for moderns in a non-mystical culture to point out that women not infrequently experience bodilessness and oceanic states in orgasm, though they may not make philosophical use of them – the problem would be to induce similar oceanic feelings in the male. This could become a project for two lovers with the woman, as is traditional, being the initiatrix. It doesn't

FOURSOMES AND MORESOMES
overleaf
Since friends already swap hints on sex it seems natural to demonstrate.

need an "orgy", the novelty of which would be unhelpful in our culture even if it wasn't, now, dangerous.

friction rub

The original meaning of shampoo, which is gentle kneading massage all over. Much more pleasant if you shed all adult inhibitions and rub each other all over with one of the non-messy scented lotions one can buy now for the purpose – a perfumery gimmick that shows a lot more insight than flavored douches and so on. Sit on something that doesn't matter and rub each other, together or in turns – sunburn oil or soap lather work well if you haven't got a special preparation. This always ends in genital handwork, then intercourse, then bath together. Semen would be the ideal medium, but it is too little and too late – bottled lotion is a substitute for this particular fantasy. She kneads his muscles, with fingers and a vibrator as well if they like; he concentrates on her breasts, buttocks, loins and neck. With practice these sensations are well worth cultivating. The Los Angeles massage parlors may get busted regularly, but they have nothing one can't do at home – apart from the fact that they are male-orientated, not mutual, and lay on a whole troupe of girls for every man. Presumably a devoted woman could call in friends to help – or a devoted man, to make things equal. This could make a good two-couple game, short of wife-swapping, provided the couples like each other.

g-string

Useful sexual accessory – for how to use it, see *Clothes*. For actual use in intercourse, as opposed to dressing up, it is best to make your own. We print a pattern. White or black pure silk are the best materials. When on, it should be absolutely tight and skin smooth, covering only the vulva and pubis. Cotton will do – nylon has the wrong texture. Other materials can be used as turn-ons, for looks, but can't really be kissed through – if you want to use these, wear them over the silk 'leaf.' Open-fronted panties aren't the same thing.

gadgets and gimmicks

The boom in sexual apparatus is quite extraordinary. The great exponents of this sort of hardware previously were the Japanese: in a sex manual one really needs a consumer study of the market, which we have not so far undertaken.

Judging from travellers' tales, most ethnographic sex aids are used by men at the instance of women; they must be unusually keen to please in order to bore through the glans and fit a 'spritsail yard,' like the Kayans, or insert pebbles under the skin of the penis itself like the Sumatrans. In softer cultures such devices are external – chiefly rings

G-STRING *opposite*
White or black pure silk are the best materials. The size should be about 8 by 3 inches – according to the individual.

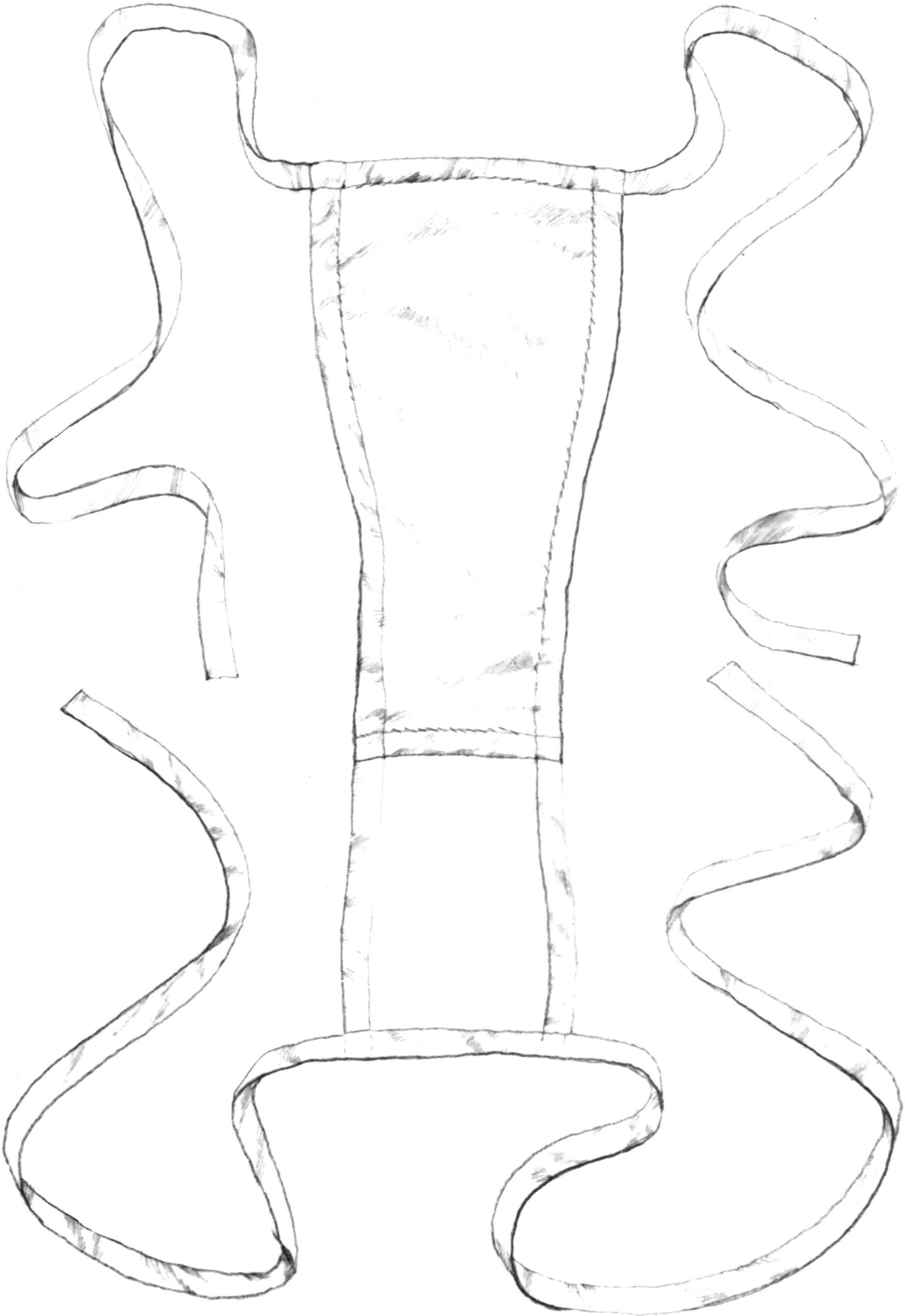

which fit round the coronal groove, made of feathers (palang unus – Malaya), goats' eyelids sewn back to back (Patagonia), or little hair brushes. These things are in museums, or one would wonder if somebody was putting an impertinent ethnographer on. The remarkable thing is that they should stay in place during intercourse. Nearly all are damnably uncomfortable to wear, and either pinch or get caught with hairs.

European equivalents are warty condoms, rings and the like, and dildoes – penis supplements or penis substitutes.

Sheaths are straightforward – they come in all manner of shapes and contours, the aim being to roughen both the penis and the vaginal barrel. Some have knobs or fingers to tickle the cervix. We are at a disadvantage here, in that these are supposed to help the female enjoy, but we've never yet met a woman who liked them. They are not safe contraceptives. Some people who are excited by the idea, if not by the sensation, buy a full set, including all the possible variations of shape. They come complete with a drying frame on which they can be stretched for cleaning, and should then be rolled and powdered with French chalk.

If these appeal to you, they are easily made to your own specification by adding knobs to an ordinary, washable-type or round-ended condom with Copydex or some other latex rubber cement – 'brushes' or larger knobs are cut from foam-rubber and cemented on, and the whole confection well washed with tapwater to remove any irritant chemicals before use. The kind with a thick corona ring strike us as downright painful. They also destroy the direct physical contact which, in communicative sex, matters a lot, but they allow one to experiment and to combine sex with handicrafts – such sexual Easter bonnets at least add novelty if you like the idea. We think they are more likely to precipitate frigidity than cure it, unless novelty is your turn-on. Buying sex gear together from a catalogue helps some people to fantasize and communicate.

Penis extensions, which fit over the real thing, likewise; penis size, it can't be repeated too often, has little to do with sexual feeling, though a big one may be emotionally stimulating in prospect. A large hard extension can do actual damage. The most these do is to boost male morale, though, like a chest wig, one wouldn't like to be found using one.

Rings are another matter. These are basically erection-maintainers; where they work, they can be a real help to better intercourse by stiffening a part-erection after a full orgasm – this is achieved by slightly blocking off the veins of the penis at its root, to keep the hydraulics working. At

GADGETS AND GIMMICKS
above and opposite
Rings are basically erection-maintainers: the finest specimen we've seen is Chinese and made of ivory.

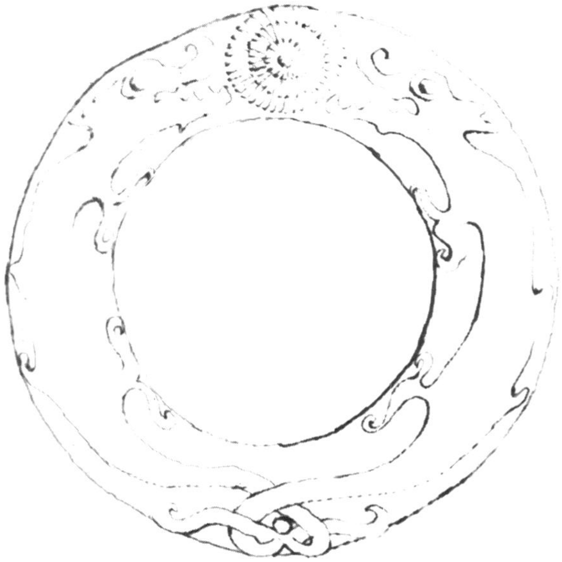

the same time, being worn over the pubis, they can also provide an additional pressure-point for the clitoris. The finest specimen we've seen is Chinese and made of ivory. The two sky-dragons are sporting with a pearl (the semen) – in use, the pearl is a small knob to fit the clitoris, the scales of the dragons open and tickle the labia, and the whole thing is held in place by a long tape passed through the hole, back between the legs, crossing behind the scrotum, up between the buttocks and then round the waist. The Chinese and Japanese also bind thin leather round the whole penis, or its base, and the Japanese favor openwork tubes fitting over the whole thing – in each case, pressure at the base plus roughening of the shaft and pubic area constitute the point. Others are belt-like devices which hold back the foreskin by pulling on the penile root. There are now several up-to-date models in rubber or plastic, which fit round the base of the shaft and have a clitoris tickler to supplement the man's pubic bone.

Quite a few of the clitoral knobs strike us as over-hard to be comfortable, and all rubber rings are apt to pinch one or other partner. We have yet to meet anyone, male or female, who got much out of them. None of these things are surefire erection devices, and most work at all only in the absence of any impotence anxieties. One, the Blakoe ring, goes round both penis and scrotum-root (it opens and clips shut), to maintain agreeable erotic sensations and hence boost morale. To stiffen erection, a ring needs to go round the roots of both penis and scrotum – some lovers use a turn of cord. Professional ladies, and some good amateurs, use it to produce elaborate 'cockties' which compress the root, separate the testes, and hold the penis in a bent-double position, giving a sensation rather like continuous suction. One can buy assorted leather harnesses with similar effects. Don't bruise the urethra by over-tightening, or leave on too long. Metal rings frequently have to be removed at Outpatients when they get stuck on an erection. One wearer, on his way to an assignation, set off an airport metal detector. He told officials it was an article of his religious faith.

Dildoes are artificial penises of varying sophistication (some include warmth and ejaculatory capacity, others built-in vibrators). These go back to the most ancient times and presumably have takers – the modern ones have excellent texture. Most women do not naturally masturbate by vaginal insertion, but since the ladies of the Turkish harem 'were not suffered a radish or cucumber to their diet except it be first sliced,' some, with sexual experience, evidently do – and the sight of a woman using one is clearly a turn-on for some males. They can also provide a second penis for simultaneous use. Single dildoes with a harness, or double-ended dildoes, are intended for woman-woman relations.

Merkins are vagina-substitutes – traditionally a warm-water container with a rubber or plastic vagina. Attached to an inflatable plastic doll or not, we doubt their utility – there is no substitute for what they attempt to replace, and, like the traditional hole in a watermelon, the only excuse for using them in two-way sex is if the sight of a merkin in use excites your partner. Vagina substitutes with a pump 'to enlarge the penis,' apart from bolstering the folklore about penile size, are capable of permanently damaging the natural hydraulics and should be avoided.

Chinese bells (now usually Japanese – rin-no-tama) are something else again. These are hollow ivory or plastic spheres, one empty, one containing mercury, and the third a large steel ball and a number of small metal tongues. They can either be inserted (in reverse order) into the vagina or put between the labia. Some are single, egg-shaped devices. Movement, including walking, then produces a quite unique pelvic sensation more intermittent and intimate than a vibrator. Some can be used in actual intercourse, others to maintain a steady stimulation – all day, if you can take it. Follow the manufacturers' instructions.

Skin gloves and skin thimbles have only just appeared on the market, and good ones have yet to be made. These are far better worth trying than any of the foregoing except the last. They consist either of a whole glove, or better a series of finger-cots the size of a thimble, each covered with a bristly cloth ranging in texture from soft fur to hard nylon pile with a tuft of bristles where the nail would be on a finger. They are used for erotic massage of the skin in either sex. With a properly chosen range of bristles and some natural skill, these can produce an effect which ranges from the pleasant to the excruciating. A well-made set would make a fine personal present. See also *Vibrators, Japanese style, Pattes d'araignée*.

Our final judgment is that unless intravaginal gadgets

help the sexually handicapped, which we doubt, they're a waste of good money. For most people, they only spoil the intensity of normal feeling. Skin stimulation is another matter. But we may be unusual.

gamahuche

French for extended pussy-kissing. See *Mouth music*.

goldfish

Two naked people tied and put on a mattress together to make love fish-fashion, i.e. no hands. Originally a nineteenth-century bordel joke. It can be done (if you are the victims, try on your sides from behind). Venerable party game, but don't play it with strangers, or leave the players unsupervised, even briefly. There was a nice spoof of this sex stunt in the movie *Soldier Blue*. A good many women can get an orgasm solo in this way simply by struggling, especially if you put them in front of a mirror. Don't both tie yourselves, even if you can manage it – you might not be able to get loose.

grope suit

Diabolically ingenious gadget which has just come on the Scandinavian market to induce continuous female orgasm – unlike most such devices it works, at least on any woman who doesn't shy off it as mechanical. Consists of a very tight rubber g-string with a thick phallic plug which fits in the vagina and a roughened knob over the clitoris. The bra has small toothed recesses in the cups which grip the nipples and is covered all over inside with soft rubber points. Once it is on, every movement touches a sensitive area – the result can be unbearable. Can be worn under day clothes, if you can stand it. When it works, the effects on the wearer rub off on the male spectator. An amusing, and expensive, stunt, but we think it would cut down normal sensitivity if used too often. Its main attraction is novelty – might make an anniversary present. There is no male equivalent.

Less blatant clothing which maintains continuous sexual excitement is an old human expedient, and well worth experimenting with. Most of it is designed for women, not out of male chauvinism but simply because of the difference in physiology: a continuous turn-on enhances the woman's eventual response but would tend to overload the man's and make him unable to perform. The traditional instances are geared to feel sexy for the wearer and look sexy to her partner. Some of them could be of real use in re-learning the proper sexual use of our skin. They range from long heavy earrings to tight straps, corsets and belts, rough textures (hair-shirts, bamboo-ring shirts), ankle-chains, footwear which affects the gait and presses on the instep, and now, more explicitly, hot pants which fit well into the vulva. See the full history of such devices in Bernard Rudofsky's *The Unfashionable Human Body*.

Most turn women on by their skin and muscle effect and men by their symbolism, but some couples get a special kick by making her wear something wild under ordinary clothes on straight occasions, when one can't go home early. Some commercial ones lock, and you leave the key at home. Could be worth trying for men too, if only in the interest of fair shares. Continuous sexual excitement you can't stop or do anything about would at least make a dull occasion more interesting, and guarantee a good scene when you finally get home. See *Earrings, Clothes, Gadgets and gimmicks, Jokes and follies*.

harness

Quick 'restraint' system for people who can't tie knots, bruise with rope, or like the look of 'apparatus.' Come in all degrees of complication and for all postures – watch out for expensive confections which are really kinky-photo props. Mainstay of way-out Danish sex boutiques. Include some gadgets like the mono-glove which holds the elbows back without cutting into the arms. Give very tight restraint and a lot of skin pressure which some people favor. Some play up the horse-symbolism, or include chastity belts, corsets, etc. The only really useful gadget of this kind is the 'leg stretcher' – a bar of adjustable length with strap collars at the ends to hold the feet apart if you don't have a bed with posts.

horse

The horse is an erotic object (see *Clothes*) and playing at horses, as well as riding them, notoriously turns some people on. One aficionado was Aristotle, who is frequently shown being ridden horseback style by a girl friend. Medieval moralists who took this as an awful warning miss the point. Men also like to dress women up as horses, though they can't usually be ridden in this manner. This seems at least as good a turn-on as disguising them as rabbits. Mentioned here for completeness – it's not our kick – but the game (equus eroticus, pony-girl game) figures in the literature. Either sex can be the steed. Odd how often children's games and grown-up sex games converge. Some people purchase a whole outfit including bit, saddle, etc. See firsthand description in *The Nightclerk*.

horseback

Intercourse like this is attributed to the Tartars, Gauchos and other equestrian peoples. We haven't tried it, lacking the horse and the privacy. He controls the horse, and she

sits astride facing him. If you were really set on this you could – in town – try a large rockinghorse, but whether it is worth the trouble we simple don't know. Quite a few women can get an orgasm when riding (especially bareback) and when jumping.

ice

The last material one would consider sexy – yet with its increased availability we keep hearing of people who use if for its shock-effect on the skin. One sex book suggests that just before orgasm the woman should slap a handful of crushed ice on her husband's back. Other people use an ice cube to go slowly over a partner's skin, including the soles of the feet, put them in each other's navels during sexual games and so on. Some women report

HORSE *above*
Odd how often children's games and grown-up sex games converge.

using them for masturbation, even to the point of freezing an ice 'phallus' in a rubber sheath. Not so strange, when you come to think of it – cold is a strong skin stimulus. We see no objection to experiments if you like the idea – you will hardly catch cold on one ice cube. Don't use super-cooled ice, let alone dry ice; these stick fast to moist surfaces and burn like a redhot iron. Test any ice-cube you use on your tongue, cautiously, otherwise you may be in for a shock.

indian style

Now widely familiar from the *Kama Sutra*, the *Koka Shastra* and so on. Intercourse on a bed or on cushions, fully naked, but with the woman wearing all her ornaments. Many complicated positions, including some derived from yoga which aim to avoid ejaculation (see *Karezza*), standing positions, and woman-on-top positions (purushayita) which are regarded as specially devout, since in Tantric Hinduism she is Energy and he is Immanence. All, if you do it in the original spirit and not for variety only, intimately linked with the Indian love of living at several levels – not only sex, but meditative technique in which one attempts to be subjectively both male and female for mystical purposes, or modified dance in which beside making love one acts out a scene from the hagiography of Vishnu and his Avatars, or the Life of Rama. There is a section on sexual technique in the chief classical dance treatise – dancers were temple maidens or devadasis who gave themselves to the devout as part of a religious exercise. Difficult for us to recapture, in spite of a dawning awareness of the psychoanalytic rightness of much Hindu intuition. Specialities include love-cries (see *Bird-song at morning*), love-blows (struck with fingertips on one another's breast, back, buttocks and genitals), love-bites as tokens of possession, and erotic scratchmarks – much skin stimulation with specially-grown, long finger-nails, from mere brushing to a passionate scratch (classically confined to the armpit and the 'girdle path' – pantie region – where marks won't show in Indian day dress). Of all Indian techniques the standing postures are probably the best worth learning, if the girl is light enough. Few women who weren't trained from birth could, for example, stand leaning backwards on feet and hands, limbo-style, then put their arms round their legs and their head between their thighs, so as to take alternate stroke in mouth and vagina – or manage the one-leg-standing, one-leg-around-waist poses cultivated by temple girls. The best Indian accomplishment, the full *pompoir*, comes from the Tamil South, and unfortunately isn't taught in the texts, though the devadasis learned it from their mothers. See *Pompoir, Exercises*.

INDIAN STYLE *opposite*
Specialities include love-cries, love-blows, love-bites as tokens of possession and erotic scratchmarks.

inversion

Not homosexuality, which isn't in our book, but taking him or her head-down. He can sit on a chair or stool and take her astride facing – then she lies back until her head rests on a cushion on the floor. Or she can lie down, raising her hips – he stands between her legs and enters her either from in front or from behind while she rests on her elbows or walks on her hands (the wheelbarrow). He can lie over the edge of the bed, face up, while she sits or stands astride. With orgasm the buildup of pressure in the veins of the face and neck can produce startling sensations. Unless you want a body on your hands, better not try this on a hypertensive executive – remember Attila the Hun's young concubine: but it should be safe enough for youngsters. It is the way to handle those idiotic women who try to persuade a lover to boost their orgasm by throttling them – if you meet one of these, never do anything so damned silly, but teach them this alternative and equally rewarding method. You may save two lives –

hers, and, since most people's grip tightens in orgasm, her next boyfriend's, which could easily be spent in jail for homicide.

Inverted 69 is described elsewhere (see *Mouth music*). This makes a good tryout, always works if you can lift her, and will give her an idea of the quality of sensation involved; not everyone likes it.

japanese style

Intercourse on the floor or on cushions, as with most Oriental styles: partial nakedness only, numerous squatting and semi-squatting positions, a lot of bondage, a lot of preoccupation with extras and odd devices. We're talking here about the sexual customs of eighteenth- and early nineteenth-century prints, rather than the modern westernised B-girl version, which is international. What would be hard to copy is the essentially Japanese mixture of violence and formality. Other things are: elaborate finger-stimulation of the woman, thumb in anus, fingers in vagina: and a big range of mechanical devices – a glans-cap of hard material (kabutogata), penile-shaft tubes (do-gata), some of them latticed (yoroi-gata), or with a glans cap as well (yaso-gata): dildoes (engi), often strapped to the woman's heel, while her ankle is held up to a sling round her neck to give a better swing to the movement: thongs to bind tightly round the penile shaft, rendering it both rough and permanently stiff enough for insertion (higozuiki), and merkins to hold in the hand (azuma-gata). Postures cover the whole range, but the lovers of the 'floating world' greatly enjoy the simulation of rape – what George Moore called 'furious fornications' – where the artistic emphasis is on huge parts, copious secretions and so on: sex is played hard in this tradition.

jokes and follies

This, contrary to cultural traditions among squares, is pre-eminently the right place for them. The best of them, too, tend for this reason to be jokes at the expense of the square tradition. The finger-raising quality of lovers vis-à-vis society is as necessary psychologically as their tenderness to each other. That, and not just the spice of danger, is what makes love in odd places and under other people's unperceptive noses so attractive. This is childish, but if you haven't yet learned to be childish in your love-making you should go home and learn, because it's important.

One mustn't let the joke go wrong and sour things: if you can have intercourse in a public restaurant or on Auntie's dining table and bring it off, you can laugh about it after (but if you don't bring it off you'll be lucky if you speak to each other again). Most couples contain, for any

INVERSION *opposite*
The wheelbarrow.

JAPANESE STYLE *above*
Yaso-gata.

given occasion, one dangerlover and one restraining influence, and achieve accordingly a commonsense balance, helped by the angel who watches over such lunatic antics and protects lovers from the consequences. All in all, it would be stupid to recommend them but a pity to have missed them.

The amount of laughter you have in intercourse, pranks apart, is a measure, we think, of how well you are managing to love. It's evidence for, not against, the seriousness of your communication. If you have this, the laughs never fail, because sex is funny. If you haven't, you end with boxed ears or tears or no orgasm all round, through some remark 'destroying the atmosphere.' When it's really going, laughter is part of the atmosphere – even mockery isn't unaffectionate, and there's no joke like love well and mutually completed under unlikely circumstances. It's one of the few contemporary scenes which gets a laugh out of pure joy.

Taking a partner (usually female) around to square occasions nude, or in some kinky gear, under a long coat, is a danger-plus-snook-cocking game which some couples relish. The danger is there all right – if you must do it, make sure she really enjoys it. The no-panties bit is dangerous enough for most girls unless it's very much their thing.

karezza

The Alice Stockham treatment – going on and on and on while avoiding male orgasm.

This is really an exercise directed against *Hairtrigger trouble* rather than a general coital technique. Long intercourse is great, but the aim will be to ejaculate eventually. Enormously satisfying for the woman: the original Stockham version, where the male didn't ejaculate but allowed his erection to subside inside the vagina has no conceivable advantage over going on equally long *with* orgasm, and is likely to spoil eventual response. Worth knowing about, however, if you read accounts of sex yoga drawn from Oriental sources. The old Tantric-Taoist system held that semen was spiritual gasoline – the man should be careful to conserve it while drawing 'virtue' from the woman. One ejaculation could dissipate this supposed virtue. Accordingly, a great many sexual yogic positions in which movement was difficult were designed specifically for this kind of maneuver – giving the woman several orgasms while the man conserved his semen and performed what was in fact a meditative sexual exercise. Adept yogis also trained themselves to ejaculate internally – an unrewarding technique which deposits the semen in the bladder, whence it is passed with the urine: occasionally the same trick appears spontaneously as a disability and is difficult to unlearn. This explains the low male satisfaction value of many of the most elaborate Hindu positions. If you intend to use intercourse as a meditative technique, you may well use them, but there seems no rational ground against eventual ejaculation in any case.

Karezza was developed, possibly with similar ideas, by the Oneida community: it also kept conceptions down, albeit not over-reliably, as semen can leak without ejaculation. There was recently an offbeat French priest who canvassed the same idea as an answer to Vatican scruples over birth control, under the title of *continence conjugale*, but he has been put down. The method consists in total control of male movement – allowing the woman internal movements only, and the man sufficient strokes to maintain erection, stopping as soon as tension mounts. Use it solely as a training technique for long intercourse, then switch to full movement and mutual orgasm, for which the woman will be fully ready. See *Pompoir*.

leather

Probably the most popular super-skin turn-on: black hide also looks aggressive or scarey and, being skin, all leather fixes natural sex odors. Unlike rubber you can now wear it fashionably without being thought kinky, which yet another example of the arbitrary social choice of sex turn-ons in clothing. Some men like women encased in it: those who like the ferocious buckled-up look don't go for wet-look, soft leather, and vice-versa. If your partner likes it on you, let him or her do the buying. This is one object turn-on which women respond to as well as men, especially if it feels and smells right – soft leather jock-straps seem to please some people of both sexes. Don't pay racketeer prices, however; most of the elaborate gear in fetishistic toy-shops can be improvized, though if you want an Avengers suit you'll have to pay to have it made. See *Boots, Clothes*. Even if the texture doesn't appeal, try a leather-based (*cuir de Russie*) perfume – it is probably the closest to the normal female attractant odor.

masks

These excite some people: if this seems odd, remember that they are the oldest human device for getting mystical as well as sexual inspiration, by making the wearer menacing, other than themselves, and 'possessed' by the mask, and by altering the body image through partial sensory deprivation. There are inflatable helmets on the market which accentuate this last effect. We find sex better without our head in a bag. Putting the girl's panties over the man's head, an old professional trick, works on quite a different basis (see *Clothes*). Masks, like corsets, were once a general fashion. Don't fool around with plastic bags – these are dangerous and obstruct breathing.

mirrors

These have always been an important part of sexual furniture in any bedroom not wholly devoted to sleeping. They turn love into a viewing occasion without loss of privacy and help the mise-au-point at a practical level. They also provide a turn-on by letting you see yourselves – he can see his own erection and movements without stopping. She may be turned-on by seeing her own body, watching herself masturbate, seeing herself bound, or any of the other fantasies one can enact, so that both get viewer as well as participant pleasure. Those who don't like them, by contrast, say they spoil the shut-in, non-spectator feeling they need to appreciate sensation to the full, and make the bedroom less like a womb with twins in it and more like Tiffany's. If you have never made love in front of a big mirror, try it. You really need more than one to enable both to see clearly without having to shift around. The exercise is worth it, not only for voyeur effect but to show you how unridiculous you look making love. Sex in cold blood description sounds undignified, but seen as one participates it is natural, attractive and formally beautiful to a morale-boosting extent, even if you aren't beautiful figures. If there does come a time when it's better to feel than look, we haven't reached it yet, in middle-age.

What you have on your premises is your business, but if you want to entertain guests, have the mirrors inside cupboard doors or on a stand. With all the publicity given to the one-way variety some couples are inhibited by anything they can't walk behind.

Old-style bordels went in for rooms of a hundred mirrors. Expense apart, these may or may not work for you; 100 couples acting in unison may be your turn-on, or they may remind you of Red Square on Mayday or an instant Roman orgy rather than lovemaking.

motorcars

These approach our ideal form of locomotion, the 'double bed with an outboard motor.' Big American cars come very close to it (there is room to lie flat, even on the rear seat) – Volkswagens call for neat handling of anything more than breast-and-petting work. The classical postures (she on the back seat, he kneeling between her legs, or both sitting, her legs round his waist) were developed for use by Emma Bovary in hansom cabs. All cars, whether adapted to petting or coition, have greenhouse-like properties unless you live in a climate where the windows quickly mist over. If you rely on condensation it is still a good idea to have a powerful light ready to dazzle cops or

MIRRORS *opposite*
Sex seen as one participates is natural, attractive and formally beautiful to a morale-boosting extent, even if you aren't beautiful figures.

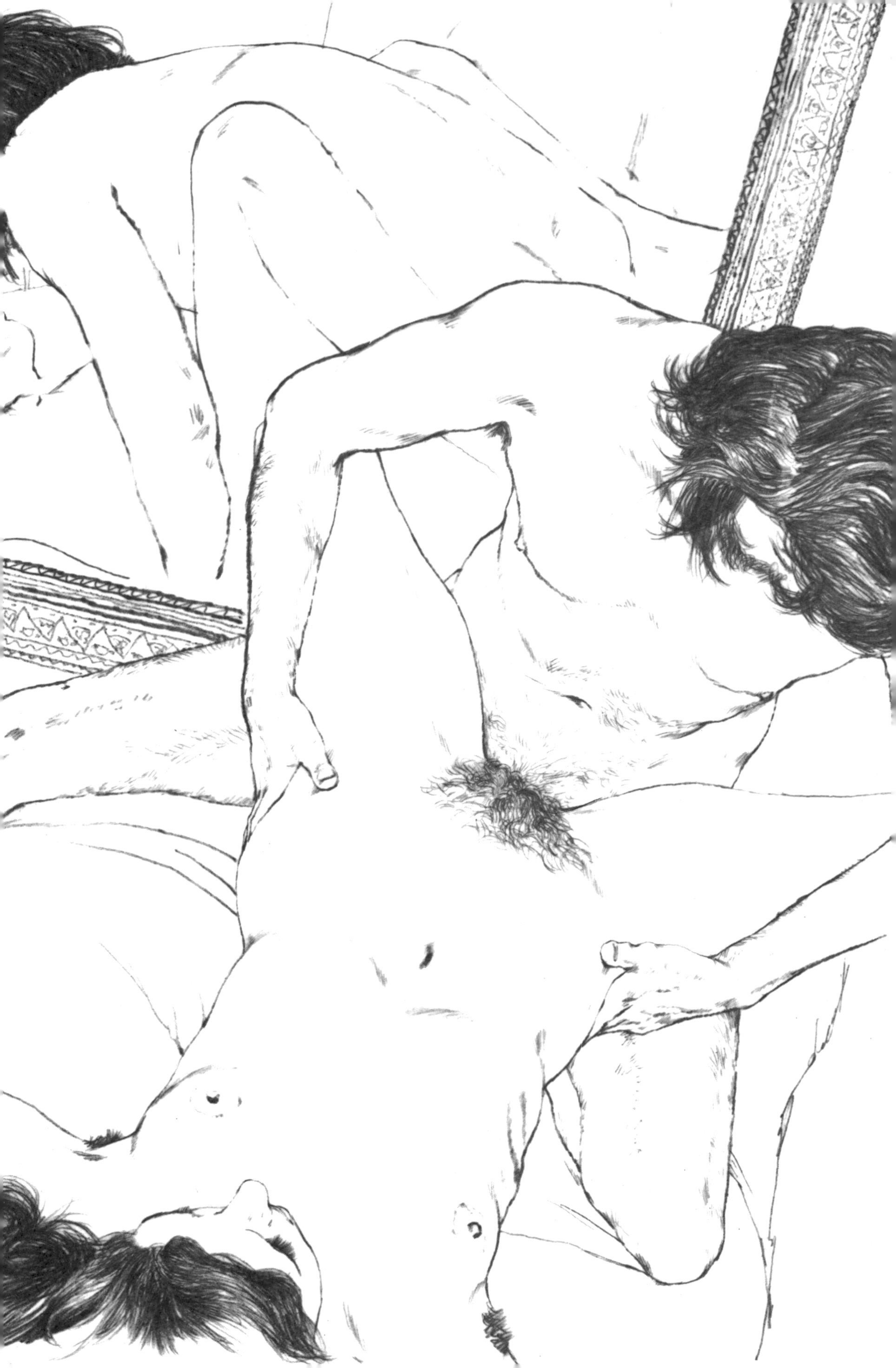

prowlers – a really bright one will give you time to get dressed before sight returns.

For alfresco love the least-screened parking site is the safest, like a French eighteenth-century bower, because you can't be crept up on. If you want to do much of this, buy a small van, or one of those mini-campers known as adultery wagons, which are in effect mobile houses. It takes confidence to strip naked in any of these. For security the best ploy is to make it a foursome, taking it in turns while the other couple drive, or sit stonily in front behaving themselves and providing cover. Mutual masturbation while driving, and trying to score number of orgasms per gallon, are popular fantasies, but against the interest of safe driving. Seatbelts can be worn, or you can tie the non-driving party to his or her seat and work slowly.

motorcycle

Increasingly popular sexual venue, which combines the symbolism of the horse with leather gear, danger and acceleration. Has serious safety drawbacks, calls for the wearing of a hard hat, and you can't rely on the machine to look after itself as a horse can, but if you have access to a private road the hazards are yours. Better not attempted on the public highway. Another limitation comes from the fact that the passengers, m. or f., sit behind, and you can't, or shouldn't drive with one on your lap – clothed or not. Probably better as a preliminary to love than a venue for it. Don't let her liking for increased G override your judgment. Nobody looks virile dead.

open air

Countries with a warm summer have advantages which can't be overstated. In England, to have regular and full love out of doors you need to be frostproof and own a park. In Ireland or Spain, even though it is warm in Spain, you need to be priest-proof as well. Most parts of the U.S. should count their blessings. What is odd is that they don't do more about garden design. The walled or hedged gardens of Europe are nearly all practicable, at least by night.

Outdoor locations in wild areas are often flawed by vermin, ranging from ants and mosquitos to rattlesnakes and officious cops. Surface-wise the best venue is often sand dunes, which give shelter and keep the heat, besides not harboring stinging insects. Lawn grass is fine if well-screened. The safest cover, if you intend to strip right off, is the thicket standing on its own, where you can see out but they can't see in, the 'bower' of Fontainebleau painters. Europeans, who live in crowded landscapes, are adept at quick dressing and using places like Hampstead Heath and the Prater. With so much of America to choose from, there should be no problem – if you do take risks, however, cultivate the quick getaway and the weather-eye open; danger turns some people on, and others, of both sexes, right off. Enthusiastic larks one gets lost in, like stripping right off or tying each other to trees, call for very remote areas or a walled garden.

What you can do safely in Hyde Park, London, would be asking for gang-rape in Central Park, New York. When traveling, Catholic countries are more up-tight than Protestant, and Stalinist than other-style Marxist such as Jugoslavia, but anyhow you don't want to offend local feeling. A flat roof at night is a standard Oriental venue – you can make love and see the whole city.

Ultimately there will be scheduled areas – we give it another five or six years.

pattes d'araignée

Pattes d'araignée, literally spider's legs, is tickling erotic massage, using the pulps of the fingers, with the *lightest possible* touch, aiming to stimulate not so much the skin as the almost invisible skin-hairs: not on the genitals, but all the next most sensitive places – nipples and around, neck, chest, belly, insides of arms and thighs, armpits, hollow of the back, soles and palms, scrotum, space between it and the anus. Use both hands; keep a steady progression of movement going with one, and make surprise attacks with the other. The whole essence is in the extreme lightness of the touch – more electric than tickling. Feathers, bristlegloves or vibrators give a quite different sensation. If you are agile, don't forget you have toes as well as fingers and hair in various places, including eyelids, to vary the sensation. A set of finger-cots with textures from cardcloth to mink are easy to use; the real and original French style with fingertips is difficult to learn but unforgettable by either sex. It's one of the two general skin stimulants (the other is the *Tongue bath*) which work even on not very skin-conscious males.

pompoir

The most sought-after feminine sexual response of all. 'She must . . . close and constrict the Yoni until it holds the Lingam as with a finger, opening and shutting at her pleasure, and finally acting as the hand of the Gopala-girl who milks the cow. This can be learned only by long practice, and especially by throwing the will into the part affected, even as men endeavor to sharpen their hearing . . . Her husband will then value her above all women, nor would he exchange her for the most beautiful queen in the Three Worlds. . . Among some races the constrictor vaginae muscles are abnormally developed. In Abyssinia, for instance, a woman can so exert them as to cause pain

OPEN AIR *overleaf*
If you do take risks, cultivate the quick getaway and the weather-eye open.

to a man, and, when sitting on his thighs, she can induce orgasm without moving any other part of her person. Such an artist is called by the Arabs Kabbazah, literally, a holder, and it is not surprising that slave dealers pay large sums for her.' Thus Richard Burton. It has nothing to do with 'race' but a lot to do with practice. See *Exercises*.

pornography

Name given to any sexual literature somebody is trying to suppress. Most normal people enjoy looking at sex books and reading sex fantasies, which is why abnormal people have to spend so much time and money suppressing them. The only drawback of the commercial stuff is that because it is based on fantasy, and often inexperienced fantasy at that, it's not much help with sex practice. Depiction of any of the range of sex behaviors we've described helps people to visualize them; porno stories tend to be dull, repetitive, and a strain on credulity: frankly antisocial fantasies about torture and so on worry legislators and others for fear they might induce idiots to imitate them – it's equally possible that by enabling not very bright people to fantasize their unacceptable needs vividly they help to keep them from acting them out, but there is no good evidence one way or another.

Straight couples can use 'pornography' constructively in the exact proportion that it's well done, i.e. it describes feasible, acceptable and pleasurable sex activities they'd enjoy, or fantasies which, though not feasible, turn them on. This is what literature in general does. Many people, male and female, find sex books a real help in raising the level of feeling to bedpoint. Use them as football enthusiasts use books about football – even if the players in the story show superhuman shooting-powers. It isn't true that only men are turned on by sexual literature: it is true that women are most turned on by it if it's written with awareness of other than male feelings.

If you've got literary or artistic ability, use it to express your own fantasies to the full, for private use between you. Most of the squarest writers and artists have done this, even if they didn't publish the results. It's one way of dealing with the things you can't, or wouldn't wish, to do in fact – a kind of accessory to dreams and to play.

The idea of children getting hold of pornography terrifies some people. If it deals simply with normal lovemaking, this fear is probably not justified – young children are likely to be bored: the main objection lies in how badly most of the Mafia stuff is produced – some is enough to put adults off. Some adult fantasy-material, if it's odd or cruel, could be actively frightening, though no more so than non-sex material such as newsreels or religious books. If you do see your children with pornography, remember far more harm would be caused by any uproar you make about it. For adolescents it's probably innocuous unless they're obviously very disturbed over sex.

postillionage

Putting a finger in or on your partner's anus just before orgasm. Popular in French erotic books, and works on some people. Most prefer firm finger pressure just in front of the anus; in men this can produce an erection used alone. Use a small vibrator rather than a finger if you prefer – don't put it into the vagina afterwards, if you've actually inserted it. Firm pressure with a heel behind the scrotum or between anus and vulva works as well in some postures.

railways

An old and favored site for 'different' sex – now going out, as they won't let you fly united. This means, of course, the oldstyle wagon-lit or roomette. Whether it's the motion and acceleration or the association with love on the run that provides the turn-on isn't clear: it used to be fashionable in the classier Parisian and Viennese bordels to have a compartment fitted up, complete with train effects and noises, and vibrated by a motor and cams. Since it is probably the motion and variable G which score, choose a hard couch and a winding track with numerous intersections and switches. In emergency there is just room for an upright in the washroom.

remote control

It's an old story that you can seduce a complete novice, who has no idea what you mean, by slipping a thumb into a closed fist, or between your lips, and absent mindedly moving it in and out, in and out. We'd like to see this. All of the people we have seen it work on have known very well what it was all about.

This is one version of the pompido telecommando. The lip one works better, nail downwards in the appropriate rhythm – she will feel it where she should. She can do the same 'at' him, for example in eating (see that wild sequence in *Tom Jones*). Once habituated to either of these tele-control devices, most girls and some men can be radio-controlled as to excitement, erection and even orgasm – even by rubbing the lobe of one's ear – from several places down a table, the opposite side of a room, or the opposite box at a theater. The funniest use we've seen of this was when the lady was dancing with someone else, who spotted what was going on in his arms but thought he was the source of the signals – which actually came from her lover, who was sitting out.

The original telecommando is the 'blower' which

connects the restaurant with the kitchen downstairs. Appropriate.

rocking chair

Tried by some as an indoor substitute for that classic piece of sexual gear, the swing. Actually it feels quite different, lacking the sudden bellydropping acceleration which is the source of the swing's effects on women, but more like the sensation of love in a train (see *Railways*).

It works best with an ill-made chair on a very hard, rough floor – better, an erotic rocking chair with a dozen flats or studs on each rocker, hard cushions and no arms. This still needs a hard, preferably stone, floor and is infernally noisy – useless for an apartment if people live under. Normally you sit astride facing, but other positions are possible. We've seen a stool with a powerful vibrator in the top cushion which looks worth a trial, though the feel would be quite different.

rubber

This turns some people on, and is a wholetime fetish with others. Effect seems to depend on its status as super-skin combined with tightness and odor. The odor of latex rubber excites a lot of people if they have come to associate it with using condoms – it also enhances the normal female perfume. Wash anything rubber in soapy water, dry, and keep in french chalk – this includes condoms, ticklers, g-strings and larger items. Black seems to be the preferred sexual color. The livid pink condoms sold in some places don't look as good as the normal translucent variety.

Rubber clothes are one of the few very common turn-ons which for some reason, if you leave out skin-diving and water-skiing, have never got to be fashionable, probably because it's not specially empathic for women (or because it's unbelievably hot).

saxonus

Coitus saxonus – pressing firmly on the male urethra near the root of the penis to prevent ejaculation and (hopefully) conception. No use as a contraceptive, since sperms are around long before he ejaculates – but some women do have the knack, during masturbation, of stopping and restarting ejaculation by urethral pressure so as to spin out the male peak. This is best done by pressing on the shaft near the root with two or three fingers, but you need to press hard (don't bruise). Some people press midway between scrotum and anus. The idea is to allow ejaculation to occur piecemeal. If you stop it altogether, he will eventually ejaculate into the bladder. There's no evidence that this is harmful unless done

ROCKING CHAIR *opposite*
Like the sensation of love in a train.

violently and often, but it's probably better avoided. Interrupting ejaculation is also probably harmless but it is difficult, and won't work on everyone. Women who have this as a party piece say it is appreciated, but that may depend on their partner. You might as well stop just short of ejaculation, then restart the whole business a few minutes later.

shoes

A sex turn-on connected with the foot-pussy equivalence we've mentioned elsewhere (see *Feet*); symbols apart it's interesting that shoe-leather 'fixes' from sweat exactly the same fatty-acids which are present in the vagina and turn on male sex behavior in monkeys and apes. Though these smell rancid rather than sexy, they may still have a subliminal turn-on effect in man. High heels attract some males, chiefly for their effect in increasing the wobble in the female gait, another instance of making the woman more woman-shaped. Probably something of a hide-and-seek effect, too – Chinese women had to hide their feet but could show their genitals. Even for us bare feet are symbolic of nakedness, which is why lady pop-singers shed their shoes.

For most lovemaking you really need bare feet.

slow masturbation

Prostitutes aren't usually much good at advanced sex: this is about the one old-time bordel trick which is worth trying. To make it work, you need to know how to tie your partner (see *Bondage*) and to have a partner who likes struggling against resistance, but it works for a great many people. Traditionally, the woman does it to the man, but it works in either direction. You need good access and a completely helpless partner, though you can try it without if bondage games turn you off, but the result is quite different and you can't get so far. The knack lies in playing on your partner like an instrument, alternately pushing them forward and frustrating them (compare *Relaxation*).

The woman starts by tying the man to her satisfaction, either staked out, or wrists behind and ankles crossed, knees open, naked and on his back. She then 'signs her name' (*le coup de cassolette*). To do this she knees astride him, facing him, and performs a tasteful striptease as far as her panties. Next, holding his hair in her hand, she rubs his mouth firmly over her armpit and breasts, giving him her body perfume. Then she locks her legs carefully round his neck and presses her covered pussy on his mouth. Finally she strips off and gives him the direct genital kiss, (brushing first, then open, taking her time over it), pulls his foreskin well back if he has one, and stands back for a few moments to let him get excited. If she knows her job, he

SLOW MASTURBATION *opposite*
The knack lies in playing on your partner like an instrument, alternately pushing them forward and frustrating them.

will be unable to move, while the kiss ensures that he won't lose the feel of her. Coming back she does the same all over again, stiffens him by hand and mouth if necessary, and starts in real earnest.

She has two focal points to attend to, his mouth and his penis, and the knack, during this warm-up period, consists in keeping both of them occupied continuously, without pauses and without triggering ejaculation. The possibilities are obvious – hand to each, hand to one, mouth or pussy to the other; varied by a touch of her breasts, her armpit, or even her hair. Between the two poles she will work over his most sensitive areas with her fingertips (*les pattes d'araignée*), her tongue, and her pussy – this last with one hand on his penis and her other palm over his mouth, never letting the rhythm slacken. If his erection begins to go down she stops, tightens him up

(this is the moment for thumb-tying if she is strong enough to turn him easily), then re-stiffens him. Then she can begin slow masturbation proper.

This is about the most mind-blowing (and, while it lasts, frustrating) sexual sensation of which most males are capable. (If you still want to know why we include it under bondage games, try it for a few moments with an *un*bound partner.) Sit well up on his chest, with your buttocks to his chin, and put each of your ankles inside the crook of one of his knees. Hold the root of his penis with one hand and with the other pull the skin back as far as it will go with finger and thumb, thumb towards you. Then start quick, sharp, nervous strokes–each one quick, that is, but timed at one per second, no faster. After about twenty of these, give about ten very quick strokes. Then resume the slow rhythm. And so on. If from the turmoil under you and the general scene you think he is about to ejaculate, drop the speed (you can sense this with practice). Keep it up as long as you think he can stand it. The excitement is his, but is less one-sided than it sounds; the male response is enough to turn most women on, and you can press your open pussy hard on his breastbone, but don't let your attention wander. Ten minutes is about as much as most males can stand. If he goes limp, put him out of his misery, either by quickly masturbating him to climax, or by mouth, or by turning and riding him. When he does come, get him untied as quickly as possible – delay after orgasm will leave him as stiff as if he'd played a hard ball-game.

The domestication of this experience, which veterans will recognize as the Japanese-massage-special-treatment routine, may be the one good thing America gets out of the Vietnam war – the only bar to making it at home, like sukiyaki, is if your are a big girl. The Japanese are artists at making their knots, like their dishes, look really nice, and Japanese masseuses are small enough to sit on a man's chest without killing him. If you are a Brunnhilde, try tying his legs apart and taking your weight on your knees, with your pussy on his mouth: in the story Brunnhilde tied up King Gunther on *his* wedding night, probably for a similar routine – we've given the small woman version. And let him try the same techniques on you.

The man has three points to concentrate on – mouth, breasts and clitoris. A fairly tight couple of turns round the breasts helps (careful!). He can start as she did, with the *coup de cassolette* (armpit and glans) and then rub his hand over *her* cassolette and put it over her mouth, to play back her own perfume. He needs to watch from her sounds and movements how heavy a touch on the clitoris she can stand. He can copy the spinning-out technique and excite her by postponement, but usually he will get better results by simply pushing her as far and as fast as possible. If she is a responsive subject and not frightened of the whole business the reaction will fully test his skill in securing her. He should kneel astride, but not sit on her, nor hold her down – she should be quite helpless anyway. Finally, and with experienced lovers this will be when she is semi-conscious, he will switch to a few moments of tongue work for lubrication, then vigorous intercourse, and make her scale another, still higher range of peaks taking his own orgasm early on. He should know by the feel of her when to stop – this bears no relation to mewing and struggles, which reach a peak just short of climax. He should then untie her quickly, skillfully and painlessly, so that she comes back to earth lying quietly in his arms.

One unexpected trick is for the lady to tell her partner she's going to give him the time of his life, tie him, and then, when you've made sure he can't get loose or make a sound, make him watch while you masturbate to orgasm. This is more exciting for both of you than it sounds: he, if he's already excited and expecting something else, will go beserk, and his useless struggles will turn her on. Afterwards she can make it up to him – slowly.

south slav style

Well-documented because of the very rich erotic folksong literature of what is now Jugoslavia. Intercourse naked, emphasis on the importance of genital perfume as a stimulus, several reputedly 'national' positions or approaches. Serbian intercourse (Srpski jeb) is mock rape – you throw her down, seize one ankle in each hand and raise them over her head, then enter her with your full weight (do this on something soft – the traditional bare earth is beyond a game). Croatian intercourse (hrvatski jeb) is a woman's ploy – an elaborate tongue bath, with the man free or staked out, followed after leisurely stimulation by riding him astride (reputed by local wiseacres to be 'exhausting'). The Lion position is a male masturbation method – squat down, heels to scrotum, place the penis between your ankles, rest on buttocks and hands, and move legs together. The style is passionate and affectionate as befits a race of bride-stealing warriors whose women were formerly, and still are, natural partisans: tough plus tender.

stockings

Can be a sex turn-on – often the preferred ones aren't the fashionable kind but old-style black stockings which look prossy. Tights are an obstacle unless crutchless, and only erotic, for most males, if worn without panties, and then chiefly visually. It is said that if you can get one stocking off her you're home. Actually in quick undressing or actual

STOCKINGS *above*
Often the preferred ones aren't the fashionable kind but the old-fashioned black stockings.

lovemaking modern nylons usually get ruined, but if you keep your nails and fingers smooth taking them off gently makes good foreplay, along with mutual undressing generally. Long gloves turn some people on – they suggest the old-style great lady. Unless you find shoes sexy, lovemaking is best with bare feet and toes.

substitutes

Handwork and oral love aren't substitutes for vaginal intercourse but techniques on their own. The listed 'substitutes' are what Europeans formerly used as contraceptive techniques which would ejaculate the male without masturbation and were less taboo than oral sex. The old 'substitutes' have their place – some, like mammary intercourse, can be fully bilateral and all are occasionally fun – during a period, for example, or if she is very pregnant. The *Paradis Charnels* of 1903 gives nine sites: hands (she joins her hands, thumbs crossed, fingers interlaced, and makes him a vagina, wetting her palms first with saliva – an old way of ending straight intercourse without risking pregnancy, though it isn't in fact a safe contraceptive method), mouth, between the thighs (see *Femoral intercourse*), the *Breasts*, the *Armpit*, and also the fold of the elbow and the knee. The other two substitute sites are the hair (long hair or plaits can be rolled into a vagina, or the penis lassooed with a loop of it, though some women may object because it's a bore to wash. Such techniques might be helpful for "safe sex".

swings

These are one erotic extra which emphatically do work. Swinging solo has given many little girls their first orgasm, because the acceleration produces pressure in the pelvis like nothing else. Swings are of two sorts – those mentioned by Eastern writers are simply suspended garden-seat beds, not capable of this kind of acceleration, but giving the agreeable feelings that go with a slightly unstable surface, the proverbial jelly-on-springs. For him, this is like having a woman with infinite buttocks, for her it is a swimmy sensation, devoid of the drawbacks of an over-soft mattress, since the actual surface can be firm.

The real high-velocity swing is the woman's turn-on unless she gets air sick first. The operative thing is the swoop, the falling-elevator sensation of negative G. Swinging with a well-implanted partner is a sensation every girl should have at least once in a lifetime: solo swinging with the Japanese rin-no-tama (see *Gadgets and gimmicks*) is another wild experience of inner movement. A plastic eggshaped saltshaker containing a really large ballbearing will do at a pinch. For intercourse, he sits on the seat, and she astride facing – he works the swing, or a third party pushes (traditionally the maidservant). Ideally one should try the Roller Coaster, but we haven't found a showground which permits that. On a garden swing, watch out for the occasional girl whose orgasm under these conditions is so intense that she blacks out, even if she doesn't do so normally, as she may fall if you don't hold her. Start at rest and penetrated, and use the movements of working up the swing to drive your coitus.

VIBRATORS *overleaf*
Lovers often find them an extra sensation to incorporate into the ritual of skin stimulation.

turkish style

The Sultan of the Ottoman empire, so far from living 'mit Saus und Braus,' was the bottom man of a huge pyramid of functionaries and eunuchs, who lived in fear of his life and was obliged to sign a stud-book at each act of sex. Often he had spent his youth in the company of mistresses known to be sterile, while waiting to know if he would reign or be strangled at the accession of another heir. His innumerable harem were taught the arts of pleasing, but these are not recorded. The chosen lady would enter his bedchamber naked, and in darkness dive under the covers at the bed foot, wriggling her way up alongside him to wait his pleasure. Recalcitrant newcomers were brought in by the Aga Bashi with their thumbs tightly tied behind, and frequently beaten into submission by flogging the soles of their feet. Delinquent concubines were drowned in sacks – silk ones if they were kadins. In spite of the facts, Turkish erotic scenes were a great nineteenth-century fantasy in Christian Europe. They need not be so biased towards the male – she can equally well be Gulbeyaz receiving a chosen Christian stud. Take it in turns.

vibrators

A new standby, which have proved very useful in teaching sexually inexperienced women to stimulate their own responses. There are two main kinds – penis-shaped, which can be used on skin, breasts, clitoris or deeply in the vagina (the small size can be used anally) and larger motor driven kinds as used by masseurs, which strap on the hand like a glove, and can impart wild sensations to almost any part of the body. Vibrators are no substitute for a penis – some women prefer them to a finger for masturbation, or put one in the vagina while working manually on the clitoris. Lovers often find them an extra sensation to incorporate into the ritual of skin stimulation. Vibrating hotel beds, operated by a coin-in-slot timer, are also well spoken of, but are apt to run out at the critical moment, or make you ill. Careful vibratory massage of the whole body surface is a better bet than over-concentration on the penis or clitoris, but it requires skill. Penile gadgets of various kinds for attachment to the standard vibrator base don't seem to have much beyond novelty to commend them.

viennese oyster

Lady who can cross her feet behind her head, lying on her back, of course. When she has done so, you hold her tightly round each instep with your full hand and squeeze, lying on her full-length. Don't try to put an unsupple partner into this position – it can't be achieved by brute force. You can get a very similar sensation – unique

WET LOOK *opposite*
Try showering in a clinging cotton shift: this both feels and looks sexy.

rocking pelvic movement – with less expertise if she crosses her ankles on her tummy, knees to shoulders, and you lie on her crossed ankles with your full weight. Why 'Viennese' we don't know. Tolerable for short periods only but gives tremendous genital pressure for both.

voyeurs

Title to be kept for those who treat sex as a nonplaying, spectator sport. Any active player is likely to be fascinated to watch his game being played, provided the players are worth watching. Real couples are worth watching – the bored, semi-erected participants in blue movies seldom merit the trouble. Real human mating behavior is as interesting as that of birds and far more instructive. If you can watch others, do, unless it violates your sense of privacy. We lose a lot in this society by not being in the habit of making love in company. If we did, fewer books such as this one would need to be written.

wet look

Another super skin releaser which is getting popular – it makes you tight and shiny. Some people like the real thing with real water – try showering in a clinging cotton shift: this both feels and looks sexy. Transparent plastic raincoats worn over the bare skin do something for some wearers and spectators and are a fairly common male turn-on. Ask, try it, or both.

Problems

and what to do about them

age

The only thing age has to do with sex performace is that the longer you love, the more you learn. Young people (and some older ones) are firmly convinced that no-one over fifty makes love, and it would be pretty obscene if they did. Ours isn't the first generation to know otherwise, but probably the first one which hasn't been brainwashed into being ashamed to admit it.

Some couples may be starting on some of our suggestions when they've been through the groundwork and reached the thirties. Since, however, we shall all get older, and superstitions still persist, it is worth giving the facts.

Neither men nor women lose either sexual needs or sexual function with age. In men, the only important changes over the first seven decades are that spontaneous erection occurs less often (accordingly they need more direct penile stimulation from the woman), ejaculation takes longer to happen, which is an advantage, coital frequency tends to fall, but given an attractive and receptive partner, decent general health and an absence of the belief that one ought to run out of steam, active sex lasts as long as life. In later life, the ability and need to ejaculate frequently get less. It's a good idea not to try for it every time, which will give you more mileage and no less mutual pleasure. Women lose their fertility at the menopause, but that in itself often helps rather than spoils their sex life. In fact, there is little if any physical decline in any attribute except frequency up to 75 and beyond. From a quarter to a half of all couples of this age still have regular sex, and that includes all of the people who never had much of a sex life when they were younger. Since continued activity keeps hormone levels up, for couples who make love often it's probably closer to 75 per cent and the other quarter will have stopped because of arthritis or the other ills of age, not impotence or frigidity. 'The things that stop you having sex with age are exactly the same as those that stop you riding a bicycle (bad health, thinking it looks silly, no bicycle).' The difference is that they happen later for sex than for bicycles. Over 50, the important thing is never to drop sex for any long period – keep yourself going solo if you don't for the time being have a partner: if you let it drop you may have trouble restarting (see *Health*).

Women can, of course, be kept menstruating indefinitely with hormones. There's probably little point, unless it boosts morale. A few find they get dry vaginally and need some estrogen, but in fact the results of continued sexual activity and of hormone pills are just about equal.

As with so many things, later life is the time when you've tried everything, and settle down to the things you like most – together.

opposite and overleaf Two further paintings from *Loving Couples* by Hokusai

bisexuality

All people are bisexual – that is to say, they are able to respond sexually to some extent towards people of either sex. Being 'homosexual' isn't a matter of having this kind of response, but usually of having some kind of turn-off towards the opposite sex which makes our same-sex response more evident or predominant. How far people act bisexually will depend on a great many things, including the society they live in, their opportunities, and how far the same-sex part of their response worries them.

Being actively bisexual makes problems in our society, not least with the other-sex partner on whom, obviously, most of most peoples' most worthwhile sex life depends. It is difficult enough to have to make out with half the human race without trying to make out with the whole of it. Moreover today, although bisexuality is not "unnatural", as evidenced by the homosexual dreams all heterosexual people may occasionally have, and by what we know about primatology, a male who has been actively "bisexual" in the last ten years poses an active threat to future partners because he may – especially if he had a homosexual experience in the USA – be an unwitting carrier of the AIDS virus.

Medicine is concerned about this group becuase, together with people who have injected drugs or been given intravenous blood products, they spread the HIV virus into the general sexual community (bisexual women don't present this risk unless they became infected incidentally, because AIDS does not pass between lesbians; women far more readily respond to other women than men do overtly to men, because intimacy between women is socially acceptable, while anything looking like male-male affection has been tramped on with society's heaviest boots.)

Although the homosexual community has responded rapidly and intelligently to the threat by altering its sexual behaviours, a high proportion in some areas are, tragically, already infected. In consequence the only safe male-male sexual activity is mutual masturbation. In threesomes and two-couple interactions, which were becoming commoner and less taboo, an infected man can infect not only the woman, but even more probably the other man as well if he has intercourse with the same partner immediately before him, since semen is the vehicle for infection. Overtly bisexual men are a high-risk group, and both they and their partners of either sex need to be aware of this and take defensive action. This is tough, but becoming a carrier of a lethal disease is tougher still.

children

Children are a natural though not a necessary consequence of having sex. They impose responsibilities – not

least those of being willing to stay together and rear them, and of having to restrict one's immediate sexual spontaneity for several years. For most people, they are well worth these restrictions, but if you aren't prepared to accept the restrictions, don't have them.

Full blooded sex is not exclusive to the childless, but if you want it you must arrange your own privacy. Never involve children in adult sexual activities: militant and exhibitionist liberals who try to acclimatize children to the naturalness of sex by letting them in at any level on their own sex lives probably do at least as much harm as was ever done by the prohibitive sex-is-dirty generation. It is possible for your children to see that love and sex are good from their awareness that your relations outside the bedroom are unanxious (if they are anxiously demonstrative you will transmit the anxiety). What happens in other cultures is no guide here, because our society lacks their other supportive and educative mechanisms.

Most young children are biologically programmed to interpret the sight or sound of adult coition as evidence of a violent assault (they are aware of it earlier than you would expect, so don't keep babies in the bedroom), and the awareness of mother-father sexual relations is on all counts far too explosive a matter to be monkeyed with in the interest of Reichian experiments. Treating their own sexuality (masturbation, interest in the other sex and so on) with acceptance and naturalness is a different matter, but don't push encouragement to the point of incestuous interference with their private lives, either in toddlerhood or in adolescence, or you'll end up trying to use them to enact your own unrealized fantasies and turn them off altogether. Good sex education starts with being unbothered but not exhibitionistic, respecting your children's modesties, answering their questions, and letting them see that you regard this as a topic for pleasurable interest, naturalness – and privacy, not secrecy. Arrange the privacy with an eye to the fact that a normal toddler sees you as a rival, i.e. don't just lock him or her out.

Modern housing makes these counsels of perfection unless you are rich, but if you aren't prepared to make the necessary concessions, stick to having sex and don't have children. Nudity is another matter with which militant liberals can embarrass their children – there is a whole built-in biology of toddler response to adult parental genitals: we would say, 'Don't push it.' Children should see each other and non-parental adults naked. Some parents normally and unanxiously go about naked; but any element of a special educational parade is probably a bad idea. The good thing about family attendance at nudist clubs is that the nudity of people in general lacks the biological and psychological anxiety-overtones of

BISEXUALITY *opposite*
Women seem to relate more easily to same-sex stimulation in a group scene, and women exciting each other are a turn-on for males.

nude parents, but don't push this either, and don't be surprised or discouraging over modesties among your offspring you don't as adults share. Don't forget that father's penis is a dominance signal and mother's vulva an ambivalent object to the normal 3- to 7-year-old boy. If you are being deliberately emancipated you're probably overdoing it.

Preadolescent children should be told about normal sexual phenomena such as menstruation or masturbation before they happen and before more anxious advisers (clergy, teachers and other children) get there first – present them as what they are, part of the process and privilege of growing up: *all* sexual enlightenment, including where babies come from and the nature of intercourse, are best given even before they can be understood, so that the child gows up knowing what is what, and proof against scaremongers.

Egging adolescent children into sex experience is pathological. By that age the test is whether they trust you and are sure enough that you will talk sense to ask your advice, but don't be shocked if they still keep their own counsel. If you are anxious or see trouble, say so frankly and directly, but don't bully. If you've done the job properly and your kids are endowed with reasonably good personalities they will have no less sense, if less experience, than you have. A friend of ours found condoms in his 13-year-old daughter's possession and phoned the parents of her best friend 'to warn them.' Questioned by her father, the best friend said, 'Yes, I know: I bought them for her. She's going with a boy, she wasn't taking precautions, and I didn't want to see her in trouble!'

Parents whose sex life is really unanxious will probably be good parents in this respect, but in our culture they are rarish, and we can't help our anxieties. Not much point in trying to hide these (many of them are built-in to man), and play-acting, whether moralistic or with-it, is bad education and is seen through by children. If you are seen to be honest about your own feelings, that is as good as you are likely to get.

Finally, anyone who deliberately sets out to use a child or a pregnancy to prove something, to 'keep the marriage together,' to boost their ego, or thinks it would be great to bring up a child or children solo, needs to think again. Of course children are ego-boosting and having them is a natural part of being a person, but they are people, not psychiatric procedures. Adoption agencies are on the lookout for those who regard a child as a medicine, a medal or a missile and screen them out. If we could cut out equally motivated natural parenthood it would make for less mental illness, as well as solving the population problem in rich countries.

climateric

Old name for the menopause, the time at which the woman ceases menstruation. Old John Fothergill the Quaker doctor wrote in the eighteenth century, 'There is a period in the life of Females to which, for the most part, they are taught to look forward with some degree of anxiety: the various and absurd opinions, relative to the ceasing of the menstrual discharge, propagated through successive ages, have tended to embitter the hours of many a sensible woman – some practitioners, in other respects able and judicious, if they have not favored these erroneous and terrifying notions, seem not to have endeavored to correct them, with the diligence and humanity which such an object requires.' That about sums it up.

Menopausal changes are complex. The end of ovulation means the end of fertility, and for some women this subtly affects their self-esteem quite apart from any physical effects of a shift in hormone balance. For others it represents a sexual release, when they no longer need worry about contraception. While a few things, like irregular bleeding or hot flushes, are hormonal, personality changes like irritability and depression could be both hormonal and due to the fact that a milestone has been passed and one has stopped being young. Men, who don't have a menopause or any sudden hormone change, often, undergo a 'male climacteric' which coincides with realizing what they haven't done among the fantasies of youth, and that they had better do it now. This can lead to injudicious thrashing about, actual illness, or simply reassessment of their aims and opportunities very like a second adolescence.

Sex life for women doesn't end with the menopause unless they have been convinced that it should or feel they are 'no longer women.' Often it really begins then, if pregnancy has been a worry. Whether the symptoms are physical or mental, such as mood changes, hormones are often worth trying to ease over the readjustment (under medical supervision). The Pill can obscure the menopause by altering or suppressing the cycle: don't stop it until you are sure you are not still ovulating or you may get surprisingly pregnant. After the menopause, a few people need estrogen to combat dryness or soreness – but continued sexual activity seems to work nearly as well as medicine in preserving the function of both sexes far into later life. See *Age*.

defloration

Odd, how this major obsession of past ages has stopped being a problem at all. There was a time when it was a constant preoccupation for the promiscuously-minded male and a real worry to most girls. The change can't be due to the shortage of virgins (there has to be a first time for everything) nor even to the invention of vaseline – it more probably is due to petting (perhaps) and a change in sexual folklore (certainly). Most girls are now carefully stretched beforehand by considerate boyfriends, and the others don't grow up on the stories of blood, sweat and tears which their great-grandmothers used to tell. In the eighteenth century a girl was disgraced is she didn't bleed like a pig on her wedding night; most modern lovers would reckon not to make her bleed at all unless she asks to be 'deflowered' in the good oldfashioned way. Even then, unusual anatomy apart, it shouldn't hurt her 'more than it hurts a vain young miss to get her ears pierced.'

The first night is a special situation we needn't handle here. Our point is that with the bogy of real defloration exorcized we can revive the eighteenth century play-wise and deflower her again as often as we and she like. The Houris in heaven grow new hymens daily and are perpetually virgin, but so is every woman if she likes to pretend she is. It's not a bad way of celebrating an anniversary. Real enthusiasts can do the whole thing properly, honeymoon hotel and all; the result usually works far, far better than a real first-shot honeymoon. One can even book the same room in advance. Or one can do it oftener, at home, and at shorter notice. All she need do is to say, 'Tonight, I'm a virgin.'

depilation

One way of getting rid of hair you don't want (see *Hair*). Japanese women use a sharpened finger-ring, or you can use chemical pastes (not round the genitals – they often sting) or have hairs taken out individually by electrolysis. This costs several dollars per hair, and is usually only worth it if a girl has a lot of hair on her face.

doctors

There is no special reason why doctors should advise us on sex techniques, but traditionally they often have done so. In fact Avicenna wrote that it was a highly reputable part of their job, because pleasure in sex is 'pertinent to generation.' We'd probably say that it's also pertinent to being a whole person. In view of the clutch of health worries about sexuality which we still inherit, the doctor would be a very good counselor if he knew anything about it. In the past, particularly the Victorian past, medicine collected superconformists with all their age's anxieties and superstitions, plus a line of omniscient homespun moralism which is still with us, occasionally, over things like abortion and the Pill. This isn't the reason, however, that so many people, not only with problems, but simply with straight questions about sexual matters, draw a blank from their physician and write either to magazines or to total strangers.

The trouble is that normal human sex behavior simply isn't taught and until lately, with researchers like Masters or Kinsey, it couldn't be taught because there was only folklore to teach. When we were medical students thirty years ago, not even birth control was on the syllabus, though at least we were urged to read Havelock Ellis. Also most of what was in the textbooks was tendentious bunk. The sort of folk commonsense which used to figure in ballads and stories had gone, and so had the worldly wisdom of eighteenth-century doctors like John Hunter. Accordingly with the best will in the world, a doctor who wanted to counsel on sex behavior either had to research it first himself, or read it out of one of the books, or go on his own experience – the last of these was fine if the experience was varied, but it could be limited, or eccentric, or absent.

We think this has changed, especially with the younger generation, along with the change in cultural attitudes, though some conscientious office doctors are a little inclined to realize their lack of background and push quite simple matters off onto the psychiatrist, who isn't necessarily any better qualified.

However, sex problems, especially if they involve health, anxiety, or you can't get answers from books, are well worth taking to your doctor. If you are making a choice, a young doctor who talks the language of today or an older man or woman with some personal experience (if you can gauge this) is the best bet. If you have a bad problem and get no joy, persist; if the doctor you consult is hostile or embarrassed, change doctors. Avoid evangelicals – Catholics have hangups over sin, but are often worldly-wise beyond their convictions. Shop around – medicine includes all sorts, and you don't have to put up with a Hippocratic oaf.

It's unfair to your doctor to take the Pill without telling him (if it disagrees with you, he'll have deal to with it); to be shy of letting him know, for example, if you have potency problems (they could be due to medicine he ordered, or explain a lot of other symptoms you've been getting); or to be unnecessarily reticent about your sex life generally, any more than you are about your digestion. If you don't trust the man (or woman), he or she can't help you and you ought to change doctors.

excesses

Quantitatively, in sex, these don't exist – nature sees to that; the woman gets sore, the man can't go on. Medical and moral old-wives have spent centuries teaching that sexual overactivity is debilitating – they were never so admonitory over excessive work or excessive exercise, and rarely over excessive eating, which is our most dangerous hangup at the moment.

Sex is in fact the least tiring physical recreation for the amount of energy expended. If you are flat after it, suspect either your attitude towards it, or (more commonly) secondary loss of sleep. Male lovers forget that women who work or run a home or both aren't as fresh, even though they are as willing, as the idle occupants of the oldstyle Ottoman seraglio. Girls forget that though sex is the perfect tension-relief for both sexes, preoccupation rather than physical fatigue can cause impotence, especially when it goes with a wholehearted wish to perform up to and beyond Olympic standards as a matter of personal pride. Different sleep-needs and sleep-patterns, unrecognized and unaccommodated, can really threaten a sexual partnership. Deal with all these things by speaking out – being really in need of sleep only looks like rejection or sulking to very insecure people who can't communicate with each other.

Sex commonly makes women langorous to the point of sedation. It may make men the same, or boisterously productive – in the second case get up, produce, and let her sleep after a suitable interval of shared quiet and love. At night there is no sleeping pill as good as violent and shared orgasm – active lovers don't need barbiturates.

If ever you do run yourself into the ground, there's no temporary exhaustion a few hours' or days' rest won't cure. Contrary to some belief, plenty of sex makes better and better sex – it damps down overfast orgasm without lowering the peaks: the terrific 'high' after a separation doesn't depend on continence but on reunion. You can both masturbate daily while apart and still get it. Frequent sex also preserves function long into old age – not only is it a habit, but hormone levels depend on it; so, therefore, do looks and vigor.

exhibitionism

Most people from babyhood get a kick (though not in front of adults) out of showing their genitals to the opposite sex – they are, after all, some of the best things we've got, and showing them to a partner is the start of better things. The self-adhesive label gets stuck on people who for a variety of reasons can get their sex in no other way, and show their genitalia to strangers. This would be a harmless but unrewarding activity (these timid characters are by definition not rapists) if people weren't shocked or frightened by it, though it's a disability to the fellow who can't get further than that. Under our extraordinary system, we reward them with public disgrace, imprisonment, etc. No woman need be scared if she meets one.

There was a famous French lady who, when a man exposed himself, remarked 'Monsieur, won't you catch cold?' Exhibitionists don't commonly attack children, and wouldn't frighten them if they were sensibly raised, though adults making themselves look ridiculous, or behaving abnormally in any way, usually upsets them. Children are conservative and easily embarrassed. If your child meets an exhibitionist, tell them the unfortunate chap is stuck at the baby stage, and has so many problems they'd better stay out of his way.

fetish

Something you need instead of, or as well as, a partner in order to reach full sexual response. Less often evident in women than in men, so far as concrete objects or routines are concerned, though women can make fetishes of such things as security, fear and subtler nuances of setting. Can be of all kinds – embryo fetishes are present in almost everyone, and their satisfaction is part of the art as well as the function of love. Many men perform best with a woman who has a particular hair color or length, or big breasts, or looks boyish but are less frank about other turn-on requirements. Particular garments come next – she is more desirable with stockings, or with shoes, or with earrings. Use any of these turn-on circumstances to their fullest extent (see *Clothes*).

A real fetish is any non-sexual circumstance which is obligatory for potency. It becomes a problem if it swamps everything and develops into a consuming anxiety, (shoes only, not even women with shoes) or if it happens to be a fantasy which turns you on and your partner off, or if the performance gets more and more complicated and anxious until a halt has to be called. Normal marital play can meet nearly all demands of this kind if there is real communication, and find them fun, but the partner who is stuck with an anxious ritual can be a big problem which lets-pretend fails to solve.

For a start, a person with a real hangup of this sort, even if fully enacted, can lose interest in anything but his preoccupation. This is a medical problem, however, and time to shout for help. It goes with other personality difficulties of which the loss of interest in love is only a symptom, since most of us at some level have one or more preferred turn-ons, and, if we can't communicate with our partner, tend to get more and more guilty and sensitive about them. Discharged as play, this doesn't happen; but if they can't be discharged in this way, get help. We're talking, remember, about persistent and quite inordinate obsessions which get in the way of the ordinary business of intercourse–refusing to try anything but the missionary position is as much a fetish as only being

FIDELITY *opposite*
What suits a particular couple depends on their needs, situation, anxieties and so on.

potent when wearing a diving helmet. Normal sex involves both fantasy-preferences and variety – variety is the one thing the handicapped ritualist can't enjoy. There's not much wrong with anyone who is willing to try anything once.

It may sound brutal, but don't, repeat don't, take on a partner with a major sex problem such as homosexuality or compulsive ritualism in order to 'cure him by love.' You won't – though if he has your love and comprehension cure by an expert, or at least coming to live with himself, will be much easier. If you have taken on a problem of this kind – and the measure, we repeat, of whether it is a problem is whether it causes anxiety and interferes with sexual joy – work it out between you without fear or recrimination, and go to an expert. It's as much a medical problem as a slipped disc if it interferes with your mutual enjoyment as much as a slipped disc would.

fidelity

Fidelity, infidelity, jealousy and so on. We've deliberately not gone into the ethics of life-style. The facts are that few men and slightly more women in our culture go through life with sexual experience confined to one partner only. What suits a particular couple depends on their needs, situation, anxieties and so on. These needs are a particularly delicate problem in communication: if mutual comprehension is complete and ongoing you can count yourselves lucky. Active deception always hurts a relationship. Complete frankness which is aimed to avoid guilt or as an act of aggression against a partner can do the same. The real problem arises from the fact that sexual relations can be anything, for different people and on different occasions, from a game to a total fusion of identities; the heartaches arise when each partner sees it differently.

There is no sexual relationship which doesn't involve responsibility, because there are two or more people involved: anything which, as it were, militantly excludes a partner is hurtful, yet to be whole people we have at some point to avoid total fusion with each other – 'I am I and you are you, and neither of us is on earth to live up to the other's expectations.' People who communicate sexually have to find their own fidelities. All we can suggest is that you discuss them and at least know where each of you stands.

fighting

The occasional fights, often physical, which all lovers have would have nothing to do with sex if some couples weren't directly excited by them, often without knowing it. That real anger has erotic effects is a matter of true folklore. The

French have a song which goes:

Hey, mister copper,
Colin's beating up his mistress:
Mister Copper, let them get on with it –
It will end with kisses.

Or, as one woman put it, 'We found the old tenderness routine wasn't enough: he likes to use violence and it excites me to resist him. I find the pain exciting, but he's started to hurt me in other contexts and I'm afraid how far it will go.' The trouble is that, as we've several times remarked, our image of love is up-tight about the very real elements of aggression in normal sexuality – which makes us prone to mix erotic violence with real spite or real anger, and confuse two quite distinct things, the quarrel which lets off steam, or is an appeal for help, and sexual stimulation. We aren't talking here about borderline sadists. There are women who unconsciously want violence (and have timid partners) who needle the man into a fight without knowing why. The mixture is a bad one, and usually goes sour.

To need some degree of violence in sex, rather than the glutinous unphysical kind of love which the tradition propagates, is statistically pretty normal. But the way to meet this need isn't to use rows to fuel it, but rather to learn the purposive uses of play. True, the over-gentle spouse is likely to be blocked about aggression, and nonplussed by a demand 'Now try to rape me.' He's been taught not to treat girls like that – if he's excessively over-gentle, he may be sitting on a strong need to do so. But if these things can once be talked about, you can make him (or her) learn the uses of sexual play – which is why we've included some pretty rough-looking games by Marriage Guidance standards – and this without the need to mix them up with real day-to-day angers and frustrations which can get out of hand, especially with the wrong partner. If he's over-gentle, don't needle him, teach him. Real, spiteful violence from a partner is the commonest cause of death or injury in women. Don't put up with it, and don't give second chances – leave, or go to the police. Sadistic bullies are incurable by love.

With a normal partner, don't be ashamed if you really fight (most people do) but don't treat it as a kick, or a way of turning on a partner's aggression. Use play, and keep it in the sexual situation. Cultivate pillow talk to unblock fantasies – ask each other just short of orgasm, 'What would you like to do to me, like me to do to you, now?' – 'now' meaning at the fantasy level. See *Birdsong at morning*.

Also, as nearly always with man, symbolisms are generally bigger kicks than over-literal enactments. But some couples get a lot of fun out of extended struggles, premeditated or impromptu ('love wrestling' in the old Viennese athletic tradition). Enthusiasts go in for elaborate handicaps: time limits, no-biting-or-scratching and so on. Most people find fairly robust but reasonable tussling quite enough, others play elaborate finding-fault-and-spanking games (don't play these over *real* faults). Women who dig an extra sensation of violence and/or helplessness differ whether they feel this more held down or tied up: men can take out quite a lot of the violence component in the actual process of penetration and working for orgasm. Once understood, none of this range of needs is scarey, and can be stopped spilling out of sex into cruelty, or the normal resentments felt by any two people who live together. Actually, it tends to discharge these.

Nothing we've said excludes the tenderness of sex. If you haven't learned that sexual violence can be tender and tenderness violent, you haven't begun to play as real lovers, unless you are people (and there are such) whose tenderness is abolutely unalloyed: these needn't worry about the risks of fighting. See *Bondage, Discipline*.

If you do have a real fight, make sure to end it in bed. At least it's the best way to finish.

frigidity

This does not mean failure to enjoy sex when one is dead with fatigue, when children are hammering on the door, in the middle of Union Square, or, generally, with the wrong man, at the wrong time, all of the time every time, or with the wrong vibrations. Males of the vending machine type (put a quarter in and an orgasm comes out) should take note of this. Nor does it mean failure to get a mind-blowing orgasm on every single occasion. If it does mean these things, every woman is frigid. Nor does it really apply to non-response if the man is clumsy, hurried and phallus-struck. We assume you know all this. Real frigidity is when a woman who loves her man and isn't consciously scared of any part of sex still fails to enjoy it when they've both taken trouble to see that she should. This condition, unlike male impotence, which can often be removed by simple reassurance (though not always), isn't easily helped by books. Female sexuality is much less arranged in a straight line than male – where a woman has difficulties of this sort they *have* to be dealt with on an individual basis.

A few cases of non-enjoying are simple; the Pill can produce big swings in libido either way. So can the woman's own internal chemistry, which is cyclical, unlike the man's, and undergoes more sudden changes. If intercourse hurts, that is simple too – see a gynecologist and have it attended to. Pregnancy and having a baby can affect response, physically and psychologically. Assuming

it's none of these, and you have a husband whom you can talk to and fantasize with, and you've eliminated obvious turn-offs like having an overweight lover on top of you, but still nothing really leaves you feeling satisfied, get personal advice. The mix of physical and psychological causes which can produce this kind of dissatisfaction is too complicated to be dealt with in a book.

The only technique worth trying, if you still don't feel, is painstaking self-education through relaxed, gradual and private self-exploration. Masturbation in women is far more a process of continuing self-exploration than it is in man, and many women can and do teach themselves to respond in this way. On widespread testimony the use of a vibrator helps – it can produce some sexual feeling in almost any woman. Once you have found a stimulus which makes you feel at all, whether you discover it solo or with your lover, incorporate it into lovemaking and use it to the full. If you need a finger on the clitoris, or genital kissing, use them fully – the propaganda about 'vaginal orgasm' *is* propaganda, and there is no truth in the value-judgment that unless you are fully satisfied only by deep penetration you aren't a woman; some women are satisfied by it, others aren't. Some women get many orgasms – some so many that they merge and can't be pinpointed as a single event – others get one, like a man. Some women only enjoy breast stimulation, or genital stimulation. Find your pattern. If you haven't experimented with changes of posture, do – by this time we assume you have. And with play and fantasy. If none of these things give you any lead you can develop, you need individual help (or more correctly help as a couple – if you see a counselor, both should go).

For self-training, start by getting really comfortable – naked or not, in front of a mirror or not, just as you prefer. Think and fantasize about anything which stirs any sort of response, then begin gradually to explore your own body, letting your hand go where your body wants it – breasts, the whole skin surface, labia, clitoris. Do the same if you use a vibrator – don't go for orgasm, but set out to discover what you like and what you think you would like. It takes time to learn this if you don't already know. Sometimes, if this doesn't frighten you or turn you off, another woman can help more than a man. That doesn't make you a lesbian. Don't assume that another man will be able to do better than your lover – he may, but it isn't a safe assumption. If you can imagine a situation which would excite you, try to set it up with your lover – as play, if it isn't feasible in earnest – remembering that fantasy-rape isn't real rape or fantasy-cruelty real cruelty. See if any of our suggestions turn you on in prospect. Talk to your man.

FRIGIDITY *opposite*
Doesn't apply to non-response if the man is clumsy, hurried or phallus-struck.

Beyond that, we can't help through the printed page. Female libido is controlled, oddly enough, by the male hormone. See *Impotence*.

hairtrigger trouble

Alias premature ejaculation. Any ejaculation which happens before you both want it to is premature.

Premature coming results from two causes, over-eagerness and anxiety. Over-eagerness may be delightful on occasion, but usually means simply that you are not having enough sex to reach optimal performance. One can ward off this solo by masturbating frequently and using the occasion to develop slow responses, but in the presence of all the stimuli from a real woman this can still break down. Once you get anxious it can become a physiological habit like stammering or impotence. It can rule out top quality sex and most of our suggestions.

There is a set drill for handling this hangup which rarely fails. Tackle it early.

1 Find out, with your partner, just how soon after one ejaculation you can get another erection, either by self-stimulation or with her stimulating you. Use this, holding back deliberately, and aiming not to get an orgasm but to see how long you can stay rigid. Do this often.

2 If the time interval is too long or you lose the second erection quickly, you need specific exercises. Set aside a time for practice and resolve that on the practice occasions you won't have intercourse. Get your partner to stiffen you, if necessary, and begin slow masturbation seated astride. Her aim will be simply to keep you in erection, even if she has to drop her stroke-rate to one in three seconds. If you call 'stop' she must stop. She can tie you if this really gives her better control, but as this itself is an excitant it is better if you deliberately hold still. Don't be worried if on the first occasion you ejaculate at once – try again half an hour later. Do this just as often as you can arrange it, but intersperse with intercourse, however short, so as not to build up an appetite. Either in intercourse or for practice sessions, some people find a local anesthetic jelly a help, and if you find it difficult to get the exercises going, you could try this. In about three weeks of regular practice you should be able to hold at least a second, and probably a first erection, for a full five minutes, and this will get longer and longer. Meanwhile, try and lengthen the straight coitus sessions. Use all the extras to give your partner full orgasm as often as she needs it, but she should be sparing with very stimulating techniques, or indeed any techniques, ahead of penetration. Try holding still inside her for timed minute intervals.

opposite and overleaf Two paintings by the Japanese master, Eisen (1790–1848), circa 1810–20

3 If this doesn't work, or you are getting anxious, see an expert. Usually it does work. The important thing is to set up by agreement a definite noncoital session, designed to get you into a state of sexual training. You will both benefit, and she needn't go without meanwhile: learn to use your hands and your tongue and don't forget her breasts. Having times when you specifically set out to satisfy *her* will help you to relax over any virility problems. If the problem remains, take advice before it gets to be a habit. Most men with limited sex experience are overquick to start with, and would benefit from training of the kind we've described.

At the first session with a much-desired partner, at least 50 percent of men either ejaculate too quickly or fail to get an erection. Ensure a whole night, so you can try for a comeback, but don't try too hard. If you go to sleep you will probably wake with a huge erection.

Note for your doctor: Tricyclic antidepressants such as Tryptizol (Rx) or Tofranil (imipramine, Rx) slow down orgasm enormously in some males without blocking erection: minute doses are often enough.

hazards

Contrary to superstition, very few sexual techniques are actually dangerous. Clumsy penetration with the woman on top can injure him or her; violent anal penetration can injure her, and anal intercourse with a stranger carries a risk of AIDS, and of vaginitis in the woman if you mix anal with vaginal penetration. Women liable to miscarry need to be gently handled in pregnancy, and women who are very liable to miscarry might do better to avoid orgasm while carrying. Apart from these there are a few tricks which are risky in themselves. None of these are popular, but clearly, since mischief is reported, people occasionally try them.

1 Never throttle anyone, even in play, and especially in orgasm. Many sex 'murders' are accidents overtaking women who treat partial strangulation as a kick: they can get exactly the same sensation safely by intercourse head-down, see *Inversion*. Never block a partner's airway, and be extra careful with bondage games – one can suffocate on a soft surface.

2 Never blow into the vagina. This trick can cause air embolism and has caused sudden death.

3 In spite of writers who talk about the use of household appliances for sex kicks, never fool about sexually with vacuum cleaners or with air-lines. A garage tyre inflator line has ruptured the intestine when squirted 18 inches from someone's anus (this was a practical joke). Vacuum cleaner injuries of the penis are surprisingly common and

very hard to repair satisfactorily. Water at tap-pressure is safe, but direct it at the clitoris, not forcibly into the vagina – anything under pressure can go up the Fallopian tubes and do harm.

4 Cantharides (spanish fly) is not an aphrodisiac but an irritant poison about as powerful as mustard gas. The dose which produces useless, painful erection by inflaming the penis is bigger than the fatal dose for kidney damage. Candy containing it has killed several girls.

5 Nothing you inhale is a safe kick: organic chemicals which produce dizziness also produce death rather easily. Amyl nitrite produces flushing and other sexy sensations, but is grossly unsafe to fool with.

6 Like anal intercourse, mouth-anal contacts appear from recent work to be risky, and better avoided.

Considering the range of human sexual experimentation it is a reflection on conventional fears that only manifestly idiotic sexual experiments are dangerous. Given reasonable gentleness, sex play is by far the safest energetic sport – one can be killed dead by a golf ball.

health

If you're acutely ill you probably won't feel like sex. There are very few longer-lasting medical conditions where a prescription of 'no sex' is justified for more than a shortish time, like getting over a heart attack or a hernia operation, or, of course, if you have an infectious disease such as V.D. or trichomoniasis, or are pregnant and likely to miscarry. Most doctors know this, but a few still give alarmist or thoughtless 'no sex' instructions if their own sex-lives are unimportant.

If the doctor advises the woman to avoid sex, she should find out why. He may only mean that pregnancy would be dangerous. The same applies if there's a heavy genetic risk. In that case a thoughtful male partner would have a *Vasectomy*, to be 100 percent sure. Otherwise the only indications are the ones we've given. If it's the man who gets the red light, discuss it. Even severe heart or kidney illness isn't normally a bar to having gentle sex, nor is hypertension. In these cases it might be sensible to avoid very tense or violent activities. Excitement is greatest, and casualties highest, in extramarital rather than married contexts, and boudoirs and brothels have seen more fatal accidents than the marriage bed. There can be a problem over cancer of the prostate or high blood pressure, because some of the drugs used to treat these can affect potency, and if other types of drug fail to work you may have to make a choice. The important thing is not to take no for an answer unless you've had a full explanation and are sure the doctor knows how much sex means to you (some doctors still think that sex over fifty is expendable or non-existent – see *Age*). A good doctor will know that stopping sex for any length of time is hard for normal people, and can damage an older man's sexual response when he tries to restart. Really good and informed medical advice, by contrast, may be precisely what could help you to keep going and avoid further illness – you and the doctor should work out the solution together. Some people would feel that if the worst came to the worst, it's the best way to go, and the anxiety and depression engendered by a ban on sex could be more likely to do harm than the very moderate exercise involved in intercourse. See *Doctors*. There is evidence that an improved sex-life can actually lower hypertension where this is due to general anxiety.

impotence

The basis of so much nonsense and anxiety that a few facts are in order.

1 All men are impotent sometimes – usually at a first or a hurried session with someone highly desirable whom they want to impress. The risk is proportional to the buildup. Can also happen domestically, quite without expectation or warning – often from some turn-off one isn't aware of. The only importance of these occasions is not to be thrown by them. The conventional male fantasy of being ready to perform anytime, anywhere is wholly neurotic and impractical.

Only the totally insensitive are all-time fucking machines like a stud-bull, and stud-bulls too have their off-days. Leave yourself a whole night for a first night – you should wake horny.

2 Physical factors which cause impotence do exist – the chief are diabetes, obesity, alcohol, and some drugs prescribed for depression and for high blood pressure.

3 The only other common cause of impotence is psychological – turning oneself off by apprehension about sexual performance. This is the exact analogy to the old man who took thought whether he slept with his beard in or out of the bed and went crazy trying to remember, or the pianist who starts thinking about his fingers.

4 If you can ever get an erection (by masturbation, in sleep, or on waking) there is nothing physical the matter with the hydraulics.

5 Age has absolutely nothing to do with impotence unless it brings illness. Belief that one is aging and must run out of steam has. Normal male potency lasts as long as life. The only change is that spontaneous erection gets rarer, direct skin stimulation is needed, and orgasm takes

longer to come. Impotence in old men is due to turn-offs, lack of health and an attractive partner, attempts to perform too often, or the demands of a younger partner who sets them a proficiency test. These turn normal people off at any age. Another common cause is medication.

6 Accordingly, persistent impotence means either that you are trying to perform against a specific turn-off – wrong scene, wrong partner, wrong vibrations, record attempts – or that you are turning yourself off by acting as if you were a spectator, not a participant and worrying about how you are doing. This can start if you are badly put out over one of the off-days mentioned in (1) above, and can become a habit. Deal with it exactly as for *Hairtrigger trouble*, except that in this case both of you should use every accessory excitation but with a firm resolve not to have intercourse – full description of the technique in Masters and Johnson which is easily adaptable to do-it-yourself. If this fails, get help from an expert. If everyone knew the facts listed here the task of sex-therapists would at least be lightened by comprehension.

In the past, medical study of impotence was largely anecdotal. With recent research, it has become possible to measure penile blood flow, record the degree of erection which occurs during the R.E.M. (rapid eye movement) phase of sleep, and perform other investigations. One result has been to show that organic problems are commoner than was realised: it used to be thought that 90% of erectile difficulty in people previously functioning was 'in the mind', but this now appears an overestimate. After excluding diabetes, alcohol, medications, and hormonal disorders, there are still cases where erection is incomplete through a deficit in blood supply, 'stealing' of blood by the muscular exertion of intercourse, filling defects in the hydraulics, or lax ligaments supporting the penis, making it bend. Accordingly the route lies through excluding obvious causes, checking medication, following the regime indicated in (6) above, and then, if trouble persists, going to a sexual disorders clinic equipped to do proper investigations. In an ideal world, such units would be universally available – at the moment the best place to look is a teaching hospital.

Testosterone is not a universal aphrodisiac, and is not lacking in the vast majority of men who have erectile problems, though some physicians think that additional male hormone can lower the arousal threshold. Testosterone itself has the drawback of turning off your own internal hormone supply. In impotent diabetics, and others with organic erectile problems, an alpha-blocking drug, phenoxybenzamine, can produce longlasting erection – the problem is that it needs to be injected directly into the penile hydraulics (do-it-yourself use is possible but requires medical supervision). Injected papaverine produces both immediate erection and some longterm benefit. In real organic impotence, e.g. after extensive surgery, it is possible to put a rigid support inside the penis which renders it serviceable. There is even a prosthesis which can be pumped to erection by a bulb in the scrotum and let down by a valve under the navel – no kidding. What might happen if a woman accustomed to one of these in her man changed partners doesn't bear thinking. Whether it is worth the trouble and complications, in view of the large range of enjoyable sexual behaviours which don't require erection, and the fact that wives rarely appreciate the operative result, is a judgment call, depending on your investment of selfesteem in penile rigidity.

Note for the non-sexologist doctor. For the state of the art, a little behind the research position, see G. Wagner and R. Green; *Impotence* Plenum Press 1981. For intracorporal injection of phenoxybenzamine, see G.S. Brindley, J. Physiol 1983, 342, 24P and Lancet 1984 ii 220.

infertility

A boon if you want it, a curse if you don't. Can be due to the woman not ovulating, the ova not reaching the uterus through tubal blockage, various conditions in the female organs; the man not having any sperms, or enough sperms; and probably also various chemical incompatibilities between partners. These can sometimes be helped by advice including concentration on fertile periods, surgery, or hormones, but need proper medical counseling (both of you must go – if the man has too few sperms there is no point in subjecting the woman to a lot of investigation). Anxiety can sometimes apparently block fertility – overfrequent ejaculation lowers the sperm count, so don't be over-eager. Tight warm clothing around the scrotum can kill off the sperms, which need to develop below body-temperature. Orgasm in the woman doesn't make conception more likely. Infertility can sometimes end suddenly after years, and the treatment or the life situation get the credit. Obstinate lack of sperms in the male is difficult to treat, though you can concentrate the sperms he has and inseminate with them. It has nothing whatever to do with virility judged by sexual performance. Never assume you are infertile unless it has been proved, and be careful stopping the pill around menopause time. For voluntary infertility see *Children, Birth control, Vasectomy.*

obesity

Fatness in our culture is unlovely. We know someone whose pretty, fat daughter can only get Middle Eastern boyfriends because of this norm. Renoir's women, who, when naked, look ideal for sex, would look a little too plump if clothed.

What isn't realized is that in men overweight is a physical cause of impotence. If neither this nor the esthetics of it bother you, you may still have to circumvent it. King Edward VII of Britain ('Tum-Tum'), had a special couch resembling a gynecological table made to enable him to get on target. Most stout men can manage with the woman astride, backing or facing. If this doesn't work, try lying face-up over the edge of the bed, feet on the floor, while she stands astride. An over-heavy man is a bad problem – Cleopatra could say, 'O happy horse, to bear the weight of Anthony,' but he didn't weigh 200 pounds. If you are grossly overweight, set about losing it, whether you value your sex life or only your life. That applies to both sexes. Modern girls, though supple, tend to be underweight by the sexual standards of the past, especially for rear-entry positions and for making love on a firm surface.

pain

Pain per se isn't a sexual excitant in spite of folklore. What actually happens is that once excitement starts to build, pain-awareness is reduced steadily, until any strongish stimulus, even one which normally would be over-strong, adds to the buildup. This can be true elsewhere – you can lose a tooth in a football game and not notice it until after – but with sex excitement the pain-stimulus can actually be transformed into increased pleasure-feeling provided it isn't too strong. There is a sharp point, however, at which over-stimulation becomes a turn-off, not a turn-on, and if this is overstepped the buildup collapses: tolerance increases the closer you get to orgasm – just before it people can take, for example, quite hard slaps – but the transformation stops as soon as orgasm occurs, so don't continue awkward postures or hard stimuli after this. Some people don't transform at all. If anything you do is perceived as straight untransformed pain it's either too much or too early on, or you've gone on after orgasm. Learning what stimuli are pleasant as buildup and what aren't is an art.

If any part of normal sex actually hurts, due to soreness, internal organs getting knocked, etc., you're being clumsy or something is wrong – in the second case see a doctor if it lasts more than a few days. First coitus can be slightly painful for both parties – if they are excited enough beforehand the transformation-effect will get most girls through the pain-barrier, though if you make her bleed at all give time for abrasions to heal before the next round. If it's more troublesome than this, get advice (see *Deflora-*

tion). With gentleness and preliminary stretching it can be quite painless in most women.

Actual craving for pain (mental or physical) as a sex kick isn't uncommon. Usually the idea is exciting in fantasy but a turn-off in practice, unless your partner is skilled enough to keep inside the limits of transformation by excitement, and the fantasy itself isn't too violent. A good many men who have persuaded a not over-intelligent whore to 'beat them hard' because the idea sounded exciting have been choked off a repeat performance. If your partner has such fantasies, keep well inside their powers of stimulus-transformation, subtract a good twenty percent from the fantasy, and watch out for the occasional sick character who really enjoys the idea of being injured. For sane people commonsense, a bit of play-acting, and intelligent use of the transformation effect can more than take care of the normal fantasy-range.

perversion

In books prior to the seventies, this meant, quite simply, any sexual behavior which the writer didn't himself enjoy. More correctly, it means something antisocial which handicapped people use as a substitute for the sexuality from which their hangups debar them. The commonest perversions in our culture are getting hold of some power and using it to kick other people around, money-hunting as a status activity, treating other people, sexually or otherwise, as things to manipulate, and interfering with other people's sex lives to ensure that they are as rigid and as anxious about them as the interferer. Scheduled perversions like digging up corpses or committing lust murder are confined almost wholly to borderline psychotics, and, though obviously serious, are of less social importance than the respectable kinds because they are rare and disapproved of. It's a measure of the prestige of socially approved perversion that most public utterances in legislation, law enforcement and so on genuflect to what are basically perverse attitudes, even when the speakers are privately healthy.

Hangups of this sort are extremely difficult to cure, whether they lead to sadistic mutilation, purity crusading, Belsen or Vietnam. However sorry you are for the possessors, they are dangerous people and best avoided as partners or as mentors—you will only be asking for a lot of trouble.

priapism

From Priapus, the Roman garden god with a large stiff wooden penis: erection you don't want and can't get rid of, unaccompanied by any feeling of sexual pleasure.

A painful erection which won't go away is rare, and a

medical emergency needing immediate attention. What is commoner, though not common, is being woken at night by painful, non-pleasant erections, even when one has had a full ejaculation, so that the patient has to get up and walk around or shower – intercourse or masturbation does not help: the result can be severe loss of sleep. Mentioned here because the sufferers worry themselves gray about it. The cause isn't known – it may be psychological (it often stops away from home). All normal males get repeated erections in sleep, but usually these don't wake them or are accompanied by pleasantly sexy feelings, not pain. There doesn't seem to be a good remedy for this trouble. Drugs which turn it off are apt to turn off potency. Fortunately the symptom usually goes away, and whatever treatment you were having at the time gets the credit. Does not interfere with sex at other times.

prostitution

Prostitutes don't as a rule either practice or enjoy advanced lovemaking. This isn't true in all cultures, but in ours the commonest motive for becoming a regular streetwalking pro is an active dislike of males. Their attraction insofar as it persists is in part mythological, and also due to their unshocked understanding of unscheduled sex needs, the fact that the man can at least be sure of getting sex from them without social hangups, and a group of feelings connected with sharing a woman with other males. No doubt if we treated the professional as other cultures have done – on all fours with the concert artist who gives up domesticity to an art – the personnel of professional sex would improve and it would lose its present psychopathology, and be of help both to bothered clients and the girls themselves, but general sexual freedom is more likely to displace monetary sex altogether, except for those for whom it arises from unconscious needs.

Apart from the attractions we've mentioned, any woman who herself is ready to enjoy and understand sex, and meet her partner's needs as fully as a professional but with love, can outclass anyone hired. She can learn from periods and cultures in which the courtesan was a repository of the art of pleasing, but what we call whores' tricks ought to be called lovers' tricks. A woman who can make love with love and variety needn't fear commercial competition.

Prostitutes – especially outside Europe – are a major hazard in transmission of AIDS: partly because the illegality of prostitution makes it an available income source for addicts who inject drugs. Amateurs, B-girls and pickups on overseas visits are particularly dangerous – European pros insist that the trick wears a condom. Don't take risks in this area.

safe sex

This topic only surfaced with the outbreak of AIDS (see *Venereal diseases*). The reference is to the fact that the virus is more easily spread by anal than by vaginal intercourse; the fact is that provided neither partner is an AIDS carrier, the whole range of close-contact sexual behaviors is safe – if either is a carrier, virtually none is safe, though vaginal intercourse with a condom is the least risky. Accordingly self-defense virtually rules out chance acquaintances, especially if you live in New York or California (or are travelling in Africa). Folk wisdom sums it up as 'only screw blood donors – they're tested'. The test in question shows whether one has encountered the AIDS virus – a positive result may or may not indicate that it is active, but all positives are carriers – and fullblown AIDS is 100 per cent fatal.

Known positives present their partners with the greatest problem: it's an agonizing situation to have to decide whether to withold sex or to run the risk of getting AIDS. Counselors manning the AIDS hot lines now available will have the most recent experience to draw on and can help you both to deal with the problem. If you are not already infected, make sure that semen – which seems to be the main vehicle of infection – and, of course, blood itself are kept out of contact with any region where there may be an abrasion. Unprotected vaginal intercourse carries about a seven per cent risk to the woman; using a condom should reduce that risk level still further. But there's still a risk.

We can't at present quantify the risk where a woman is the carrier, but she has to avoid pregnancy for the sake of the baby, and menstrual blood has to be considered as a possible vehicle of infection, which it normally isn't. The development of a reliable genital antiseptic could change all this, but although research began in the last century, it has been the subject of studied neglect and a good deal of moral hostility. Perhaps AIDS will change this.

termination

In a well-conducted sex life it shouldn't be necessary. All ethics apart, neither you nor the doctor can be quite sure how a woman – or a couple – will react to it psychologically. The present boom is due less to permissive legislation than to the fact that women who have been scared off the Pill by deliberate alarmism, but have experienced the effects of really reliable troublefree birth control, are simply not willing either to go back to the old makeshifts or to have unwanted children.

At the factual level, early abortion (in the first 3 months) done by a qualified expert in a properly equipped hospital is, physically, a minor and safe operation. Done by an unqualified person, a backroom consultant, or a do-it-yourself method it is dangerous and psychologically searing. Done too late (and some physicians who object to all abortion on principle deliberately try to delay matters until it is too late, and then tell you so with a superior grin) it involves killing a potentially viable child.

If you plan your sex life properly and take informed and conscientious contraceptive precautions, you shouldn't need to terminate a pregnancy except on exceptional grounds. Odd that the main moral woe-criers on abortion are also the people who have done most to block proper birth control and starve research and education about it of funds.

transvetitism

Many people enjoy dressing in each other's clothes on occasion for the hell of it. That isn't transvestitism. A transvestite is a person who, while staying fully in his or her own sex role, feels an intense compulsion at times to dress the opposite sex role, and an intense release of anxiety (not so much a kick) when they do so. They are not 'homosexual,' and a bisexual person who dresses the opposite sex to please a partner isn't a transvestite. A transexualist is a person, usually male, who actively wants to turn into a person of the other sex, by surgery if necessary, and feels totally miscast as they are. In some simpler societies there are roles or ceremonies which discharge these needs (wizards often cross-dress). In our society they can cause intense anxiety. A transvestite with an informed and unscared wife usually finds that his compulsion, whatever its cause, doesn't spoil his sex-life in the male role (if he has to keep it secret or she thinks he's queer or crazy, which he isn't, he can get really sick from worry); a transexualist needs expert help and may or may not be the happier for a sex-change operation. A lot of unhappiness could be avoided if people knew the facts to the point of not being scared or shocked if they come across them. If you have a partner with any of these problems, help them by comprehension and see they get help from an expert.

vasectomy

This is the one reliable, once-and-for-all male contraceptive method. It consists of closing off, by a small surgical operation, the tubes down which the sperms travel from the testis. The operation is done under local anesthetic. It hurts rather less than having a small cut stitched, and you can go straight home. The long-term result is a completely virile but infertile male. (Repeat, competent vasectomy carries absolutely no risk of physical interference with, erection, ejaculation, sexual feelings, or virility generally – under the name of 'Steinach's operation' it used to be done as a rejuvenation treatment and virility booster.) If you have all the children you want (which, if you have a sense of responsibility, shouldn't in most cases be more than two) consider it seriously. Certainly consider it rather than making your woman undergo the much bigger operation needed to sterilize her, or keeping her on the Pill if it doesn't suit her.

There are a few more factual points to consider.

1 Vasectomy doesn't make you sterile at once. Sperms can hang around for months, so you must stick to your previous birth control method until you know you are clear. After that you can both forget about birth control.

2 You can't change your mind. Vasectomy is sometimes reversible, but you mustn't count on that. It's a calculated risk that you might suddenly want to father children later, but not worth hanging back for if otherwise it looks right for you. No decision one takes is one hundred percent safe, but if you wanted more children there are unwanted babies wanting adoption, assuming you are fit people.

3 On the other hand, make sure you know your own feelings – which in any matter connected with sex and reproduction are never wholly reasonable. If the doctor refuses to do the operation 'off the shelf' without discussing your general self-picture of maleness, that only shows that he knows his job. If he refuses on principle or because he doesn't like your life style, consult another doctor.

If you are married, have had two wanted children or don't want children, and have any contraceptive problems, give vasectomy serious thought. If you're spread wider than that and have any sense of responsibility, you should be vasectomized. You can buy a 'vasectomy tie' or pin to advertise the fact. Wearing one when you haven't been operated is a cad's trick – far more so than wearing Guards or Ivy League colors you aren't entitled to. In case of argument, the girl can check the two little scars.

It may be possible eventually to store some of your sperm in the deep-freeze as an insurance, but you won't be able to do this now.

venereal diseases

These have been covertly fostered for several generations by straight Society as God's punishment for sin. On the other hand, they are a real hazard of having intercourse, or heavy petting, with people you don't know. When we first wrote this book, the two commonest venereal diseases were gonorrhoea ('clap') and syphilis. Both are still around, but today the commonest appear to be chlamydiasis (non-gonococcal urethritis), genital herpes, and trichomoniasis ('trich'), and by far the gravest is AIDS.

Acquired Immunodeficiency Syndrome is a virus infection caused by the HTLV or HIV virus, which leads to the collapse of immunity. Sufferers die from unusual tumours, weird infections, and a steady attrition of their health. The disease is at present incurable. The virus is contained in blood, semen and vaginal secretions – the most important routes of infection are intercourse, especially anal intercourse, and exposure to injected blood products. In consequence it has chiefly attacked homosexuals, especially those with many partners, drug addicts who shared needles, recipients of infected transfusions, and haemophilics treated with blood Factor VIII.

Because of its long incubation period (3–5 years or more) AIDS spread widely in the gay community. This is a tragedy, because once the fullblown disease appears, death is inevitable, though antiviral drugs are being tested which can postpone it at the expense of severe side effects. The last years of sufferers are embittered by ignorant public ostracism, and, in America, medical-bill-induced penury. While there have been several thousand deaths in America, and a few hundred in Europe, a much larger number of exposed people are symptomless carriers who can infect others – what proportion of these carriers will eventually develop AIDS is unknown, but it is certainly over half.

The disease can be spread by heterosexual intercourse, though much less readily than by anal sex – judging from the spouses of infected haemophilics, the infection rate is about 7%. Women are more easily infected by men than vice versa: the virus is also passed on to the unborn child.

Western society, having reacted at first by indifference (it only affected gays and drug addicts, so who cares?) and moral self-satisfaction (AIDS was God's judgment on the sexual revolution) is now reacting predictably by panic, which will increase if the incidence increases.

The moralistic prescription, predictably, has been to shut down sex altogether and confine it to marriage. This might slow the spread of AIDS but would not stop it – your virgin fiancée could have had a transfusion of blood bought off the street by an American commercial blood bank. It is also historically unlikely to work – in the nineteenth century, syphilis was pandemic, deadly and more catching, but people remained reckless.

The prudent answer is that with anyone except a lifetime partner one should totally avoid the main modes of known sexual transmission – anal intercourse – and contact with blood or body fluids (intercourse during menstruation, possibly swallowing semen). AIDS is not spread by kissing, ordinary social contact, bathwater or food, though razors and toothbrushes might conceivably spread it. Ordinary vaginal or oral intercourse can be rendered safer by a condom, if you use it properly and do not permit it to leak: it is less effective in anal intercourse because thin condoms are likely to tear. Condoms should become de rigeur in any case where you aren't sure of your partner. If your newly-found love won't use a condom, you are in bed with a witless, irresponsible and uncaring person. Love "under the influence" is particularly risky – it makes you temporarily witless, irresponsible and uncaring. The condom test is a good way of knowing whether or not you've found a decent, sensible partner. But will women know how to insist on a condom?

One fact of potential importance is that nonoxynol-9, which is used in contraceptive foams and suppositories at 5–8%, is viricidal at 0.08%. There are no direct figures on its effect on AIDS transmission (there are very few, based on the experience of prostitutes, for condoms either) but it offers some protection to the woman, who can use a contraceptive foam without reference to her partner, as well as to the partner if the woman is a carrier. Nonoxynol-9 plus a condom is likely on a belt-and-braces principle to give a high degree of protection, not only against AIDS, but also against the classical venereal diseases, hepatitis, and human papilloma virus, which is a probable cause of cervical cancer.

In World War I, crude genital antisepsis reduced the incidence of gonorrhoea and syphilis from 25% to 5%, after moral and patriotic exhortation had failed. Research in the civilian application of this astonishing finding was quashed by uproar over "condoning immorality". It should now be revived as a matter of urgency, together with research on a vaccine to protect against AIDS, and an eventual chemotherapy for it. The viricides now on test give present sufferers a hope of living long enough to see a cure. Meanwhile, the sexually prudent adult will (1) strictly avoid partners in any of the high risk groups – bisexual men, drug users and ex-drug-users, prostitutes, especially in Africa and the Orient and in the USA, partners who had had numerous partners (2) in any case of doubt, avoid known hazards like anal intercourse and menstrual intercourse (3) use both a condom and a local contraceptive (foam or suppository) which gives nonoxynol-9 as its main ingredient (4) treat all unknown quantities as potential carriers (5) in a stable relationship, recognize their responsibility not to take risks and introduce a lethal virus. Anonymous sexual exchanges of any kind are out for the duration of the AIDS epidemic.

If you are unlucky enough to test positive for the HIV virus, whether through infection or through exposure to blood products, you must confine yourself to sex with other known positives, or, as in the case of many haemophilics and transfusion subjects with still uninfected spouses, protect your partner by using both a condom and a spermicide. This is an agonizing dilemma for both parties, and you will in any event need counselling from one of the many AIDS support services now in existence (your doctor can refer you, and should).

The current test used e.g. to screen blood donors can give false negatives if infection is recent or frank AIDS is present. Moreover the fact that a partner says he or she tested negative in the past is only an indication of safety if they weren't exposed to infection since the test was done.

Of other prevalent venereal diseases, NGU (non gonococcal urethritis) behaves almost exactly like gonorrhoea but is due to the trachoma organism, not the gonococcus (one can catch both in a single dose), and accordingly it calls for a different antibiotic regime. Genital herpes has been blown up into a panic by interested parties. True, it can recur painfully in some people, exactly as its humbler cousin the cold sore can recur, and both are 'incurable', i.e. you can't eradicate the virus with drugs. On the other hand, herpes is only infectious when the blisters are present, and in the vast majority of people it is self-limited, the attacks getting less and less frequent over 3–5 years. A number of newer drugs are effective in cutting down the severity of the attacks. Herpes is mainly important in pregnancy, because an attack during labor can injure or kill the foetus. As with all venereal infections, refer this one to your doctor early. Whether the herpes virus plays any part in causing cancer of the cervix is still unclear. It is also unclear why, media campaigns apart, it has suddenly become prominent, for it is not a new disease. Neither is trichomoniasis – this is an irritating vaginal infection with discharge ('whites') which has been endemic in the past (most women in some times and places had it chronically) and which is not always spread by intercourse. It can be caught from a partner, because the male is a symptom-free carrier: in treating it, both partners have to be medicated to avoid re-infection.

Gonorrhoea and syphilis are still with us. Gonorrhoea is getting harder to eradicate because of the appearance of resistant strains: syphilis still responds quickly to penicillin. Don't in either case attempt to treat the disease yourself with antibiotics: don't cover up, and have the decency to warn your partner or partners. If it were not for the aura of magic, either of these diseases would be preferable to severe influenza or adult measles, because they are readily curable.

Index

More Joy

A Lovemaking Companion to The Joy of Sex

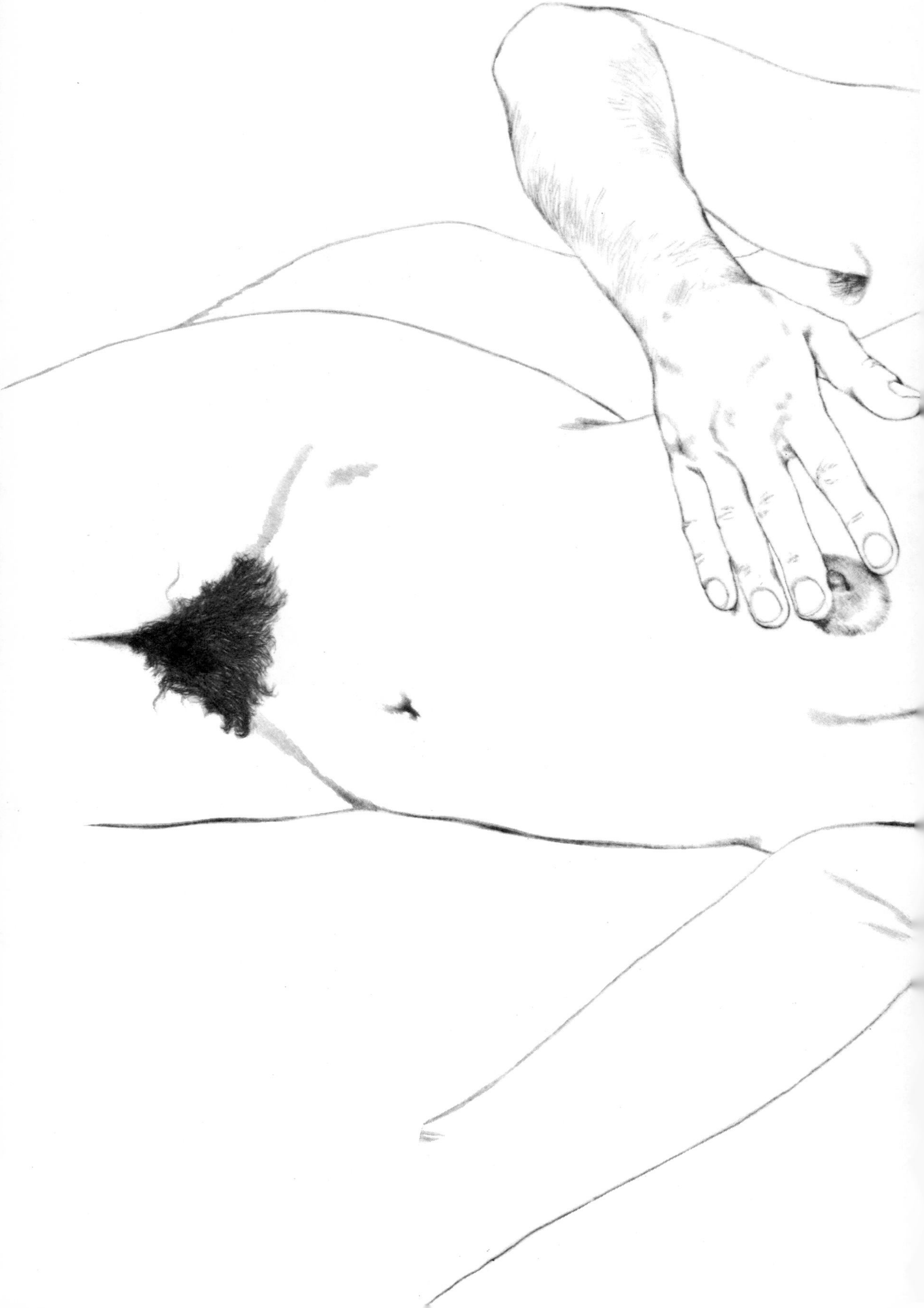

More Joy

A Lovemaking Companion to The Joy of Sex

Contents

This book was originally published prior to the recent identification of Acquired Immune Deficiency Syndrome (AIDS) and other medical conditions. These conditions may be sexually transmitted. The advice and/or information included in this book should be considered in the light of the present understanding of such health risks. The reader is advised to consult a physician about these risks.

THE JOY OF SEX® series

Resources 175

Special Needs 199

Preface

The first edition of this book was written in 1973. I intended it as a supplement to *The Joy of Sex* – a "why" book to supplement a "how" book. The background against which it appeared was very different from the situation today – we were dropping the book into a climate of widespread, not to say frenzied, sexual experimentation. Sexual undernourishment was giving place to sexual indigestion.

It is clearly time for a new edition. The gains of that period have been assimilated, openness has been established in the discussion of sexuality and is unlikely to be dislodged, there is less acting-out in our public approach – we are using our equipment, on the analogy of a quadraphonic stereo, to play music, not to see what noises it is capable of making. The 1970s declassified sex – we are now (hopefully) learning to domesticate it. To this extent, any "sexual revolution" which there was, so far from having failed, has in fact succeeded and become integrated into ordinary folks' lives.

The unwelcome newcomer is, of course, AIDS. This wholly new disease-factor does in fact modify our sexual options (and will do so still more when the public comes to realize how serious it is). It is also avoidable and controllable by simple behavioral changes, such as avoiding anal intercourse and consistent use of a condom (see text). Frankness, unfortunately, spreads slowly to governments, who at the time of writing still mumble in giving out the facts: the media, with creditable exceptions, have followed the maxim of the Ruritanian Navy: "When in danger or in doubt Run in circles, scream and shout" and the New Right is, predictably, in full cry.

One function of a new edition was accordingly to look at the options which the present scene presents, to reiterate information which remains valid, and, hopefully, to dispel some of the hysteria over AIDS and replace it with commonsense precaution. Readers are the judges of my success in doing this.

The joy, so far as I have been concerned over the ten odd years since *The Joy of Sex* and *More Joy of Sex* were written, has lain in the repeated testimony I have had that people, from kids to middle-age couples, found them helpful. I have always asked such people "Did the books teach you things you did not know, or make you more comfortable with things you knew already?" I have had both answers. As to criticism, some people found the impression overly technical and the emphasis on relationship insufficient. This is a real difficulty in book-writing: books on sexual behavior have to be explicit in order to be informative, but exhortations to tenderness, relationship and responsibility are not very effectual for those who are handicapped by a lack of them. I tried to cover this type of exhortation indirectly, by the character of the illustrations. Another handicap – obvious to women – is that a male author works unavoidably from male experience. I have done my best to control this – we could well do with a moratorium on all writing by males about female sexual experience, and I sympathize with the criticism. In the rewriting of both books I have tried to improve the score on this count.

In the preface to the 1973 edition I said that I thought the underlying attitudes of the book would have been more or less assimilated by "middle class morality" in ten years' time. I think that this has proved true in regard to frankness and partially true in regard to the sore question of the loved one as property. At the same time, nobody expects to de-fang the human capacity for sexual anxiety-making: those who worried in 1973 if they enjoyed the behaviors described in sex manuals (which are menus, not curricula) now worry if they do not enjoy all of the behaviors so described. Moreover every change exposes the need for further change – we badly need to refocus the moral indignation which our ancestors lavished on such things as masturbation and homosexuality upon targets which do have moral significance – irresponsibility, exploitation, sexual chauvinism, and bad parenting. Anger directed at these things is generous rather than spiteful, and we could use some of it.

Since this book seems to have acquired a life of its own, this revision will not be the last. For this purpose a dialogue with users is essential, and I welcome it. As in the case of the 1973 edition, the main use of the book is that you should read it as a discussing couple.

Alex Comfort

Beyond Advanced Lovemaking

In *The Joy of Sex* we described how to manage the physical side of sex relations. This, like good cookery, is something you can learn, improve and appreciate through learning, and since we have more culture-encouraged anxieties about it than about cooking, books can help by reinforcing our own experience and reassuring us.

On the other hand all sex except masturbation involves at least two people. It doesn't happen at random or in a vacuum, and it is, therefore, about relationship: to have good sex you need a relationship to have it in, whether that relationship is a lifelong partnership or a casual romp between friends. Moreover, all human relationships are sexual, even when they don't look it and don't involve the genitals. We're the only mammal which, probably for reasons connected with our family structure, has used what were originally sexual behaviors as the building-blocks for nearly all our social activities. Some apes use dominance: we use that too, but we sexualize it.

Accordingly, all sexual behavior involves relationship, and most relationship involves sexuality at some point, especially where feelings about our identity, acceptability and so on are concerned. It's not by any means true that sex is the only thing in life, but it is true that getting our sexual identity straight is often the most important way of getting ourselves straight, and that physical sex and the relationships it involves can be the most effective source of self-comprehension if we take the trouble. Half the joy which a couple get from good sex is in their mutual regard and acceptance, and in being actively male or female in a context where there isn't much heart-searching over which is which. Important, too, is finding that fantasy experiences they've always wanted can be shared – and that they work, physically and emotionally. You can feel yourself to be a person in other contexts – landing on the moon, doing a job, winning a match or painting a masterpiece – but sexual identity is a two-way experience. Having had the joy at this level, real lovers will want to take it further; not by devising any new kicks, or even going over old ones to see if they missed any, but by developing the other, relational aspects of sex. They will know by this stage that sexual interchange involves warm feelings of identity and concern, more complicated feelings of dominance and hostility, and tensions between wanting to possess one another and not wanting to be wholly possessed. Rather than be scared by any of these they'll want to understand and experience them.

In *The Joy of Sex* we deliberately stayed off the relational aspect. We assumed that you were either a couple with a relationship who regularly made love together, or that you had some other pattern in which lovemaking took place. To elaborate that and talk about sexuality as a source of personal growth involves going over some of the things we left out.

None of this would probably need saying if we lived in a culture with a fixed pattern, where sexual and social roles weren't open to much choice. If you were a male Plains Indian, you either had to be a warrior, with exorbitant standards of endurance, or dress as a woman to show you wanted out. Men in our culture can be anything from boxers and soldiers (rated very masculine) to dancers and cooks (rated probably gay, though plenty of these are as heterosexual as anyone). Some people aren't worried by this kind of ignorant classification, others are. The same kind of role-prescribing has been used to discriminate against women, who are very rightly in revolt against it.

Parallel with the decline of all this folklore about sexual identity, institutions, like the monogamous one-shot marriage as the norm for all sexual expression, are dying on their feet. People are trying other patterns and have, in fact, more and more choice, economic pressures apart. This choice will grow. Accordingly, either you are half-consciously playing along with one of the prescribed relational patterns, such as marriage, or you are trying to make your own, overcoming a lot of inexplicit learning in the process. You may well decide on a pattern that looks conventional in the end. This book, without talking psychiatry or ethical philosophy, aims to marshal some of the information you need and some of the ideas you should consider in making choices.

Moreover, most of the practical hangups in sex come from not getting your sexual identity and needs straight. Since all of us are biologically and socially male, female, or both at once, most other practical hangups – even the fact of always being put down in business or freaking out when you think you are growing old – have connections with the sense of sexual identity and can be attacked in the same way. There are two sorts of sexual joy – having a full orgasm with a person you value, and being a total person yourself. Since sexual experience is one of the main peak experiences we've left ourselves in this culture, it is on all counts a good place to start, because its built-in reward is love and orgasm. We can't fix this for anyone, but we can and will discuss some of the things involved.

This isn't so much a book about sexual technique: there would be a case for an extended one which would answer questions about how exactly to manage some of the less familiar things, but this would have to be mostly pictures. We're more concerned with the uses of physical sensation and the background into which it fits.

The first section is a discussion of body language. Massage, nonverbal communication, touching and so on have become a California-based cult in which business executives grope each other in hot pools, take bites out of the same sandwich and generally get up steam to have sex when the group leader has finished talking and gone home. If you're already sexually uninhibited it's easy to make fun of this and see it all as sensuality short of being openly sensual, like the poor cat in the adage. On the other hand, sexually uninhibited people underrate the massive block which most folk in our culture have against touching, against physical spontaneity, and against showing affection. This is especially true between males, but almost equally between man and woman, because of our obsession with getting-on-with-it sexually. Some uninhibited people have blockages they don't recognize. Often they are almost totally preoccupied with the genitals – they use the penis and vulva to make love with but not the skin – and they often have surviving hangups, which bob up in unlikely places, about the cleanness and worthiness of perfectly clean bodies.

In view of the size of these hangups, anything which helps people overcome their past miseducation about privacy, separateness, noncontact and so on is a step in the right direction. Others may be more anxious about sex than you and you for your part could probably profit from learning to touch each other, from being touched by strangers of both sexes, and from learning to use your skin and muscles for the sensations they can produce. We aren't going into touching, nonverbalism, massage and the rest as an ideology or a cult, but rather into their uses as a part of the education of lovers.

As a result of our basic cultural miseducation we have three hangups to lose: we have to learn that people aren't dangerous, that the body isn't shameful, and that no rewarding sexual sensation is abnormal or bad unless it's antisocial in some way. It sometimes takes a physical demonstration to change the mind of the child inside us, even if we know these things to be true.

In 1973, when this book was first written, it was

physically safe, though not always very rewarding in terms of personal relationships, to treat sex as a new toy: a great many did. The problems of superstition and deprivation were replaced by the problems of indigestion: interestingly, it was precisely the same people who got into trouble with inhibition who now got into trouble with the new freedom, and developed what counselors came to call the "candy-store syndrome."

That problem is beginning to settle down, but it has been replaced by another far more serious. It is wretched that a book on sexual manners should now have to begin with the discussion of a fatal disease, but unfortunately it must, because the most pressing concern in the management of our sexual behavior is now the avoidance of AIDS.

AIDS is a new disease in the Western world. Where it came from is unclear. It is caused by a virus (HTLV 3, standing for "human lymphotropic virus") and it is transmitted by any action which causes HTLV-3 to enter the blood stream – it is a bloodborne disease like some forms of hepatitis, but unlike these if the disease develops it is uniformly fatal. In the American cities where it first spread (San Francisco, New York and Los Angeles) the explosive growth was due to a combination of three circumstances – a high population of homosexual males newly emancipated after generations of ignorant and malicious persecution, some of whom practiced anal intercourse; and superimposed on these the market-economy Sickness Industry, which buys transfusion blood from hard-up donors and street people. In short order, hundreds of drug users got the virus from needles, hundreds of homosexuals from the fact that it is present in semen and easily enters the blood stream from abrasions in the rectum, which isn't engineered to act as a vagina – and considerable numbers of transfusion recipients who were given street-purchased blood. Since antihaemophilia factor is made from pooled blood obtained in the same way, and America was the main producer, a high proportion of haemophilia sufferers worldwide were also infected.

Now, about five years after the epidemic was recognized, the virus has spread worldwide, on the wings of antihaemophilia factor and peripatetic drug addicts and untypically promiscuous homosexuals. Not all carriers have symptoms either of AIDS or of its milder manifestation, AIDS related lymphadenopathy, but about 25 per cent may eventually get it. The fullblown disease involves weight loss, fever, collapse of immunity leading to repeated bizarre infections, and a black nodular tumour called Kaposi's sarcoma. There is also a risk to all carriers of longterm brain damage, since the virus attacks the nervous system. The whole thing could have been tailored by professional celibates to make sex dangerous, get back at gays, and generally create anxiety. It clearly alters the picture and has to affect our behavior.

Can Aids be spread by "ordinary", i.e. vaginal, intercourse? Yes, but luckily not very easily. Only 5-7 per cent of the partners of, for example, infected haemophilics have caught it. It has been caught from prostitutes, but many of these also shared needles with their tricks. What worries doctors is that in Africa AIDS occurs equally in both sexes and appears to be spreading heterosexually. The question is "will that happen here?"

AIDS divides the entire world population into two groups – those who don't carry the virus, don't expose themselves to it, and can safely engage in any sexual behavior with equally uninfected partners; and those who do carry the virus. The regulation of sexual contacts in both these groups involves great care to avoid crossing over between them. The critical point is to avoid exchange of body fluids. Blood is the most dangerous, semen the next most dangerous. Tears and saliva can contain the virus but appear practically unimportant. The key precautions, other than the avoidance of any partner who is or may be a carrier (or, if you are a carrier, any partner who is not also a known carrier), are the avoidance of anal intercourse and the reinstatement of the mandatory condom. With these precautions, heterosexual spread is probably controllable. True control, by immunization, and radical cure by antiviral drugs, is being energetically researched, but is probably a number of years away. AIDS has a long incubation, probably five years or more in some instances. If you are a carrier, it is irresponsible to engage in any sexual activity with someone who may be uninfected – condom or no condom – with the sole exception of a spouse or partner whom you have already exposed *and who is willing to assume the risk*. If you are a non-carrier, the condom is an added precaution, but the best insurance is a total avoidance of sex with strangers whose past history you don't know. Homosexual males are already learning to reshape their behavior to avoid the risk of infection. The people worst hit are the large number of haemophilics who find that they have exchanged one fatal disease for another through the carelessness of society.

Avoiding this extremely menacing disease – not catching it and not transmitting it – becomes the top priority in sexual decisions. The precautions necessary are reasonably simple. AIDS cannot be spread by kissing, sharing cups, shaking hands, or living in the same house with a carrier unless one has sexual relations with him or her. Panic reactions, such as demanding the exclusion from school of children who caught AIDS from antihaemophilia shots, or being scared to act as a blood donor, which carries no risk whatsoever, don't improve the prospects of containment – nor does the reluctance of public health authorities to talk openly about things like anal intercourse.

The summary is, for the purpose of this book, that with an uninfected partner who stays uninfected, all sexual behaviors which ever were safe, still are safe. With an infected or a potentially infected partner, no sexual behaviors which lead to an exchange of body fluids are safe. There are no cases so far of oral transmission, but that is presumably possible if semen enters the mouth. The only effective precaution is to limit sexual contacts, for both sexes, to people who have never been in contact with the virus. Those who caught it from medical blood products usually know they are positive (and HTLV-3 positive people, who have a ghastly problem, probably run no added risk from relations with others who are also positive. They can to some extent protect spouses, who are often negative, by using condoms).

The implications are evident, both for freewheeling men and for the large number of women who have become accustomed to sex on a friendship basis. A partner is safe only if he or she has never experimented with injected drugs or anal intercourse, or been the partner of someone who has. This, in some areas like San Francisco, is a pretty severe limitation. It rules out the casual pickup – you have to be reasonably sure of your partner's history. The era of experiments in "open sexuality" like those of Sandstone, described in the first edition of this book, did not cause any identified cases of heterosexual AIDS, but that was luck of timing. The virus did not enter this population – a similar experiment in America now would be suicidal. So would the risk taken by women who, having been disappointed by low-quality males, rush around kissing frogs in the hope of flushing out a prince, an unrewarding practice in a society populated by genuine male frogs.

You need, accordingly, to be familiar with a partner's history, not an easy requirement but possible. The beautiful French song which said "I don't need to know your story, true or false, only your name" is inoperative for the duration of the epidemic – you quite definitely need to know.

What will happen, and how will it affect behavior? Obviously, it renders slaphappy sex on impulse unnacceptably dangerous with someone who is an unknown quantity. At the same time, heterosexual spread has been extremely limited. In any case of doubt, the condom is obligatory. Condoms do not render *anal* intercourse safe – they tear, so anal intercourse and swallowing semen, as well as intercourse during a menstrual period, should be avoided if there is any doubt at all. Anal intercourse is best avoided anyway, as it can cause local damage and spread non-venereal diseases such as hepatitis and bowel infection.

Short of immunization, which looks likely to be difficult, by far the most useful development would be a safe and aesthetic genital antiseptic. The crude "safety kits" of WW 1 cut the incidence of gonorrhoea by 7.5 per cent in troops, but further work was constantly blocked under the banner of "encouraging immorality", rather as contraception for kids is still obstructed. It may be a positive feature of AIDS that it stimulates such work, as well as an advance in antiviral drugs. It was syphilis which started Ehrlich on the chemotherapeutic revolution. In the meantime the sexually active adult, while not being panicked by media or speculative moralists, will carefully monitor what happens over the next few years and not put him or herself at risk. This disease is incurable but it is also avoidable by an intelligent change in our behaviors based on accurate knowledge.

The Language of the Body

babies

The best modern sex is nonreproductive. Not only is frequent parenthood now irresponsible, but the development of a recreational erotic life needs privacy. Sexual freedom isn't compatible with a childbearing life-style, and much of what is in this book about sexual equality depends on the pill. At the same time, sexuality is originally reproductive; many people still want and have babies, and the mother-baby relationship is in itself erotic and the genesis of all of the language of bodily contact which figures in adult relationships.

Babies are where adult sexuality starts. They require both the soft texture of the mother and the warmth and probably the odor of her skin, while suckling them can turn her on. Much that is missing in adults has quite probably, on ethological grounds, been lost because we have de-erotized babyhood. People with good erotic lives will put some of that back: by nursing the baby naked; spending at least as much time, in its early weeks, over skin contact as you do in lovemaking; suckling it instead of bottle feeding, if at all possible; letting the baby explore its own body when older; avoiding dirt hangups; and both parents giving continual attention.

All this can be a deeply sensual experience for the mother. At birth, the baby is a little portable mouth and a skin texture not your own which you can carry and apply to your own skin. Normally when it's asleep you will find you put its head on your left breast (women who have had children carry even a parcel this way). The baby is programed to monitor your heartbeat (so that if you get agitated, so does the baby) and be lulled by a rhythmic sound at the normal resting rate.

Generally, the more you handle it the better – when a child is older, pushing its sensual experience can be disturbing, but not at the infant stage: prolonged naked contact is normal for the species. In spite of books you can take it to bed – "overlaying" is another name for what is now called cot death, and not due to lying on the infant in your sleep – but don't make love in front of babies old enough to see clearly. For some reason they read sex as aggression between adults, and there's a poorly understood childhood response to adult sexual odors which is probably better not experimented with until we know more about it. If you put a young baby to breast immediately after an orgasm it'll probably howl, because of your very rapid heart rate. In the first few weeks, all this apart, some couples like to include the baby in gently sensual lovemaking, suckling included – you can even experience having your baby at one breast and your lover at the other (after the baby has finished that side). This can be a most unifying experience. Don't do this later on, but equally don't cut off close skin contact

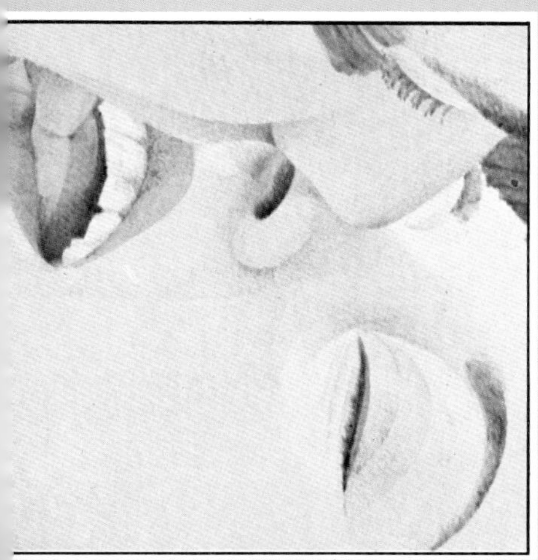

Body Language...
the tenderness and
passion of the act of
love

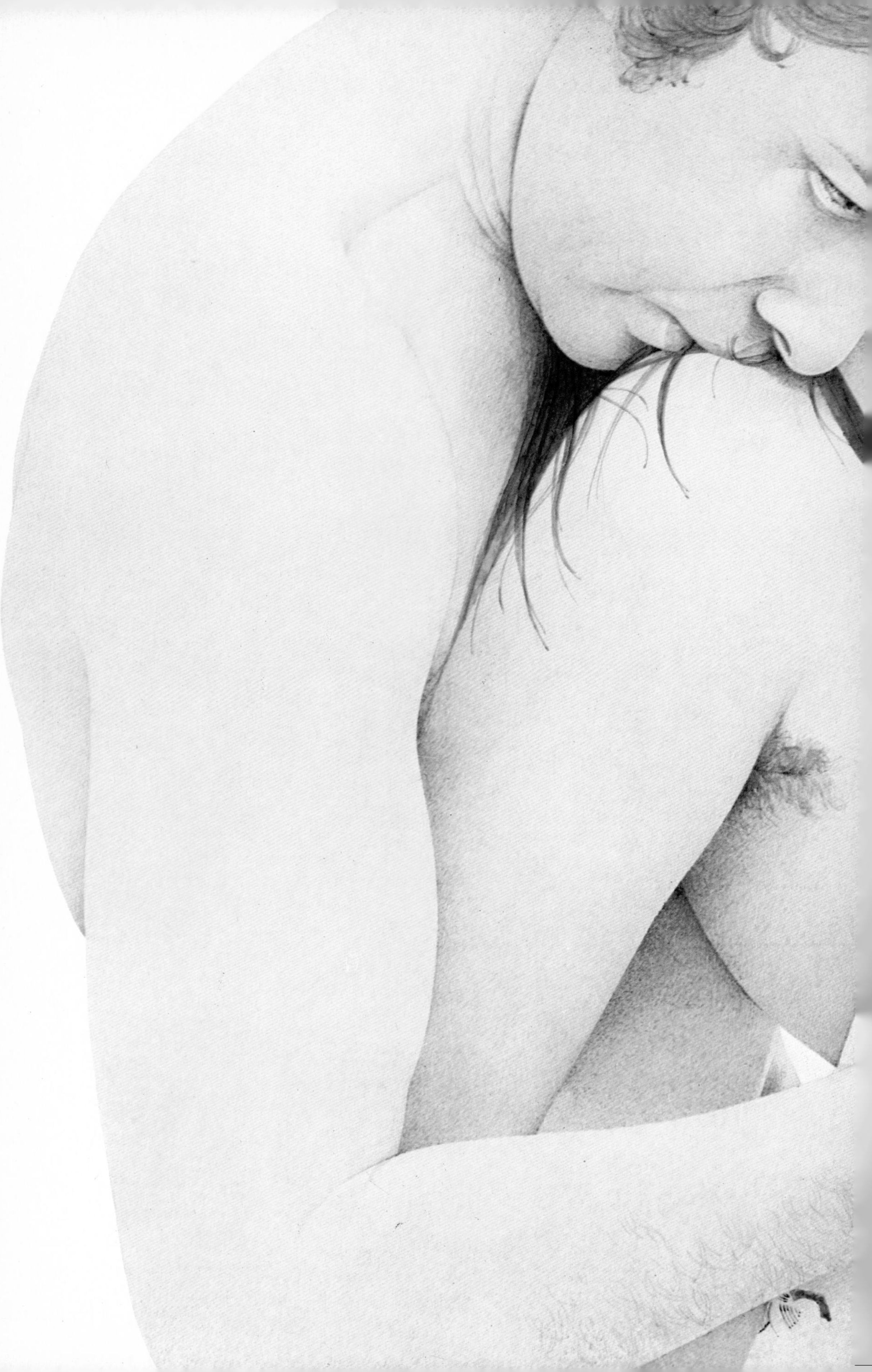

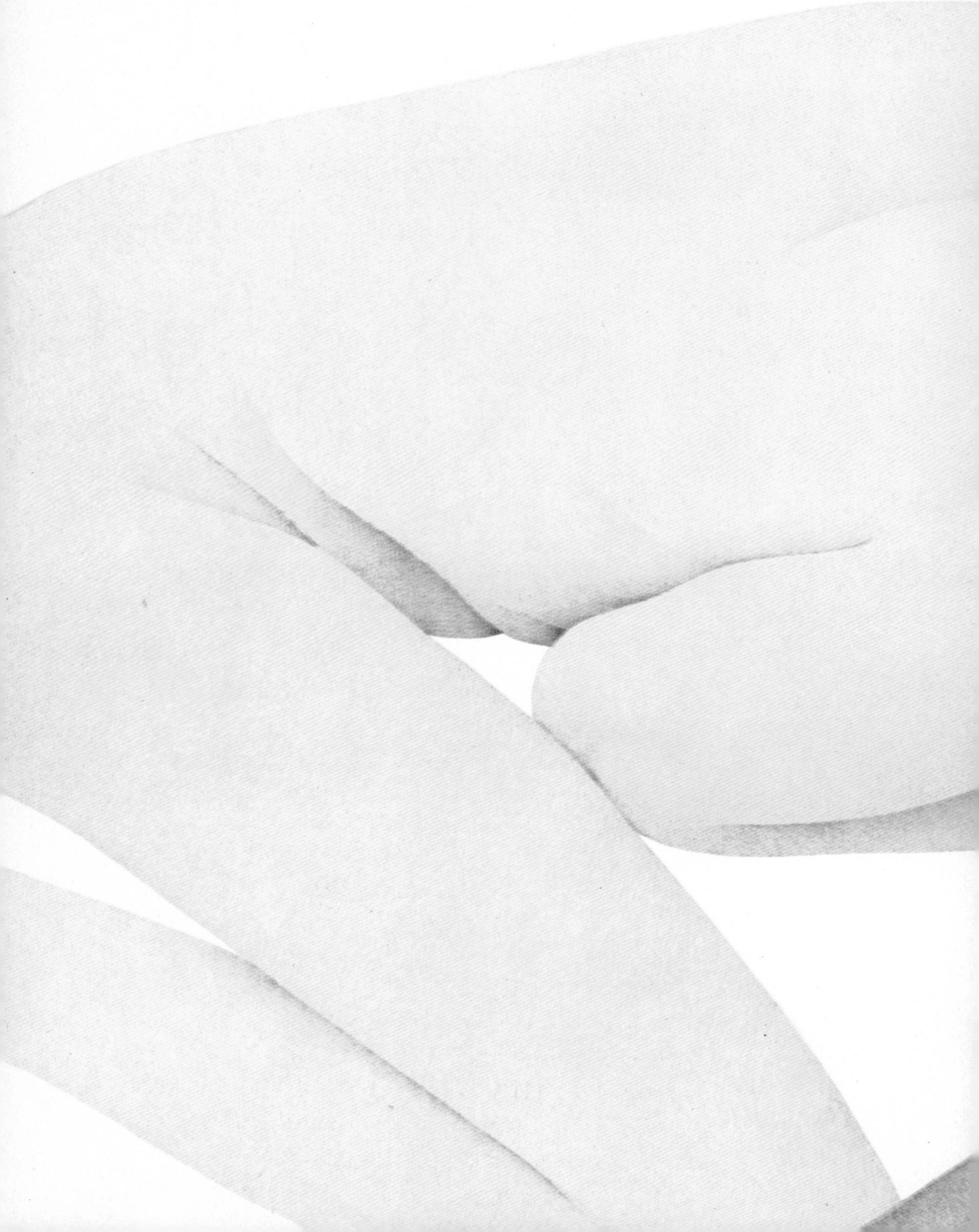

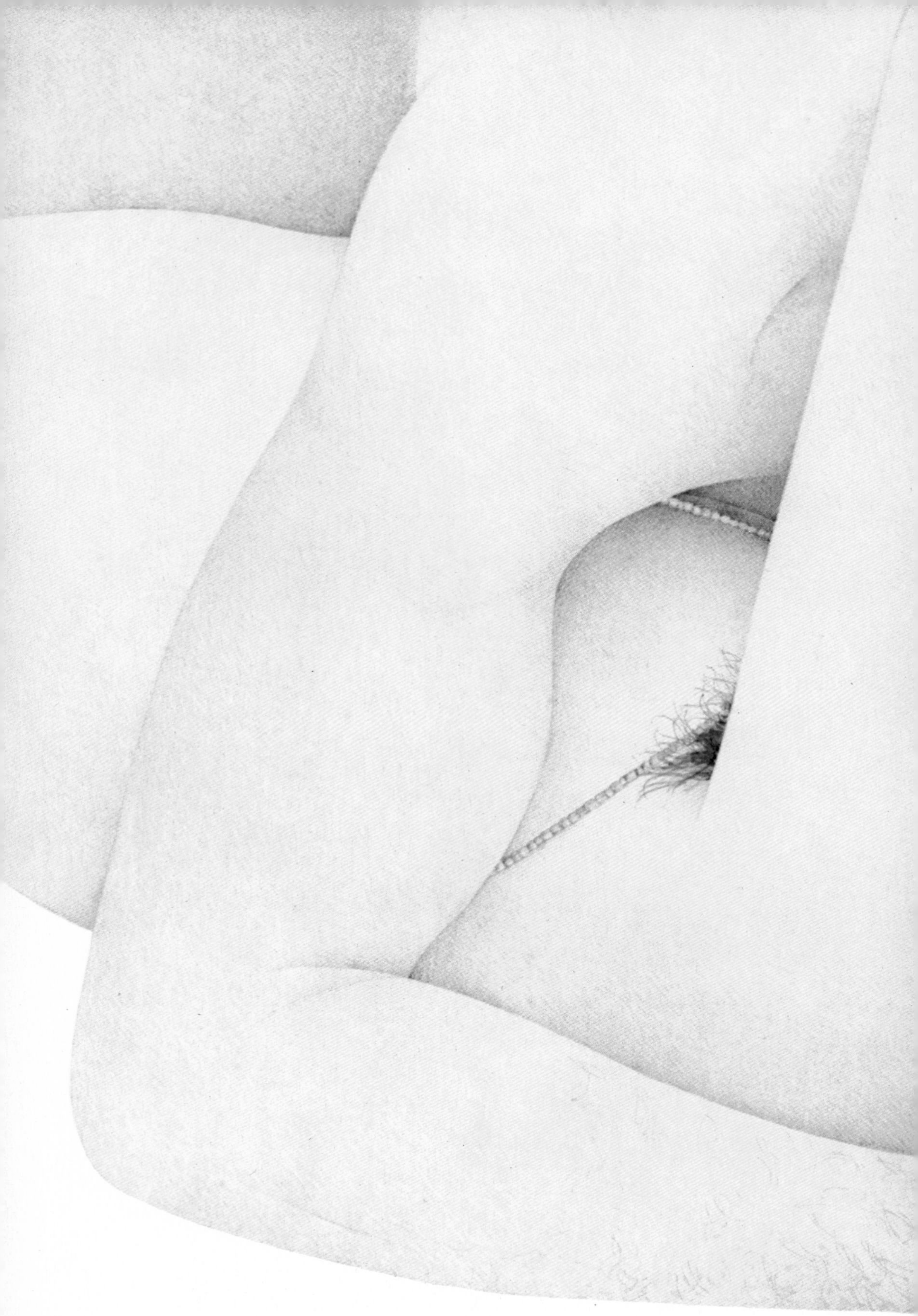

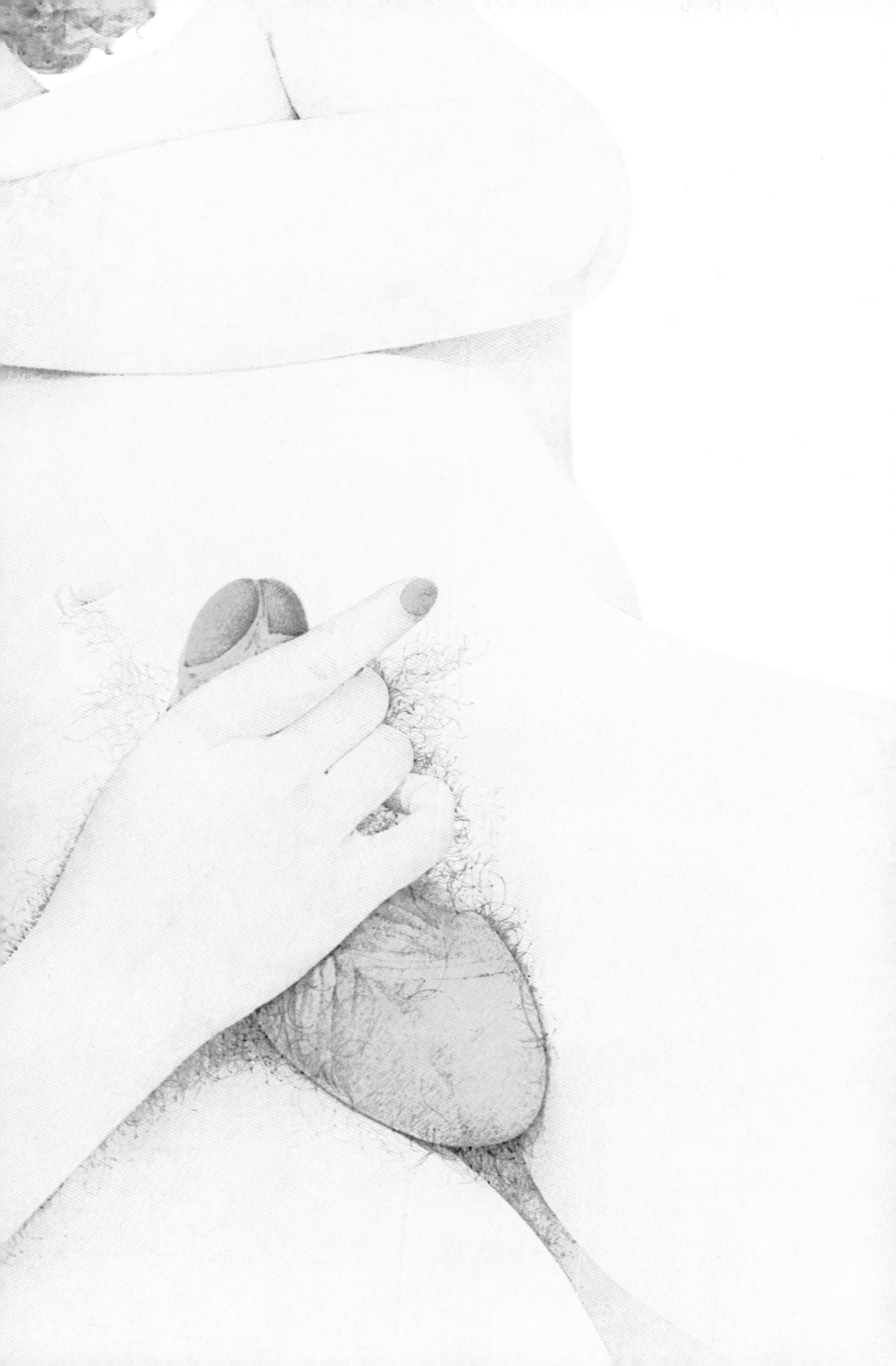

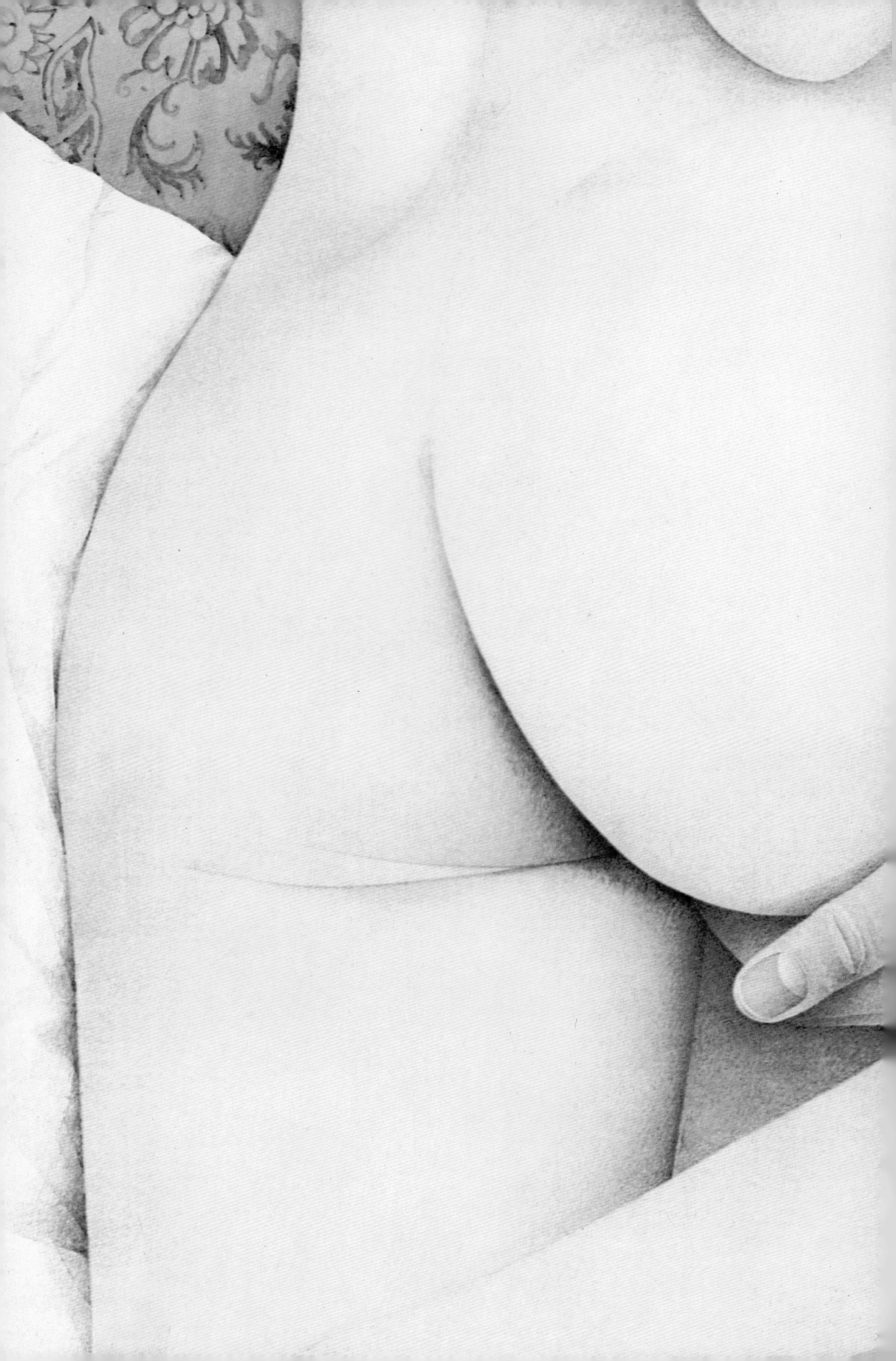

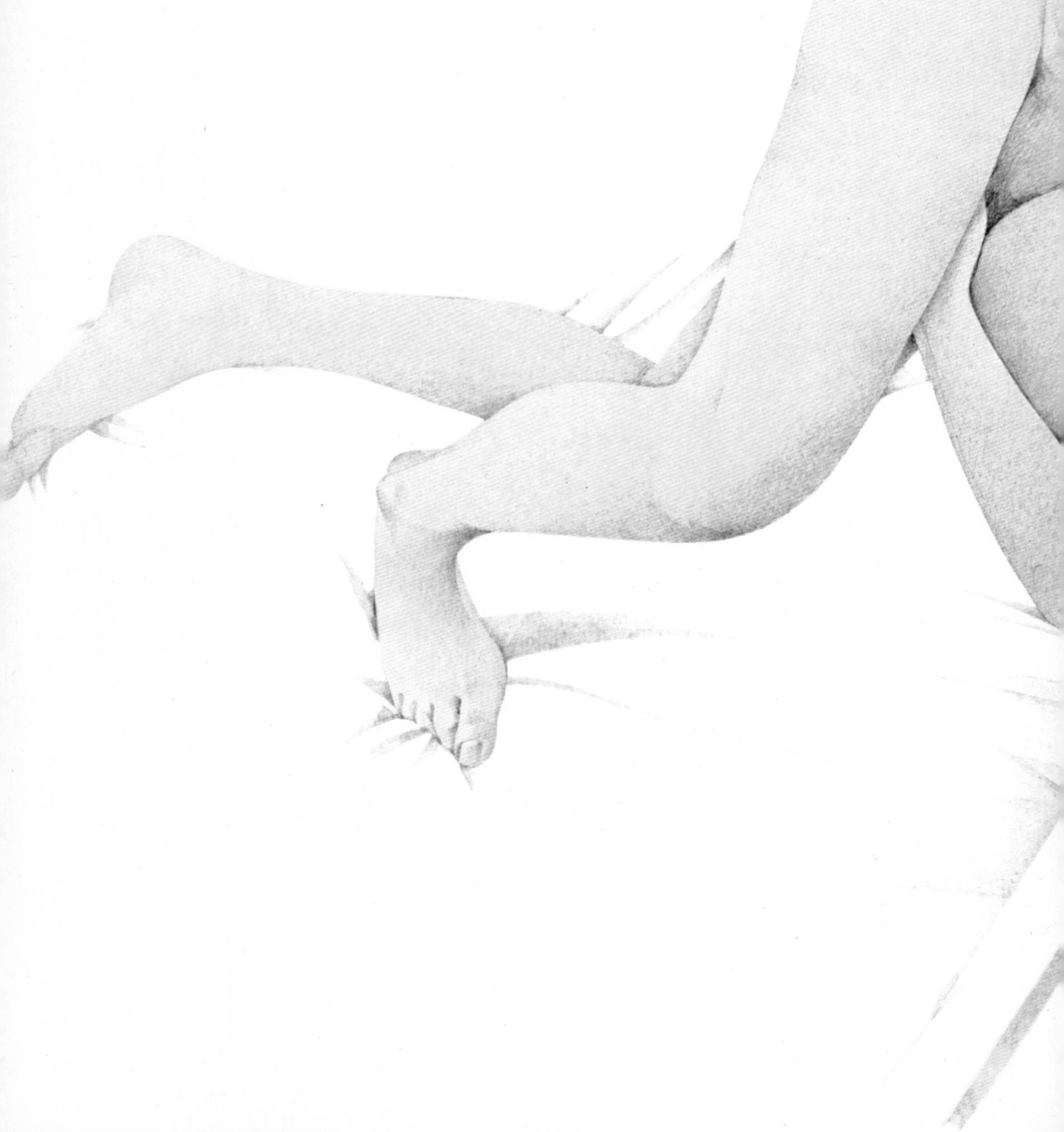

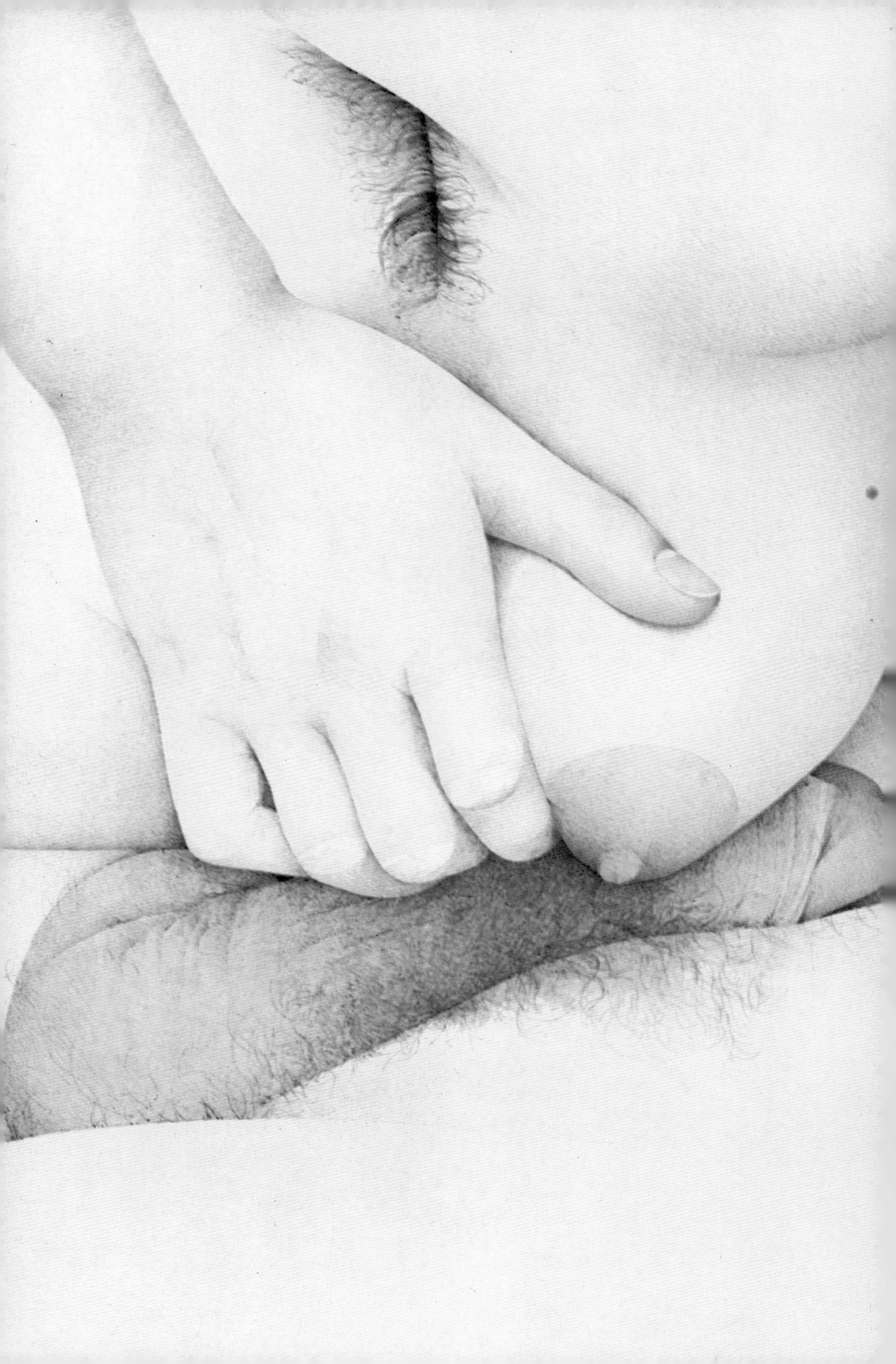

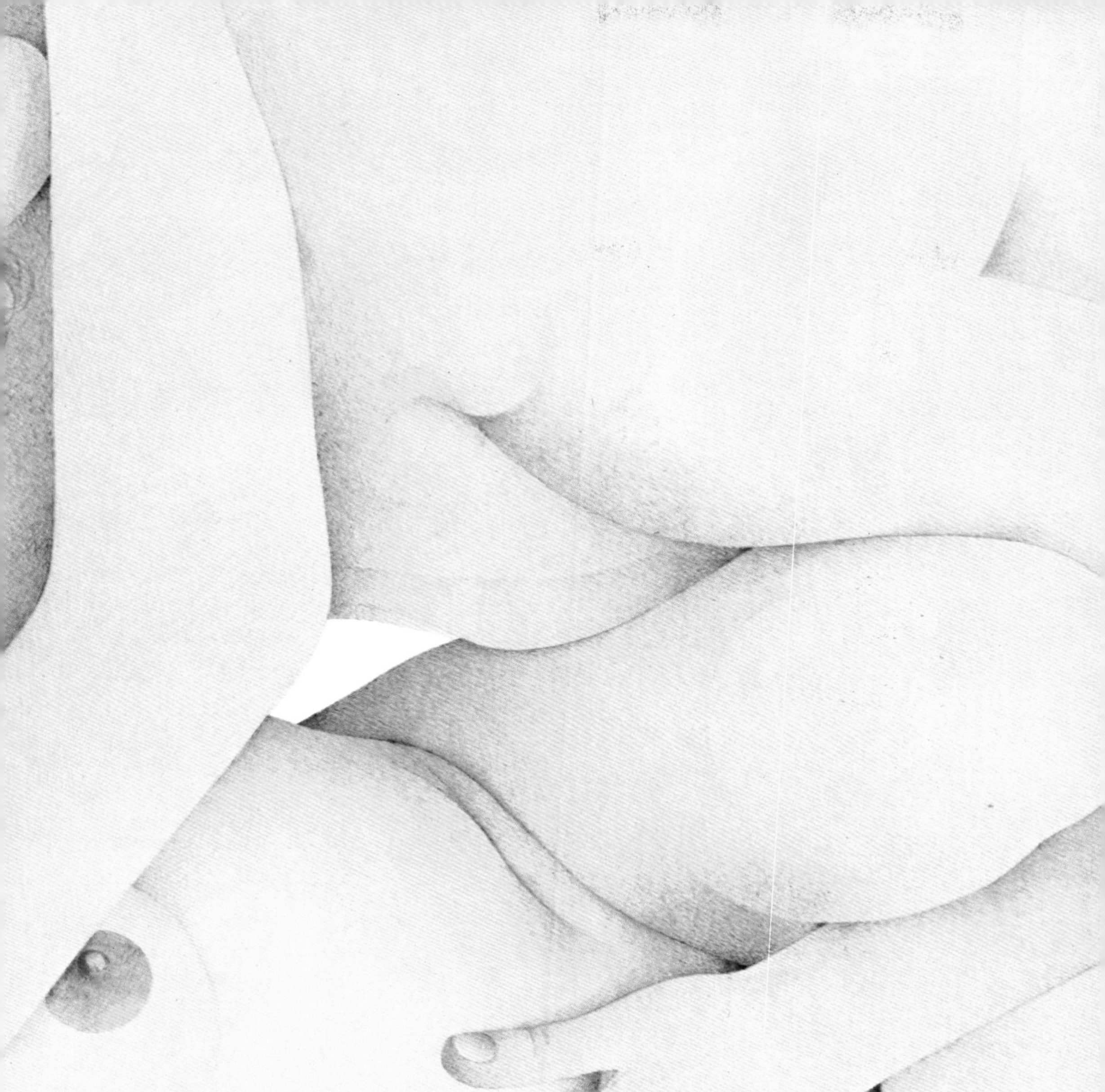

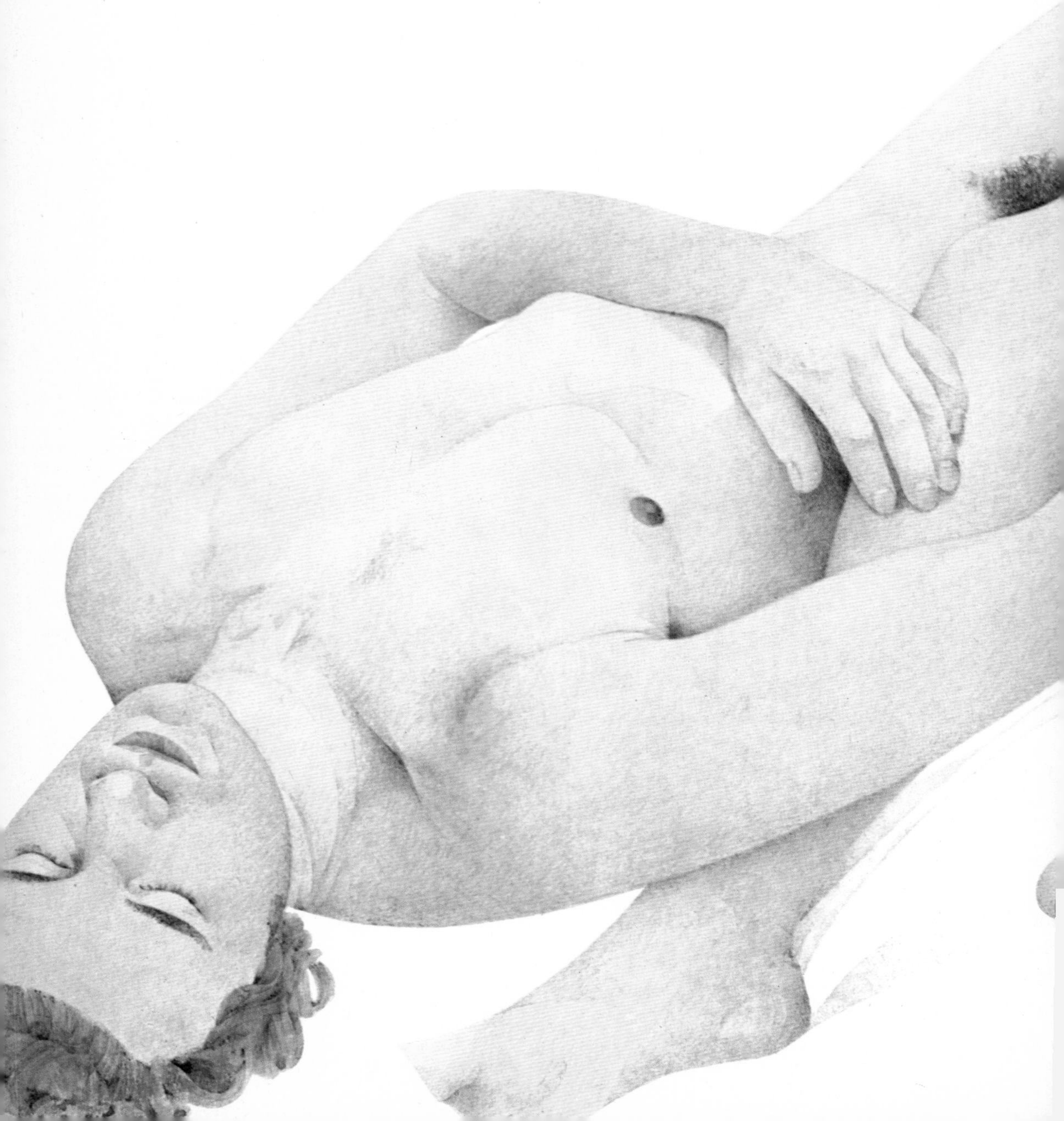

"There are two sorts of sexual joy—having a full orgasm with a person you value, and being a total person yourself"

when you can't so specifically include it in lovemaking – just follow the child normally as it becomes a separate individual. Anxiety over naked parental bodies and the father's "dominance" doesn't usually surface under the age of three.

There is an association psychoanalytically in many women's minds between a baby and a penis – both are as it were community property, regardless of the baby's sex. (Male babies, incidentally, get erections early on and nursemaids used to quieten them by bringing on the nearest thing a baby can contrive to orgasm. Some pediatricians now say this overstimulates the child: at a later age it would do, so we can't give an opinion as to whether it's wise or not, but since many primitives masturbate babies it's most likely harmless, and the baby appears to like it.) Don't retract the foreskin on hygienic grounds: it isn't normally capable of retraction until much later, and unless you are Jewish don't cut it off. Penile cancer is a rare hazard; wash, don't amputate.

Women differ about whether birth itself can be a sensual experience; if it's difficult it won't be, nor if the whole setup is clinical. Having the father there is a complicated extra – most men have guilt or co-operation feelings about a woman being in labor which are traditionally taken out as a *couvade* (sham labor for the man) or, in our culture, an attack of toothache or a totally uncharacteristic binge. You'll have to judge if participation will upset him and whether there's an element of demonstration in making him come.

We have no evidence for this, but it wouldn't be surprising if a muscle-relaxed, turned-on and fully orgasm-experiencing woman was more likely to get an easy labor than one who was a bag of tensions. Whether labor can be an orgasm in itself depends very much on luck and on the mother; some natural-childbirth mothers who can relax and haven't been trained by an overrobust nurse say it can. If it isn't, or is painful, that is perfectly easy to control – and putting the baby to breast for the first time is a sensual experience, if only of relief. It's also programed, because breast stimulation makes the uterus contract, which may explain part of the role of breasts in adult lovemaking.

Having a baby, then, is a unique function of your whole body, and a bonding experience with your lover. That's one reason, apart from the child's needs, not to do it solo if you can help it. It's one sexual experience which does commit you, at least until the child grows up.

One has to be careful saying that pregnancy is a beautiful and sensuous experience – a lot of women who have had nausea and felt like a half-loaded oiltanker rightly suspect that this kind of comment is made by males or infertile, butch women. On the other hand most would agree that quickening, one's first encounter with the baby as a person, is pretty moving. Emotional equipment and attitudes also shift in many people while they're carrying – it can be toward anxiety if it's the first time or if the baby wasn't fully wanted, but it can also be toward a gentle sensuality which the man can share. This fits the gentler lovemaking appropriate to pregnancy in all but those women who miscarry easily and repeatedly, and who – this is about the only time it's ever true – do better to avoid orgasms around the time they've miscarried before.

batacas

Soft, cloth-covered plastic-foam bats with which you can box or fence absolutely painlessly and without the least risk of damage. Two people armed with these can belt each other with their full strength without hurting, and women aren't at a disadvantage. The encounter can be merely a fun thing or a dramatization – not, as the makers suggest, of aggression only, but of our far more basic fear that our aggression and other people's would hurt or destroy them or us if it were expressed. This fear goes very deep, and this is a game to get rid of it – it also allows the body language of really violent fighting without any of the bad consequences. Pillow-fights are the nearest thing, but pillow corners can get in eyes and the wretched

things burst if you hit really hard. An all-out bataca fight with someone you love, not hate, can be a very instructive experience in feelings you didn't know you had. If it sounds untender and not the thing for lovers, you probably need it. If she always loses, give her a bataca in each hand against your one, and vice versa. See *Aggression*.

body image

The image we (as observers sitting inside our heads) have of our body. It is much more complex than that, of course, since it's really the whole computer-synthesis of sensory inputs from inside and outside our bodies, plus some added program derived from ideas we have about ourselves in terms of dominance ("feeling seven feet tall," "feeling smaller than a snake's knees") and infant experience. The trouble is that "we" are the computer,

so the interaction with our identity isn't that of a controller watching a screen, but far closer.

Most humans manipulate the body in order to manipulate the body image – crowns on kings and bearskins on guardsmen make them "feel big." Obese people who gorge and adolescents who starve are doing the same kind of thing. A whole range of sexual hangups and satisfactions are body-image phenomena, especially fetishes, devices intended to increase or decrease muscle tension, and orgasm, in which the body image momentarily "explodes."

Yogic manipulation runs the other way, and aims to manipulate physiology by manipulating the body image. We now know this is possible (see *Biofeedback*) in quite specific contexts, and nobody would exclude a more general manipulation of things like hormones, fertility, or even susceptibility to disease. This is one reason why self-image is important and goes far deeper than what we see in the mirror.

Yogis, indeed, have several centuries' start on us in investigating this (though with electronic monitors we may catch up). The point of all those odd postures is that they've been worked out to affect body image (originally with the aim of suppressing the body-image component of identity altogether, so that one feels merged with the Whole – orgasm can do the same, whence its use in mysticism). These postures depend on muscle tensions and on crossing-over proprioceptive (from inside the body) inputs – sitting in a crossed-over posture is a little similar in its final effect on body image to the old trick of holding a coin between the backs of two hands – you feel two coins. Some elaborate sexual postures, many uses of compression, restraint of movement, or even tight embracing, and many human semisymbolic interferences with the body, such as corseting or Chinese foot-binding, are basically concerned with manipulating the body image and our experience of it.

The body image is analogous to a telephone exchange and computer store for all the body languages we discuss. A great deal of the medicine and sexology of the future will address the body image as much as the body. What is vaguely described as "feeling more alive," "feeling more a person" after various sorts of experience is really concerned with our own experience of our body as the "computer" scans it. That in turn can alter our body image – and with it our posture, taste in dress, physiology and orgasm capacity. Since body awareness starts at birth and develops rapidly in the weeks when a baby is learning muscle co-ordination, disorders of the body image, often affecting later sexual behavior, probably originate pretty early.

body language

It was that brilliant eccentric Wilhelm Reich who first pointed out that we use our body as armor against our anxieties. People who feel small and suspicious do hunch up (instead of "walking tall" – the phrase makes the point), and this kind of tenseness generates backache. Other less evident tensions manipulate our body image in other ways and upset our physiology. Moreover, as Reich quite rightly pointed out, the part of ourselves we've been taught to suppress most until recently has been our sexual identity – turning off our skin in case we might feel something sensual, tensing up in case we might have an orgasm, keeping our legs closed. It's a pretty arduous business spending one's whole life keeping one's legs closed.

The phrase "uptight" is absolutely accurate medically. And being uptight nearly always goes back to some kind of anxiety over the expression of normal feelings, many of them sexual. The energy American men have spent trying not to express bisexuality, and American women in not expressing emotions men said they shouldn't have, would solve the power shortage. In uptight people, all of that energy goes into deranging their physiology and turning off their normal human responses.

Accordingly, when we start to live sexually, many of us have to get rid of the batch of cultural habit spasms which prevent us from relaxing and allowing ourselves to feel. It's perfectly good behavioral psychology that if you can persuade the hunched-up self-accuser to stand up, his self-estimate will change and others, who read his body signals, will treat him differently. The same goes for the anorgastic lady who even keeps her mouth closed – teach her to open it and she may feel different.

This is the justification for all the paramedical courses in relaxation, expression and not-being-scared which are proliferating at the moment. Becoming a live body instead of a moralized tailor's dummy can make one act sexually and socially less like a tailor's dummy (and probably cure a lot of uptightness diseases not limited to postural backache). Since half the task of sex education is to get rid of hogwash which people have been taught by disturbed people and have believed, this kind of re-education helps.

Good sex makes us less dummy-like, sickness-prone and liable to destructive pieces of body manipulation, such as compulsive overeating. At the same time, to have good sex, rather than just sex of a sort, we need the total acceptance of our whole body as a source of pleasure, not of guilt, fear, prohibitions, precautions and better-not warnings. In this respect we've still got a fair distance to go as a society. The various sensual things we describe here are intended to move that along.

Animal body language is an important part – since

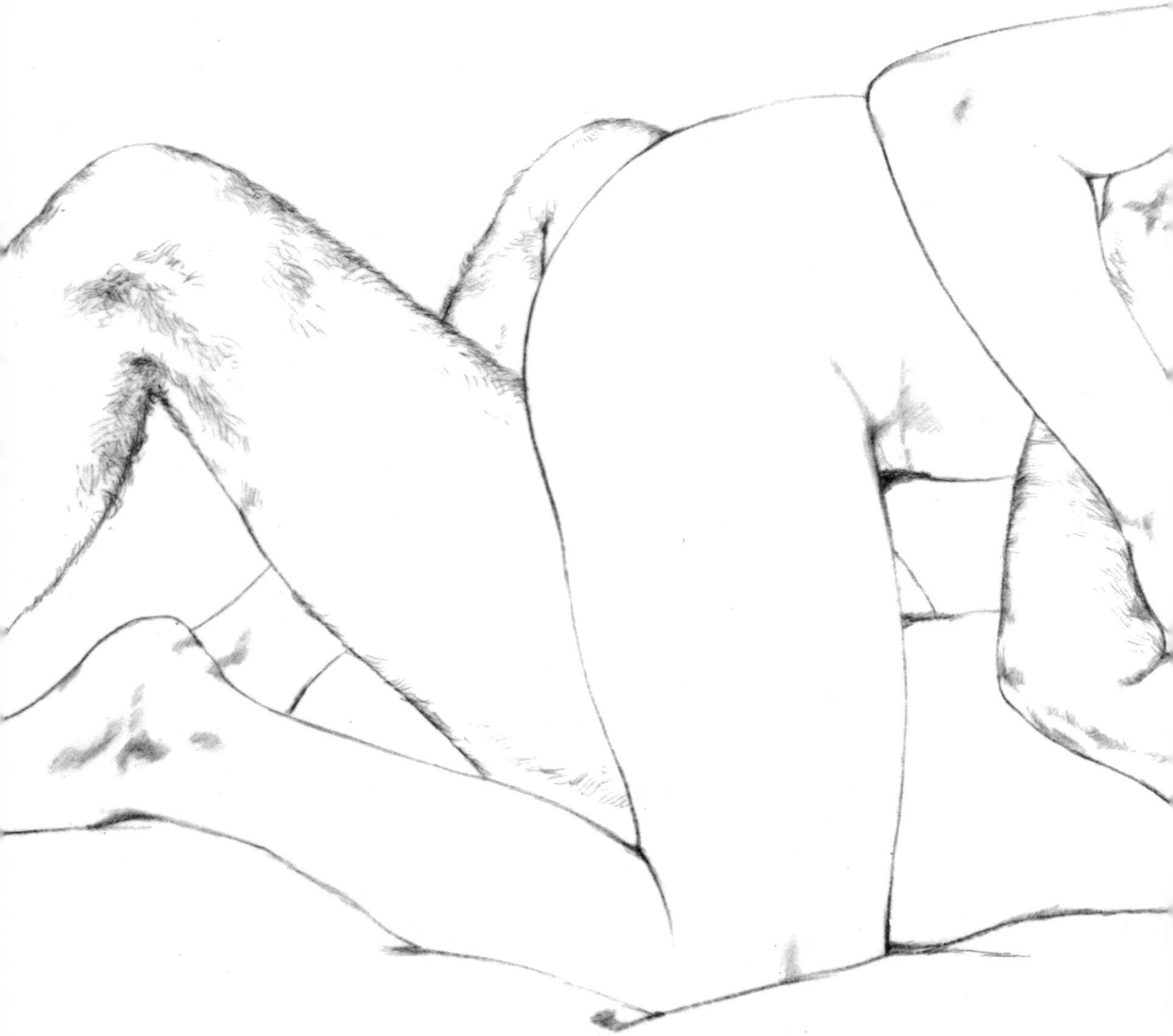

all animal communication is nonverbal – of the science of ethology. Most animals make gestures of self-estimate, which we refer to as dominance and submission. If a male baboon turns his buttocks toward another male and takes the posture of a mating female he's expressing submission, not homosexuality. Baboon society is what is called "agonic," built wholly on dominance and submission, yet this is a gesture which occurs in our own sexual behavior – does it mean the same thing, or some-

thing else, or is it that we have just kept the wiring from our primate ancestors? Chimps are a "hedonic" society: their gestures are invitations to others to behave in a particular way, or statements about how they feel – like being hopping mad. Chimps who give this hopping-mad performance get surrounded by others who are first nonplussed and then supportive or apologetic.

We see this in people, too. The hunched-up person is expressing low self-esteem, and is likely to get pushed

around, which increases his self-deprecation. Body signals which are communicative get reinforced by other folk's reading of them. The tight, mouth-closed lady is saying something nonverbally to men – in this case they are apt to avoid rather than accost her. We all read and speak body language, and more than we realize it can determine our relationships, for it acts at first impression.

hostility

Teenagers today aren't reared on Fred Astaire movies and probably don't get their ideas from *Love Story*. But they do live in a culture where sex equals love. It often does, but it's a lot more complex than that, and even when it does equal love, it can also express hostility. The version in old movies and soap commercials is a simplified version – "lurv" not love – and doesn't occur in real people. It's part of the mythology that loving involves a total takeover bid by each partner for the other ending in a kind of parasitic embrace.

We're not being cynical. If your relation with someone doesn't involve giving, protectiveness and a large measure of sharing it may be a fun thing if both feel the same way, but it doesn't go far as a relationship. At the same time to love or be loved by someone who had no streak of healthy, self-protective selfishness would be a pretty dangerous exercise, leading to unlimited and quite inhuman demand-making on both sides. In fact militant unselfishness is a smart way of making unlimited demands that are hard to combat while at the same time keeping one's end up.

Both sexes need to realize that there is a healthy streak of hostility in all lasting adult love (where it's a defense against being too taken-over by another person) and that some sexual approaches are wholly hostile: notch-cutting by either sex, for example seduce-and-abandon operations by males, husband-hunting by females. Adults can often – but not always – recognize the state of play, but in adolescence one can far more easily get hurt or trapped. In fact in the exploratory relationships common between people who are starting sex, all these components are jumbled up. If they can be expressed as play and seen as play, the attempts teenagers make to see what can be expressed in sexual relations are part of learning. Unfortunately they tend to happen at a time when people are easily hurt. If both are only trying to score, fine – but even here the hostility implied in scoring for its own sake points to a fair amount of inner uncertainty.

Girls have often been already trained by disillusioned mothers to realize that male love can be hostile (and often need to learn that even so it can be concerned and reinforcing). Boys don't always recognize predatory behavior by the other sex – and similarly shouldn't be thrown or scared if they meet it, while not falling for any kind of blackmail. More important is to look at your own reading of sexuality to avoid the risk of hurting someone else. If you think inwardly that all girls or all boys are "sex objects," are deceitful and need conquering and putting down, or are basically dangerous, you will hurt someone, and others who at heart think likewise will hurt you, unless you are tough to the point of being inhuman.

On the other hand, beginning or practicing sex can't be wholly painless, any more than beginning or practicing football. Normal people are robust enough to give a few rounds to experience. Awareness of reality as against sentimental fiction helps here, and adolescents shouldn't be deterred by parents whose own bad experiences make them distrust and hate all men or all women indiscriminately – a hostility which gets propagated in their children's attitudes and leads to another unhappy generation. You will, unless you are lucky, meet hostile people, be let down, and be sad or disappointed. You can be prepared for this, as you would be prepared to lose out occasionally in any other situation: these experiences only make it easier to avoid settling for the wrong primary relationship and recognizing the right one when it comes. You aren't made of glass or jelly, and your final primary relationship will have a few healthy prickles if both of you are human.

This book can't stand in for experience, and not all adults are any more sensible here than teenagers, despite extra years (which some of them spend reiterating the same neurotic mistakes). The best response to a letdown or a putdown if you're young is to cry or swear for not more than 12 hours, wallow in self-pity for not more than three days, then write it off to experience and realize you are that much maturer.

hot tubs

It's been said that it's immoral to take a bath alone. The communal kind is a Japanese invention. You wash before you get in, then all soak together. In Japan this isn't an erotic exploit any more than a sauna, but for us it makes a remarkably effective icebreaker and a kind of bonding. People who soak together behave as if they'd shared a warm womb.

European houses aren't geared to this – they could be, since the climate in Japan is not so different. Rich Californians sport a hot Jacuzzi pool; less rich ones buy up old winevats or construct their own outdoor tubs, fed by a small waterheater. (See *Hot Tubs* by Leon Elder, Capra Press, for practical details.) Apart from being the

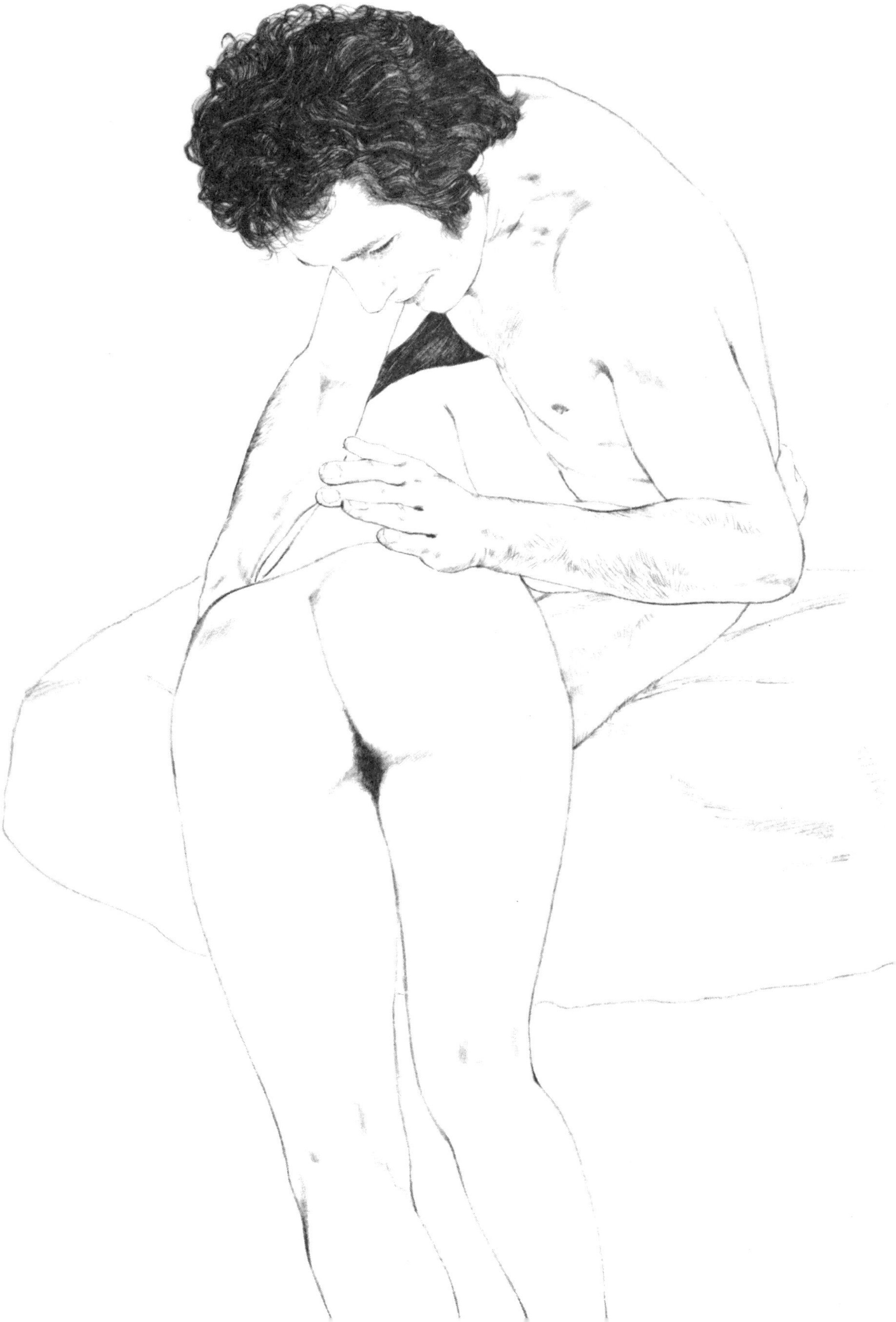

best invention for companionate relaxation since the days of the Roman Empire, hot tubbing encourages non-nudists to share nakedness more easily than swimming. Mickey Mouse hasn't so far persuaded us to wear swimsuits in our baths, so hot tubbing makes a good starter. The tub needs to be around 100°F – it's a site for togetherness and things like group massage rather than lovemaking, for which it's really too hot if you want to be strenuous. We put it in here because it is part of the repertoire of greater sensuality, between couples and between friends, which goes in turn with better sexual expression, and it's a fine start for sharing (q.v.). Ordinary baths and even millionaire "conversation" baths have none of this social quality. The whole thing need not

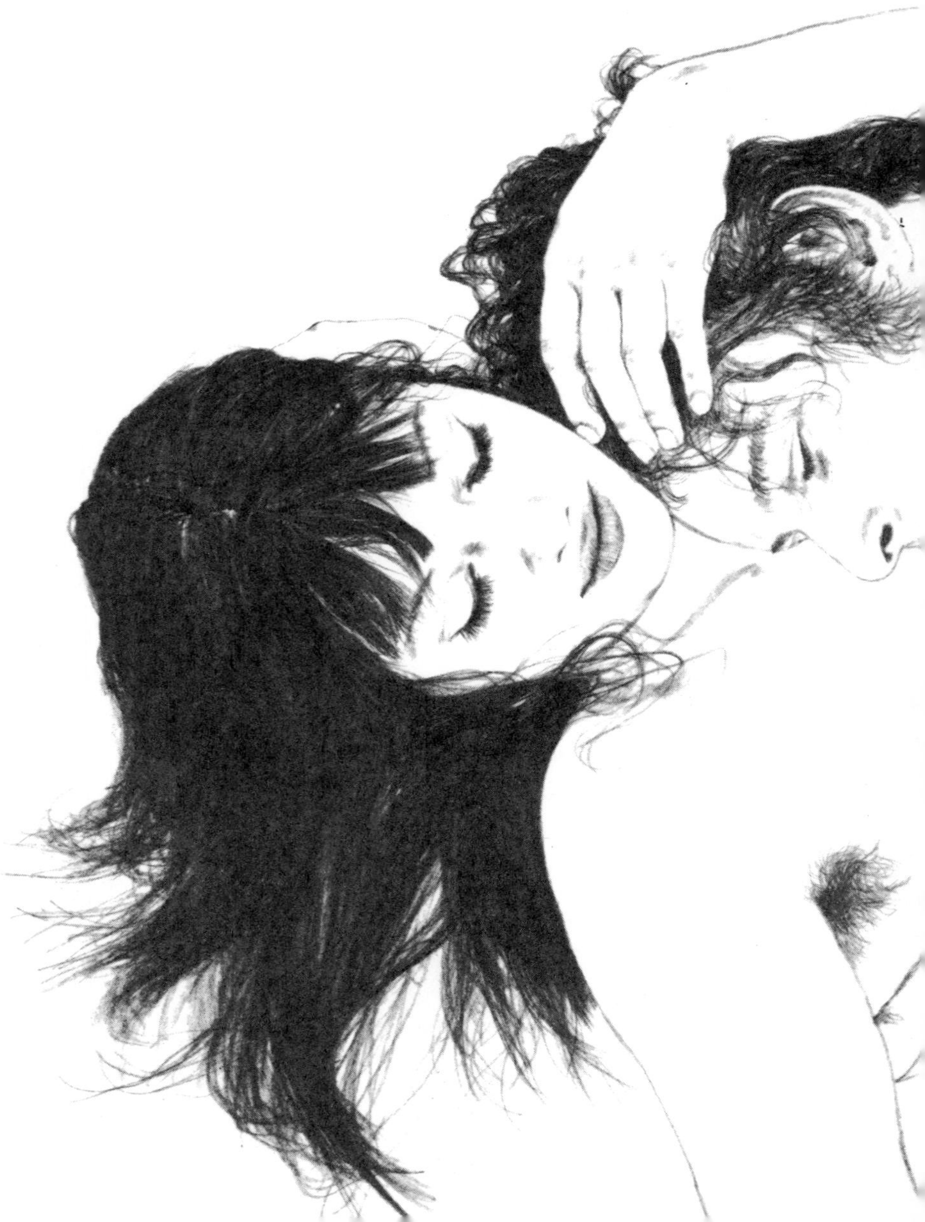

cost more than $250 plus fuel, though it would be costly to keep running – less so in a warm country. Couples who are close enough to make real use of them could own one jointly.

language of the heart

Nothing to do with pink bows and Franz Lehar. The probable reason that the heart is a traditional seat of the emotions is that its rate changes with arousal. This is only readable on close contact or for one's own heartbeat, but the mother's heart rate is a programed signal of her emotional state to a baby at breast (see *Babies*). Between partners their own heart rate and that of the partner act as arousal signals – this, plus infant reminiscences, may explain why heart-like drumbeats in music are erotic (the theme of fate in *Carmen*, the bass in Roberta Flack's "The First Time Ever").

Most lovers do genuinely aim at heart-to-heart contact, often in the infant, head-on-breast situation, so the quickening heart rate is arousing during the runup to sex and the slowdown is tranquilizing during detumescence.

Heart rates in both sexes at orgasm can go as high as in athletics, both from arousal and exertion. Even for people with heart problems such as angina or arrhythmia, however, this seems to be the least hazardous form of exercise – compared with unaroused stairclimbing it rarely produces either anginal pain or extrasystoles, presumably because the coronaries dilate in anticipation. Bed deaths are much more often due to anxiety, it seems, than actual physical exertion, because they don't usually occur in the familiar marital context – much more often during what used to be called an "intrigue."

massage

This isn't a textbook of physiotherapy, so we aren't going into the medical, nor the Oriental, sensual, erotic and other kinds now canvassed. If you want to make a big deal of it you can buy books on sensual massage which come in a kit complete with a bottle of baby oil. Do learn the art of sensual massage, however. It happens to be one of the best presexual turnons for both sexes, one of the best postcoital relaxations, and certainly the best icebreaker. We've seen couples who are really good at it – both of them – get another couple to strip with a decent social excuse and turn them on without being irreversibly seductive if the scene doesn't take off (they can always say thank you and get dressed if that's how they feel). See *Sharing*.

If you've got experience in medical massage, fine. If not, don't just rub the skin, which isn't soothing, but work on a limb or along the trunk with both hands together, kneading fairly firmly but not heavy-handedly with the thumb and fingers. If you do this regularly to each other you'll learn what soothes and what irritates. Try and get a massage from someone good, to see how it feels, and watch them (but don't try professional tricks such as those involving knee pressures on the back until you know how). Don't "rolf" people – this hurts, has no medical basis, and is best left to masochists. Don't use too much oil unless you happen to like the feel of it (you don't need oil for good massage), and when things get really erotic, don't automatically put it on the penis even if massage parlor girls do – it cuts sensation below triggerpoint in some males, though others enjoy it, especially if you're going to massage the glans itself.

You need to be naked yourself, so you can use your whole body surface. In the early stages you can vary

kneading with tapotage (very light, quick karate-chops given with the edges of the two hands alternately and close together on back, thigh and other muscles – do it as if you were chopping onions with two choppers). With the subject face-down put each of your hands on one of their hands, fingers spread, run them simultaneously down each arm, then side by side down the trunk, over each buttock, and down each leg to the foot, with firm finger-pressure. Later on, do the same with the subject face-up, going lightly over the breasts if it's a woman, then down the insides of the thighs. You can add touches from your breasts, genitals and pubic hair if you wish. Not all the most sensual effects come from the obvious areas – careful finger work between the fingers, between the toes, and on the palms and soles (without tickling) can excite most people. Take time to learn what works on each other before you try on someone else – then both of you work on a third party, one giving general massage while the other (usually the other-sex partner) concentrates on special areas such as hands and feet.

Both start together with straight body work, however, and only increase the sensuality if the subject seems to be responding – go on to fingers, armpits, breasts (don't neglect the breast and nipple area in males), insides of thighs with your fingernails (gently) in both sexes, while the same-sex partner keeps up straight muscle kneading. Finally, take a finger or toe in your mouth – if that works, you can begin tongue work elsewhere, ears, trunk skin, nipples. Don't rub the clitoris unless she is manifestly ready for it, but do brush her lips with your nipples or glans, according to how you're placed. When a man gets a full erection you can fondle the scrotum first, then go on either to full masturbation, or if you want to keep with the massage bit and make this something special, oil the glans and rub it between your thumb and finger. The point of sexual no-return is really when you start mouth and tongue work – before that it's sensual massage, afterward it's pre-sex.

Even if it doesn't get that far, being massaged by more than one person is a special sensation: tribal massage by many people, eyes closed, is an experience of deep reassurance rather than a kick. Being massaged, eyes closed, by another naked person using their whole oiled body on your body is a wilder experience. With two couples it's often best for three to work on one person before changing to one-to-one: in a threesome, change roles, or all three massage each other. Don't in either case hurry to switch to full sex, but prolong the oral part, with kissing and tongue massage. For women, when the touching gets specifically genital, the tongue is usually better than the finger. A shy person often takes better to sexual massage if blindfolded (and you may be less blocked about same-sex contacts if the subject doesn't know who is doing what). In fact, in massaging a woman, it often isn't the man who starts mouth work – or who takes it to orgasm.

Apart from its social uses, cultivate prolonged massage of each other, as a couple (oddly enough blindfolding or shutting the eyes often helps here too, even though you know perfectly well who's doing it). Don't forget the head, hair and scalp, or forget that the penis and vulva as well as the hands and mouth are skin-stimulating tools, the vulva in particular because of its warmth. So are all hair tufts, if you're agile, and your head hair and beard if you've got one.

The only problem is that it takes naturally unclumsy and sensual people to give good sexual massage. But you can better this by learning not to grab, bruise or irritate – and in so doing you'll get much better at sex generally.

Group massage, or massage between more than two people, is now a widespread feature of "new encounter" experiences. It does not have to become what society would consider sexual. It is still a good experience if it stops short of genital stimulation and is spoiled by over-concentration on that, and it carries no serious infection risk.

Probably the thing most experienced couples most often miss is that the buttocks and small of the back are highly erogenous areas. You can perfectly well turn someone on face-down by the right kind of touches, kneading, gentle slaps and so on. Practice this – from behind you can get at the neck, whole back area, buttocks, small of the back (which is an erection trigger area in males if you find the spot for finger pressure), soft insides of thighs and much of the woman's perineum. Remember you don't have to use massage only before intercourse – you can use it in intercourse (of her back in a rear-entry position, if you have good control, for example). Once she has started on the penis, however, massage of the back, etc., is apt to be swamped by local feeling or to act as a distraction – he may then prefer to concentrate on genital sensation.

How far you take massage depends on whom and where you are massaging. But it's the gentlest form, not of seduction, but of introduction. It's also an excellent way to learn to use and accept your body and other people's.

masturbation and learning

This is now a more important learning experience for the woman than for the man, because quite a few girls don't embark on it spontaneously. Men almost universally masturbate for enjoyment from early adolescence on – they may also use it to desensitize themselves and

avoid overrapid response in intercourse: the second of these has to be learned, but not the first. Women who do not climax or who are frigid in intercourse almost always have to be taught in the first instance how to produce an orgasm themselves, before learning to transfer that ability to the sexual situation. This strongly suggests that while boys need only be told to enjoy masturbation without guilt, adolescent girls should be actively encouraged to explore their own bodies. The idea that this is a beautiful love-secret to be taught them only by an idealized betrothed falls down on the inexperience and anxiety of a lot of the unidealized men they'll meet. If they don't know their own responses they can't help a man to stimulate them. The idea that learning in this way will cause them to get stuck with noncoital responses is a piece of theoretical folklore. Shy and anxious people of either sex can get stuck with masturbation because it's nonrelational, but that is as a consequence of their original withdrawnness.

To the mother who finds her daughter masturbating and wants to know what to tell her, the answer is, rejoice and be exceeding glad that she's learning a skill, and hope that if you were worried by old superstitions you didn't show it and put her off. As to "telling" her, say it's something she'll be able to enjoy all her life, a practice for adult lovemaking, and the only way to learn her own responses; warn her against disturbed people who say it's sinful or harmful. Don't give her a vibrator – some adults find that effective, but it's inclined to damp down sensitivity with prolonged use, and is better kept for people already sexually active. If your daughter doesn't masturbate, there would be a case for teaching her if parental teaching wasn't apt to be mistimed and intrusive: books, or instruction in a group as a part of normal sex education, would be a better idea.

Lovers should not only masturbate each other, but watch each other masturbate – both for excitement and instruction. Few women respond best to finger insertion which men tend to use with the idea of simulating intercourse. If your man watches how you do it, he can vary that for new sensations.

One of the most useful things any sexually experienced adult can do is to re-evaluate masturbation. When we start it as kids we don't have the experience to do this, and most of us stay with the technique we learned then and use it as an occasional. As an adult you can go back over this – it's something you enjoy and accept and you now have the privacy to do it properly. If you never saw yourself masturbate, use a mirror, settling down to it naked and in the most comfortable posture. A male should consciously look for new techniques: try with

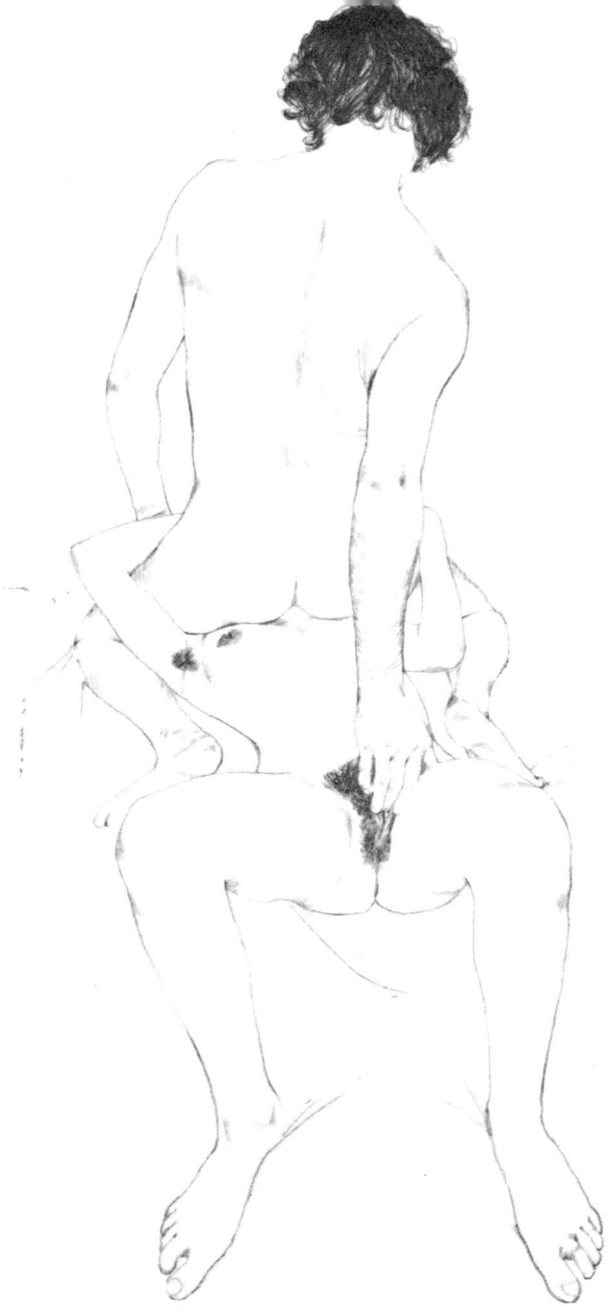

your left hand if you normally use the right (you'll be surprised at the difference), use the foreskin if you normally retract it – if you're circumcised, try wetting or oiling the glans and rubbing only that. A woman should similarly try things she hasn't normally tried – the clitoris alone, if you use the whole-hand method, and vice versa. The object is both to enjoy and to learn more about the responses of which you are capable. If any other part of you seems to need attention, notice. If you have a fantasy, notice that. Then try the same things with your partner watching. He or she will learn new things too.

muscles

Muscle contraction occurs all over the body in orgasm, especially in males, some getting what looks like a convulsion. Involving the whole musculature in the act of ejaculation is about the nearest men normally get to the whole-body sensations women experience in orgasm, though theirs is of a different kind. Most men get a partial experience of this through exertion in intercourse – a passive or totally relaxed orgasm is quite possible for men, but obviously it doesn't make use of this particular body language.

It is, indeed, a language, and this has given rise to some hangups which aren't for once culture-created, but may be basically human. The language of skin contact has been tabooed in our culture because it expresses tender sensuality. Muscular language is for some people even more anxious because it's associated with aggression or violence.

The biology of this is interesting. The male is programed to use a lot of muscular strength in intercourse, and needs to do so to achieve one variety of total-body orgasm. On the other hand a strong individual who really went for this would give his partner problems and might have to hold back, in order to stay on the bed and not bruise her through muscle-spasm. Even with not-so-muscular couples, children who see or hear intercourse are apt to mistake it for a violent assault. This could be behind the notion among social evolutionists that the male of our primate ancestors was programed for struggle because he had to catch and overpower the female (the old caveman joke), and that this tended to promote the survival of the fittest. The explanation's neat, but it only reflects human anxieties, not primate behavior. No ape overpowers the female (who can bite very effectively, and outthreaten a male), and it is normally she who does the inviting – rape is entirely a human invention.

Why we erotize intense muscular contraction in orgasm and then associate it with aggressiveness isn't clear, though it could have something to do with early infant experiences of sensuality and frustration at a time when our musculature isn't very co-ordinated and everyone else is stronger than we are. It may surface preferentially in males because they have bigger muscles and a special hormone system to maintain them: it would be interesting to see if the woman athletes who use anabolic pills to boost their musculature get the same reaction.

At the practical level, some people manage to express

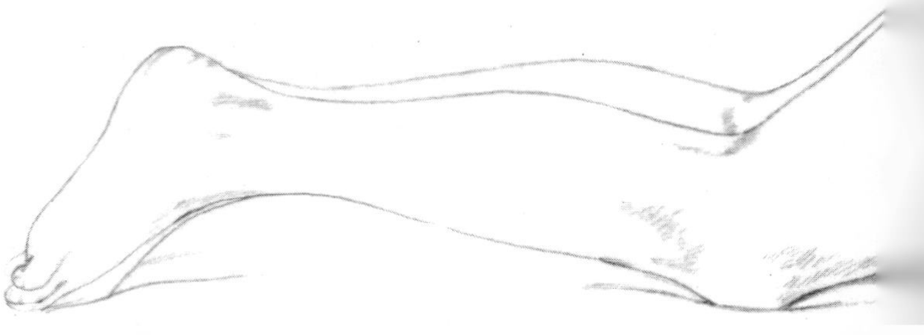

this response fully by using positions in intercourse which give them maximum muscular scope. Extracoital things like sport or actual struggle can set off sexual excitement – quite commonly, in both sexes, by watching, not participating. Watchers tend to play over at brain-level the movements they are seeing, so it could be that at least half of the arousal comes from what are really abortive or unrealized movements, though the element of nonverbal communication and symbolism helps. This may explain why "violence" is exciting – an unfortunate association for Man. Another effect of the exertion-equals-aggression equation may be that we could make good use of sexual energy in the interests of civilized behavior. In our culture we're more or less obliged to block the movements that express hostility to people like political crooks, fellow drivers and the guys at work, and lack nonhostile aggressive activities like hunting, running and heaving logs. Apes, on the other hand, make intention movements and throw things about to express frustration – if we did, we'd be laughed at.

Accordingly, although the muscle-anger equation causes trouble, especially when it's tacked on to mutual anxieties between the sexes about who is stronger than whom, learning to use the sexual language of muscles is a resource, and it can be highly reinforced by the intensity of the climax it gives. Psychiatric writers who see violent physical activity in intercourse as covert sadism are confusing activity with hostility. Real sadism – self-assertion through hurting or humiliating someone – is almost certainly a part of this normal association-sequence gone badly wrong.

Some people need to use other techniques, partly

because of the symbolisms which muscular language generates for them. Actual struggle, if it's under control, turns many men on (see *Wrestling*), and it may be because abortive movements are effective and reminiscent of infant sensuality experiences that they often wish the woman were the stronger. Bondage (i.e. binding someone so that muscular tension is maximal but they can't move or get loose) is another traditional method, and the only

one which maintains the tension right up to and through actual orgasm: you can't have sex while wrestling. Skillfully done it can give a man an orgasm in which nearlv every muscle of the body takes part, making him, in one informant's words, "feel like one huge penis" – a psychoanalytic bonus which probably contributes to its popularity.

This only applies to some of the complicated postures which give tight elbow compression. Couples who nominally tie each other as a preliminary to teasing are mainly acting out a weaker-stronger game (see *Aggression*), and women who enjoy being bound usually also like the dramatization of helplessness. This is another case of a sexual technique which can be played for symbolism, physical effects, or (usually) both. At the physical level a really expert woman can induce an all-muscle orgasm in a man if she secures him correctly, and the muscle response is stronger than in straight intercourse, however violent, because the movements are abortive or isometric, and he can use his full strength. It's been suggested that this explains what Delilah was doing to Samson. Observe, after what we've said, that both wrestling and bondage as sexual extras terrify (or fascinate) some anxious people as violent, aggressive or sadistic. They've got far more to do with body image.

At the other extreme, total muscle relaxation is sexual (in both sexes) and doesn't have any symbolisms alarming to Man because it's a statement of total non-aggression. All the same it can produce all-body orgasm in males who learn the knack, though more rarely than tension because it's not a positive effort and isn't boostable artificially. Really good massage can induce it. It's noticeable (see *Massage*) that the sexual contacts which follow prolonged massage are intense but often, to the

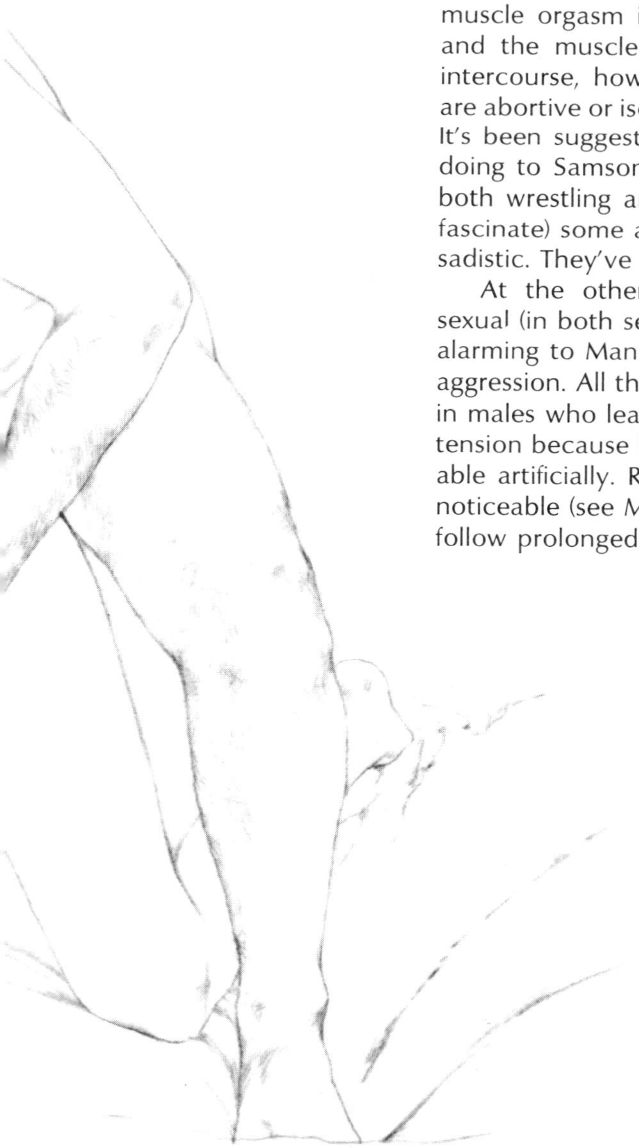

observer, rather inactive if it's been properly done. Even work on the penis or clitoris remains massage not masturbation, since the muscular key is lower. For although the feeling is as intense it's different and, with good preparation, more generalized. For the male this is much nearer to the real female pattern, and should be experienced if possible. (It could be that the male orgasm isn't as generalized as the woman's, not only because men concentrate on the penis, but because they concentrate on their muscles.)

Women, too, use their musculature in intercourse and orgasm, but it's mostly the pelvic and thigh muscles, though it may spread to the back. They have the option of cultivating this (especially the internal pelvic movements, which can be learned) and sharing a male-type muscular orgasm if they want to.

Contrary to folklore huge muscles in the male are not a common feminine turnon, any more than huge genitalia. Muscles, like genitalia, are probably a male dominance signal, which explains the cult of body-building that occupies most of some people's time. The "140-pound weakling" in those body-building ads, who gets hassled by a bully on the beach, takes the course, and then beats hell out of the bully, has some biological basis in male thinking. In the ad, his newly acquired aggressiveness enchants his formerly disappointed girl friend: this is a male fantasy, however, since with most women success in a brawl doesn't rate very high. The only muscular structures that are an important releaser for women appear to be male buttocks.

In gay sex between males, both muscularity and genital size are turnons, because here it is precisely the male dominance signals which are being erotized.

pictures

Sexual pictures are a turnon in their own right (which is one reason we've included them here) and can be uniquely beautiful (which is another). With instant cameras removing the need to get film developed, people are coming to use snapshots sexually as they've so far used them in other family contexts – as a memory file to relive good times – and for this they are extremely effective. Moreover you can use them dream-fashion and realize your own fantasies visually for keeps.

It's unfortunate that only expensive instant cameras can be set for time-lapse, and good pictures of an engrossing activity like lovemaking really need a photographer. We don't ask footballers to photograph themselves. Accordingly, photography goes best in a two-couple scene.

There are a few rules. Don't send sexual film to com-

mercial photographers, especially across state lines. Some will refuse it, destroy it, or send it to the police (and since most of us are breaking obscure sexual laws at every session this could be heavy – the courts really apply these idiocies, and you could be declared sex felons simply for giving each other head): those that don't, and print without a murmur, are commonly taking copies for sale. Unless you want to shoot movies, use a Land camera. If you want motion, save up and get videotape. Keep an album by all means, but don't show other people's pictures around without their consent, as some swingers do. Tact, and an awareness of just how mean and dangerous square authority is when set in motion, are essentials for survival if you have a full and joyful sex life, and doubly so the more people it involves.

You can of course buy sexual pictures as a turnon, but few professionals are as skillful as you could be yourselves. The best use of transparencies is to photograph flowers, lace and textures like striped Indian blankets or rows of eggs in a box, project them and walk together into the beam until it focuses on your skin. Then dance, or make love, watching yourselves in a mirror. It's less messy than body-painting, more versatile, and taps a human turnon we've nearly forgotten – a painted person is magical. If you can get good sexual films you can show them as *hors d'oeuvre*, but this isn't usually necessary when you can do instead of watching – except when you need to turn another couple on.

Keep sexual snapshots and color slides out of the general box you show socially. You'd be amazed how often, if you don't, one surfaces on an inappropriate occasion. Keep your Land camera loaded, focused and ready, so that you can capture anything specially beautiful, or funny, or original. Censor and make sure the negatives don't go into the garbage if you mind other folk seeing them.

Tapes are an even better turnon – keep the best occasions and play them as background: women in particular are often wildly excited by the right reminiscence.

positions

We didn't elaborate much on these in *The Joy of Sex* because they have been an obsession of sex books throughout history. Experienced couples usually use quite a number of them, but find out by trial and error which produce good sensations and stay with those. They are, however, a part of body language in sex, and not all the experience involved in them is simply a result of a good genital fit.

The missionary position is deservedly popular: it's excellent physically, adaptable, and dramatizes intimacy.

On the other hand it is intimacy with the man as the stronger or on-top party. She may feel more or differently turned on if she plays stronger (and on top she actually is stronger, in having more control). Some people see sex from behind as animal – according to them it's bad not to look into your partner's eyes (which most people shut as orgasm approaches anyway). But being taken from behind may be like being taken blindfold: you can't see the man, it makes him a stranger, and that can be exciting; it also gives stimulation of the whole perineum. One can find it rewarding for either or both reasons. Turning the buttocks is also a primate gesture of invitation and/or submission, and that may come into the turnon too.

Quite apart from the meaning and physical efficacy of different postures for people of different shapes, good lovers sometimes try them as a sequence like dancing, not for quick orgasm or regular lovemaking but for variety. Through them they can savor the different physical emphases and the different plays which are dramatized – lover-stranger, weaker-stronger, taker-taking – as a continuous experience, in which all their skin, muscle and genital responses are explored.

Preferred position is part of body language, but don't play it back idiotically and assume, for example, that a woman who comes on top is naturally bossy. It could be the reverse, as with many games, or she may simply find she gets better physical control that way. Equally, a man who wants it from behind is not necessarily wishing he were balling another man, or undervaluing women. He may simply find that buttocks against his lower abdomen boost his response, or like it deep and half-upright. This sort of anxiety based on the real language of intercourse shouldn't be allowed to replace the older theological anxieties it supersedes. Play it the way you enjoy it, and test your further responses by occasional sessions devoted simply to variety – a language is no good unless you speak it constantly, and the psychological overtones are sources simply of extra stimulation.

It's been remarked that describing sexual positions is a bit like trying to tell someone how to put up a deck chair. We are showing a sequence (which you might not want, or be able, to do all together) with some notes on each.

skin

The skin is our largest sexual organ, and the one through which we make close-range contact with any love object, as we did with our mothers in babyhood. If it has a language it's one of tender sensuality. For this reason generations of "gray" culture have tabooed it. They couldn't wholly taboo genital sex, but at least we needn't

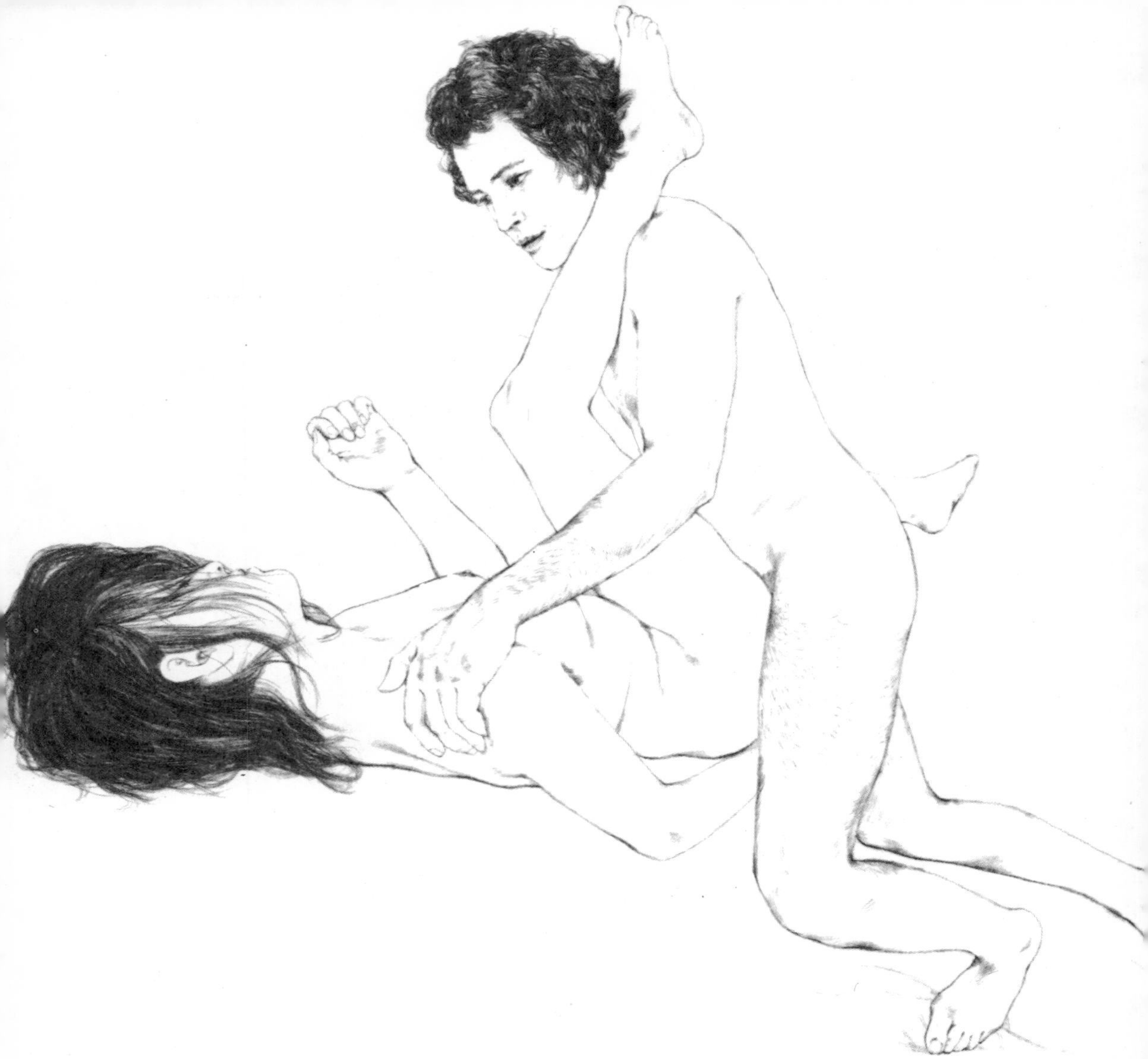

"Splitting the reed" in Indian erotology – a muscle position in which, as well as applying clitoral pressure, he is using his effort to tense her muscles by thrusting on the raised leg. From here she can easily roll over without disturbing the flow into the cuissade (half rear entry) or croupade (full rear entry) positions

admit the rest of our bodies to the operation, or we might become genuinely sensual and value trust, pleasure and touch instead of fearing them and being guilty about them. There are still people around who've had fertile sex but never touched another person's skin, or let their own be touched.

Quite apart then from lovers learning to touch one another, to enjoy skin sensation, and to turn each other on through it, there's good sense in the nude encounter setup in which you touch the skin of both sexes, to see how it feels, and let them touch yours, to see how that feels. Most cultures and all animals stylize their touching of other individuals, use it as a language, and confine it to meaningful contexts – but we've got a lot of leeway to make up. We are contact animals (which naturally touch each other rather than spacing out like many birds), and skin satisfaction is probably one of our most important infant experiences, though one on which, because of clothing, some generations have gone short.

Lovers touch each other anywhere, with fingers, skin, lips and tongue (and should devote some quiet sessions simply to this kind of exploration, enjoying the sight, feel, taste and smell of each other). Who touches whom socially is a matter of regional variation, like who kisses whom and where – cheek, forehead, hand, lips, all with different meanings. One nice thing about American women is that they aren't afraid to touch men socially; this has shifted from skin to clothing (tie straightening, for example), but is a step in the right direction and communicative not seductive. Men are intensely afraid of touching each other except in certain set situations, and most sensuality training provides the educative experience of two males feeling each other's naked skin.

It's probably best, as a turnon and for social use, to combine skin touching with some muscular stimuli such as massage (q.v.), for skin and muscle weren't programed to function separately. Don't forget that all human skin is visibly or invisibly hairy, and that the hairs can be

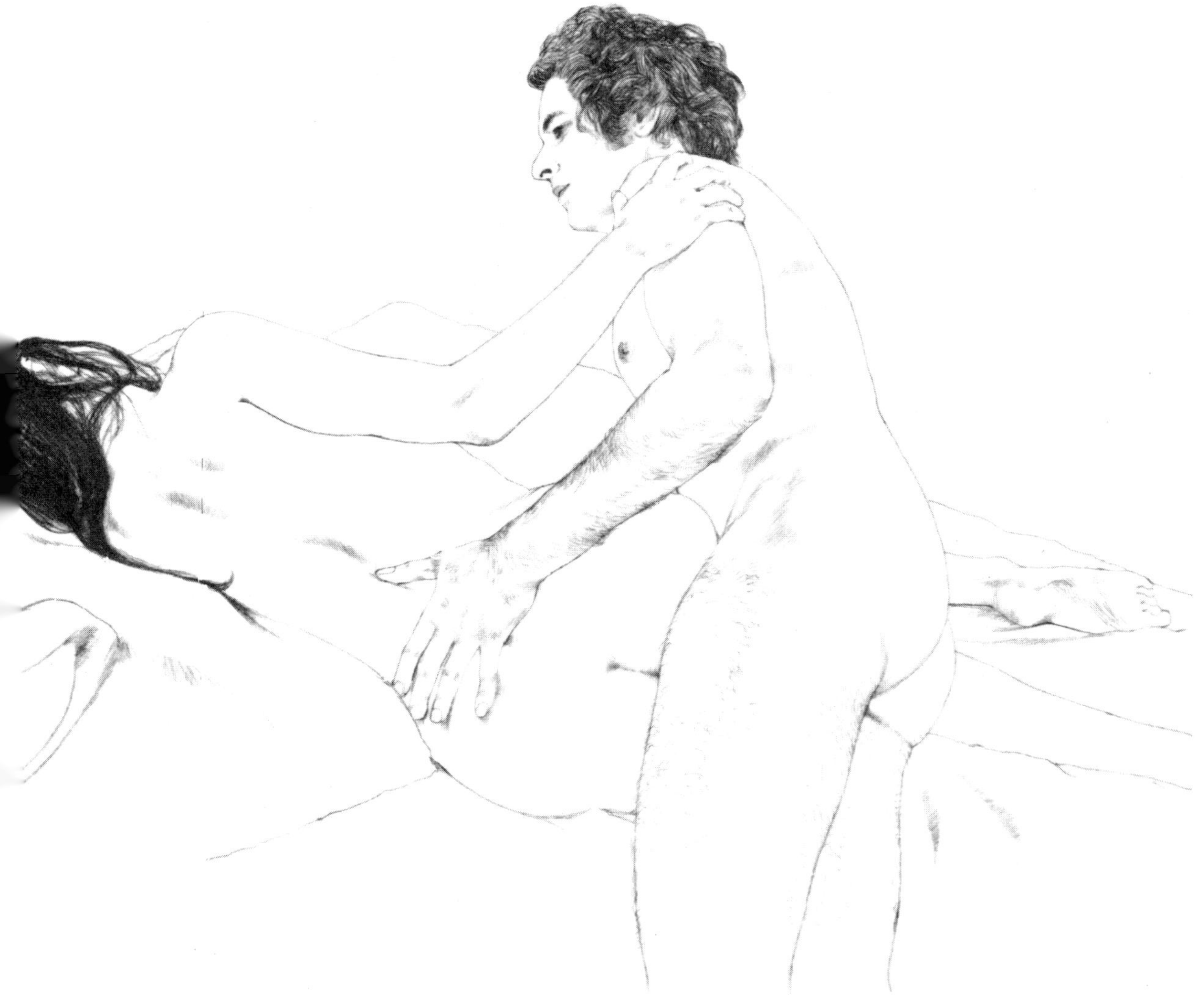

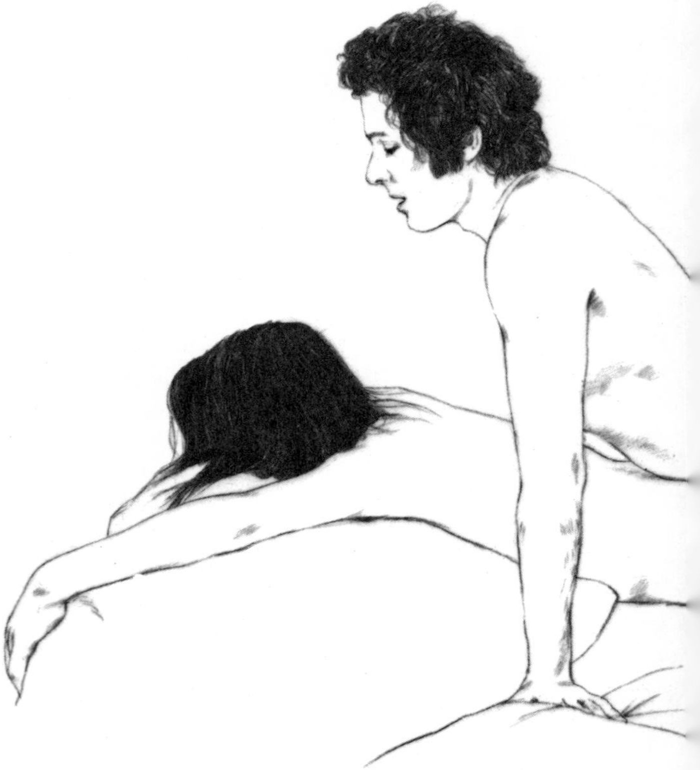

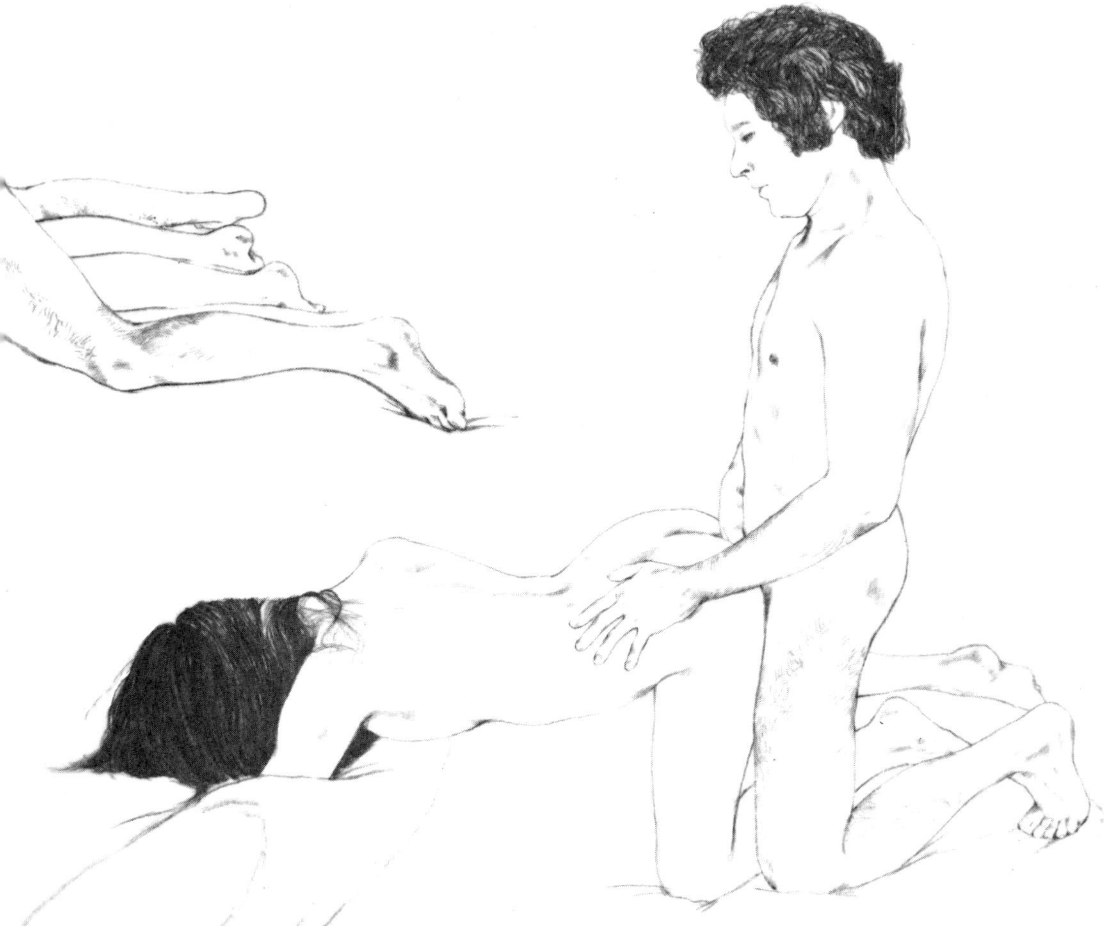

Rear entry is a whole scene. The kneeling–lying positions with the woman's hips raised give very deep penetration and contact with her whole perineum and buttocks. They are also fine for adapting different-sized partners. If he fails to get enough friction he should hold his penile skin back with one hand. Enough symbolisms to fill a book, but they are meant to be enjoyed. Rear entry also works well flat or near-flat, or you can fool around and make it acrobatic

Close astride position. He is at her breasts baby-style, and holds back his foreskin to get more friction and shallower penetration

Woman astride. She has total body and breast contact and he can caress her buttocks

Sociable, but only a good orgasm position if she has pelvic muscle control. Immensely popular in cultures which cultivate the latter – Arab and Indian in particular

When she leans back (usually as she gets toward orgasm) they get maximum visibility and muscle tension

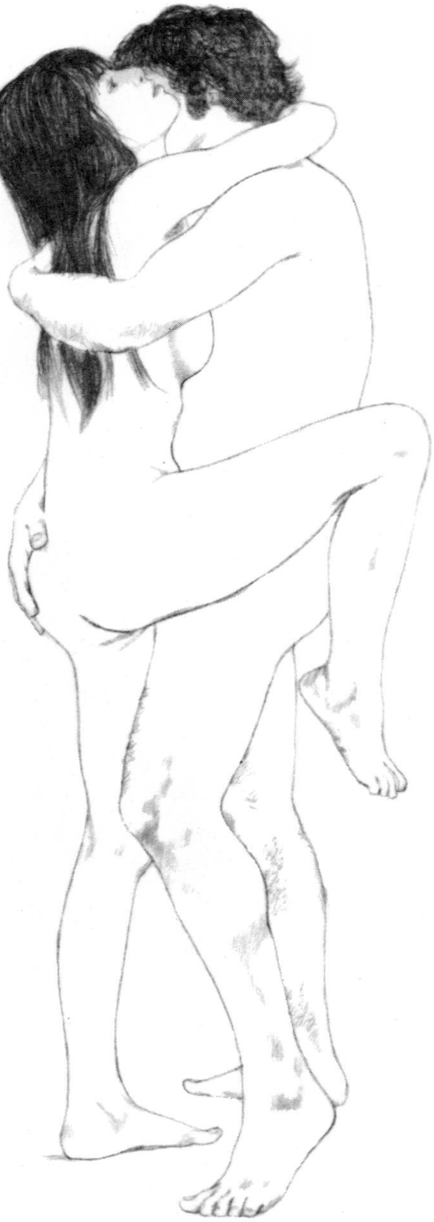

This Indian-Tantrik position is arduous, but try it if you're the right heights. Fun to do though perhaps more for meditation than orgasm

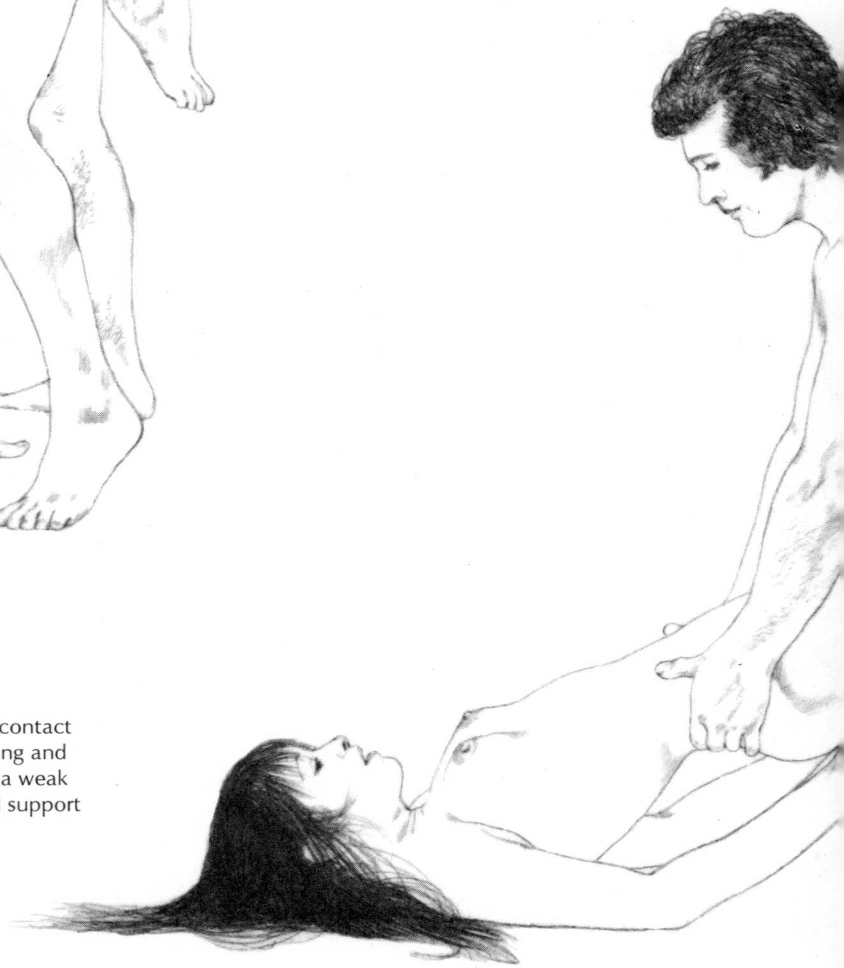

Wide open with full genital contact but shallow penetration. Tiring and not good for someone with a weak back unless he gives her full support

A rest position, reached from any ordinary rear entry simply by lying down. Her buttocks come to hand and both can make enough movement to keep erection

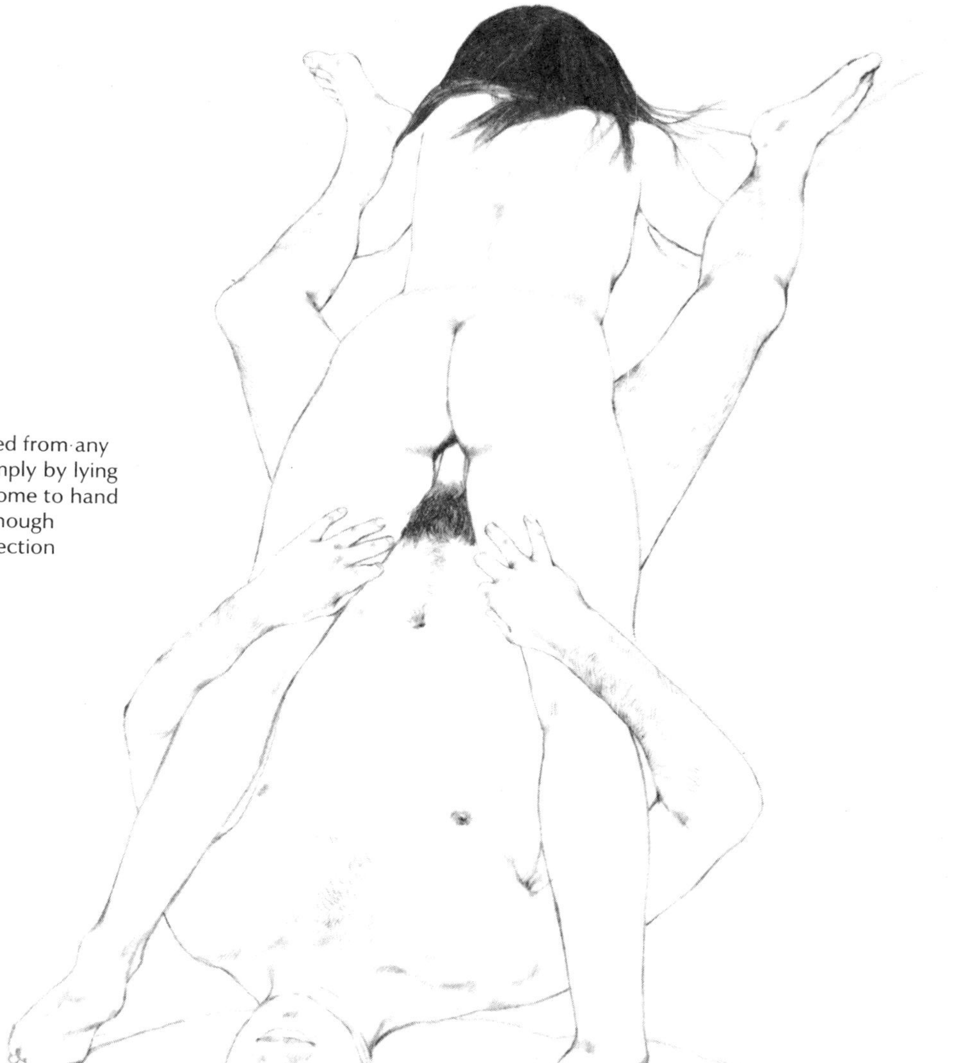

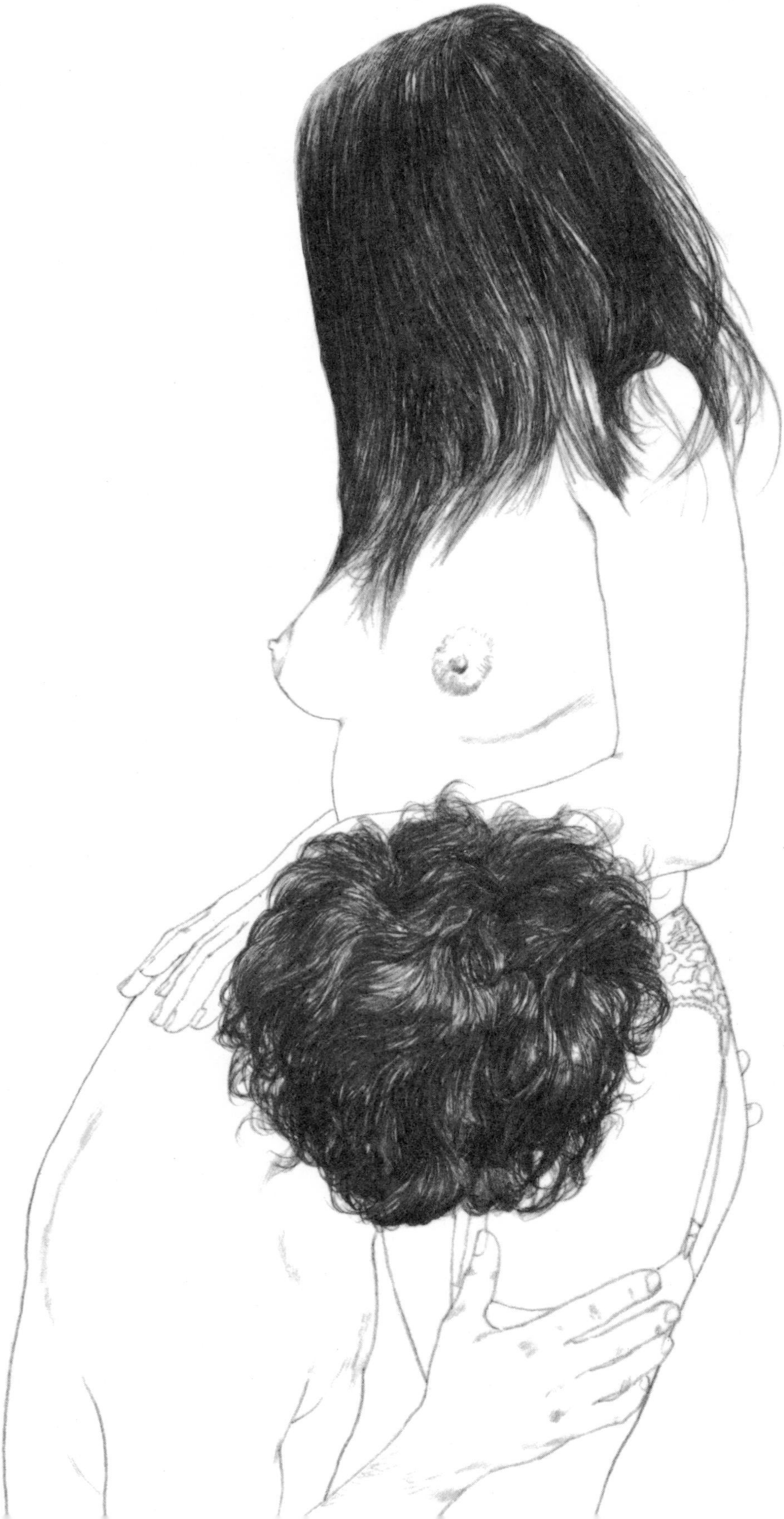

stimulated. Touching in our culture gets sexual when the lips and tongue become involved: a passing touch on the genitals doesn't say the same thing. Try being touched blindfold or eyes closed by one or several people and with different textures – feathers, cloth and so on (one group we heard of specializes in cracking an egg and pouring it on you, but this sounds like an optional extra). The point, however, is to boost your own skin awareness, and that is sensible enough. The best domestic measure is simply total nakedness in bed, though that is only a start, and not all people who sleep together naked have really developed the awareness of each other's skins. It's odd but true that you can tell from skin feel if a person's turned on, turned off, hostile, or whatever – probably from the tone of the small underlying muscles – but don't mistake being cold literally for being cold sexually, though they feel similar. You need to be warm to start this – climate and past Ice Ages may account for some human and northern hangups.

soul power

It must be the oldest human conviction and anxiety that Others (black if you're white, white if you're black) are larger, more potent and generally better at sex than you are. It would in fact be pretty odd, given the diversity of people, if all black men were better or worse at anything than all white men, except perhaps hiding on a dark night; but humans are given to idiotic racial generalizations. The old chestnut about genital size is also bunk. It probably originated from white encounters with Africans in a hot, humid climate where the resting penis isn't shrunk by cold and the intrepid explorers were clothed and couldn't see their own equipment. This sort of nonsense is insulting to both black and white.

Where black people of both sexes undoubtedly do score sexually is that Black culture has never lost its body sense as White has and isn't physically uptight. Its body language is much freer and accordingly many black people are better at sex than anxious Wasps for the same reason that they dance much better. Some degree of soul, rhythm and body sense is something we others badly need to relearn.

technique

Don't be scared of technique – "reducing sex to a matter of technique" and so forth and so on. Sex is about total body communication between affectionate people. If you concentrate wholly on technique, try to show off, or think that because your line in tongue or finger work freaked out one person it will freak out another, you're missing this: *part* of the knowhow (the most important

for tenderness) is reading the other person's responses and knowing what to do and what not to do, as well as signaling your needs to them. But if you don't know the ways in which the body can be explored – not just in theory, but how exactly – you haven't the equipment to be adaptable with.

This adaptability is one use of techniques. Most books are written as if people were morally and physically like an endless series of identical twins. In fact no two are alike. With a new partner the exploration is total, and you may be reading and meeting for the first time needs he or she didn't ever know about before. With a steady

partner, technique comes into its own, because with easier and constant communication you can devote part of your lovemaking to perfecting everything which you both enjoy – getting your manual and oral techniques absolutely right for one another, working through postures and so on.

It's not cold-blooded to do this systematically, using about half your lovemaking, and let the rest run free, declaring, say, National Rear Entry Week or National Woman on Top Week every so often, looking for sensations you've missed. Some of these won't work for you, but don't write them off until you're sure it's preference and not inexperience which makes them fail. Both of you look out intelligently for love-gifts for the other – this can include things you learn from other people, from books, or from an active erotic imagination. Don't keep switching around for its own sake, but don't let sex get routine or it can stop being exploration of each other's bodies as well as communication between them. The range of skin, muscle, genital and oral sensations appropriate to all moods and needs within a good couple is near-inexhaustible: if you did exhaust it you'd need to start over, like painting the Bay Bridge.

One justification for having a threesome or an exchange sometimes is that it freshens this sense of continuing exploration. Practice so you can do everything quickly, expertly, unclumsily and without holdups and letdowns, but (especially if you're a man) not with a touch which communicates slick routine. Given this sensitivity, only in-out sentimentalists knock technique.

Mostly they are folk who have none, with disappointed partners who've given up hoping for any.

The start of good sex is knowing what resources turn some people on and roughly why. If you have a lot of partners you need to start with this knowledge and can check it in practice. If you have one partner you can check parts of it – high skin response, high muscle erotism, whether or not they respond to oral work and so on – and concentrate accordingly. But store the other approaches. Someone who has become aware of his muscles may need to become aware of his skin for balance, and vice versa. The sex fantasies we have and volunteer represent known parts of ourselves, and a great deal of creative sex lies in exposing and developing others. So neither of you stick to known preferences except in let-go situations. Have these often, but intersperse them with deliberate experiment.

One has, in writing a book like this, to address the kind of criticism which runs: "What about the relational and affectionate aspects which make sex worthwhile and good sex possible? Why concentrate on techniques, which don't matter? You seem to reduce the whole thing to organ grinding, or a learnable skill".

True, no amount of "technique" will make a loving or a loveable partner: self-conscious and selfsatisfied "technique" will make a wholly obnoxious one, as many women in particular can testify after being treated in bed as if they were fruit-machines which pay off with an orgasm when you get three lemons in a row.

On the other hand, nobody who has done even a little practical sex-counseling will accept the notion that sexual enjoyment comes naturally to any two caring people. Society misfires. In writing this book we assume that only an idot was true, it isn't now. Accordingly, while a stinker with technique remains a stinker, caring and loving people still run aground on ignorance, anxiety, and misinformation. For them, how-to discussion is a necessity, especially if it enables them to talk to one another – about likes, dislikes and needs. This, oddly enough, is something ideally loving people find hard. Discuss "sexual performance" and you open a can of extremely anxious worms – adequacy, potency, desirability: terrifying subjects. Far better to see it in print, mark passages for the other partner to read – and, for Pete's sake, laugh about it – which will rescue the occasions when "technique" misfires. In writing this book we assume that only an idiot starts with a list of erogenous zones, fails to make a sensitive study of his or her partner, and sets out to manipulate rather than satisfy.

If you find yourself in bed with a mechanistic idiot, get rid of him or her – unless, of course, you have the capacity to educate through example.

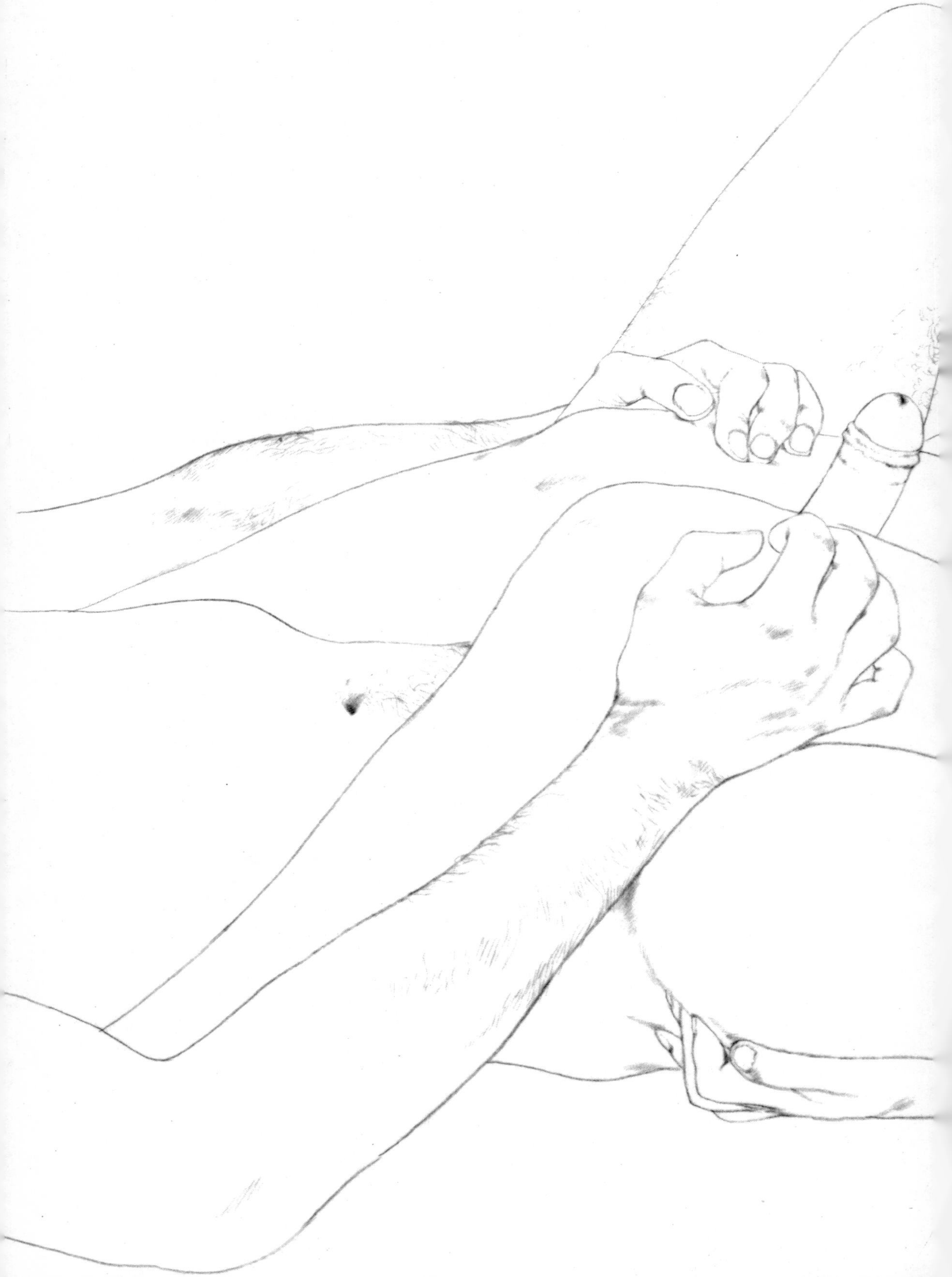

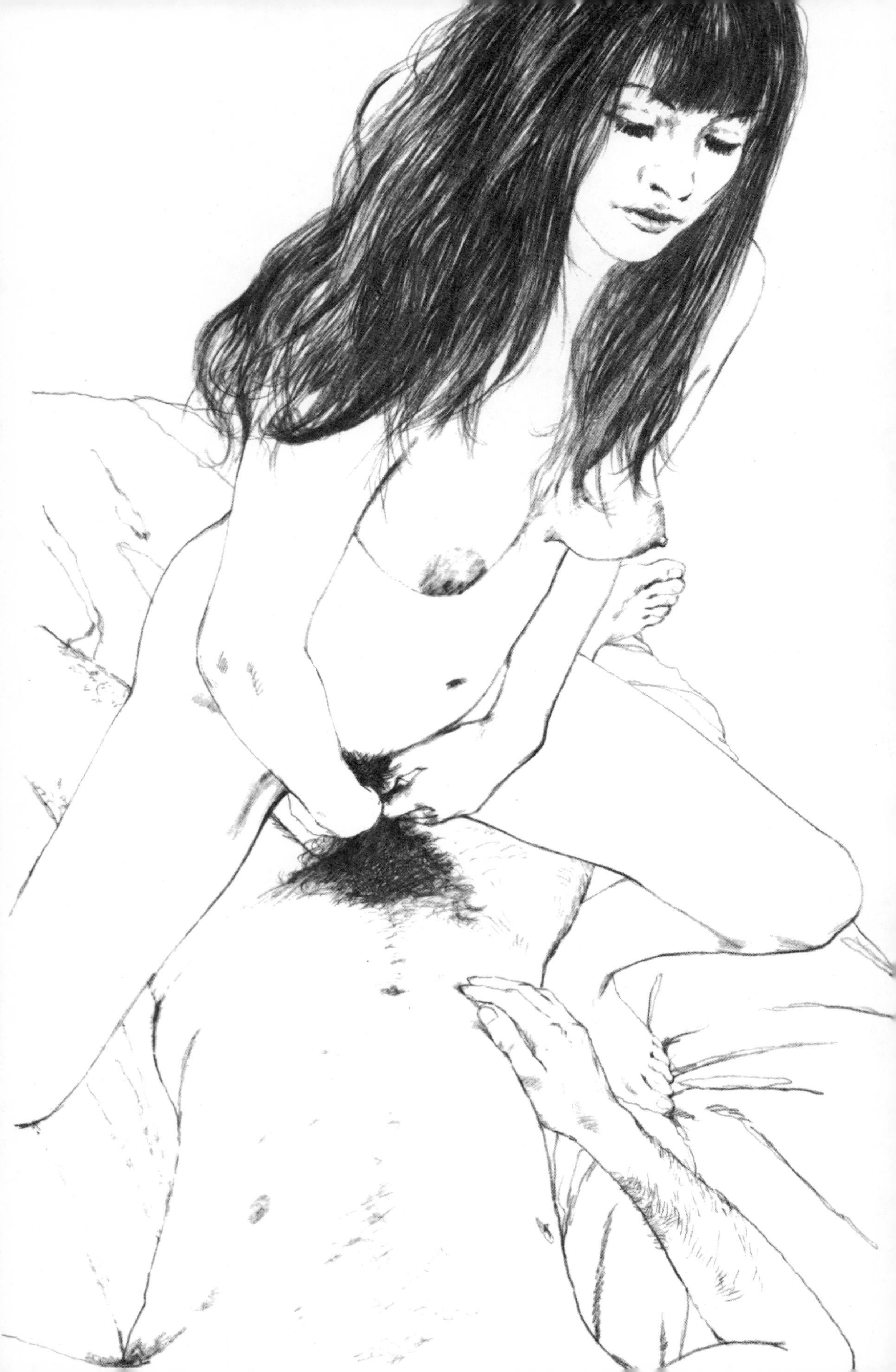

watching

Watching other people having sex is, for many couples, not only exciting but immensely instructive. (See *Sharing.*) Sex is about the only social skill we don't learn by watching: instead "gray" society has imposed ideas of modesty and privacy which imply that sex itself ought to be hidden and that other people are hostile. The result is individuals who worry if their performance, methods and tastes are normal and have had no way of checking this and no way of bettering their play by observation. You can learn more in one session by watching a few other couples than out of this whole book. If they know no more than you, you'll at least be turned on and reinforced about your abilities; if they are better at things like skin stimulation, or more creative over play, go and do likewise. Films are occasionally worth seeing, though a lot of porno directors and actors aren't enjoying themselves too much (see if the men get solid erections and the women a chest flush at orgasm – they can't fake that). But the shared scene with real people is naturally better, and you can talk as well. Some couples encourage friends to make love with them, even if they don't want to swing, simply so that they can all watch and compare styles – it's a good way to learn about sexual behavior. Most of the people who have written about sexuality never saw a couple making love – probably not even Sigmund Freud; it wasn't his scene. It's a heavy thought. How many books about football, telling you exactly how you should play it, have been written by people who never actually saw a game? It's a good question to ask any medical authority who pontificates about sex. We'd get less hogwash written.

Yes, we've watched dozens of couples, and a lot of the comment in this book is from direct observation. But don't take our word for it, try it and form your own conclusions. Watching yourself in a mirror is good but isn't the same exercise – you get no new information and no standard of comparison. Sex techniques are as varied as people – most of the nonsense in past books simply couldn't have survived even minimal direct observation. Watching and being watched is exciting, friendly and encouraging – not intrusive or embarrassing.

wrestling

Wrestling is sexually exciting. Quite a few people of both sexes are turned on by watching professionals – or the anthropoids who appear on television in Britain on Saturdays – chucking each other about. Most of us tried wrestling the other sex when we were kids: a lot of lovers enjoy wrestling. The trouble here is that in most couples it's not an equal match – in childhood one could get over this through age-difference, but the numerous males who are turned on by struggling with a woman as strong or stronger than they are may have mate-selection problems, because desirable wrestling partners don't necessarily make the best social or sexual choices on other counts. Even non-sexual struggling produces penis and nipple erection at least to half-staff in most young adults, as Classical artists knew.

If you don't mind the man winning most times, fine. No biting, scratching or kicking is a wise rule if you want to stay sexually excited and not get hurt, but this does handicap the woman. If she needs to win or he to lose sometimes, handicap him – the wrestling princess in the Arabian Nights could beat men by magic, so you agree your own magic. Or make it a numbers game – after three defeats she has the right to take him prisoner and set up her own bondage scene. (See *Muscles*.) Silly? No

more so than other kids' games: some couples simply don't relate by struggling, often because they haven't tried it. Others find loving struggle a turnon and – oddly, if you take "struggle" at its usual social value – wholly tender, a dramatization of trust as well as of complicated but quite normal needs to overpower, be overpowered, be or play at being the stronger or weaker. Kids use struggle to test their actual strength, lovers to experience feelings about strength in the relations of the sexes which they can't verbalize but which deepen their sense of identity and sharing. Being less strong than a woman is sometimes important to very strong males, and being stronger than a man on occasion lets girls try a part of the male role for size.

Never let struggling get spiteful, stop if it becomes rougher than either wants, don't do it if it seems pointless

or turns you off, but try it – sensibly – if the idea excites you. If it's working, the tender element will be enough to prevent accidents. Even real fights can end this way – see the marvelous set-to in the movie *A Touch of Class* for a very well-observed scene of this sort.

His & Hers

aggression

Most people in our culture are scared of aggression. It sounds like something which will set the United Nations dropping napalm on us, and we're indoctrinated against it, women especially. Symposia are held by medicos and welfare people on how to deal with it. In fact it's the most sloppily used word in social science, which is saying a great deal. At different times and in different mouths it means at least three things.

The first of these is hostility, the wish to clobber somebody. Clobbering people indiscriminately, either by hand or with bombs, is obviously a bad thing, but we needn't be ashamed of the purely domestic wish if it's reasonable. All lovers want to hit each other sometimes. One long-

term couple, asked if they'd ever considered divorce, replied: "Divorce never – murder frequently." This is absolutely normal.

The second meaning is assertion, wanting to make an impact on the environment – like an "aggressive" salesman or "attack" in music. One and two get mixed up not only verbally but attitudinally. Kids who feel that they are nonentities entirely surrounded by solid granite corporation offices attack people or break up property by way of making an impact quite as much as out of hostility. Pre-lib women had the problem that while men were expected, as a male performance, to be aggressive in the second sense, and often aggressive in the first sense to back it up, any attempts by women to be aggressive in the second sense were taken as aggressive in the first and put down. There is a biological relationship, of course, in that the first is often the backup when the second, which all but the most timid humans need, is frustrated.

There's also a third component related to both these – dominance. This is a zoology term for a behavior by which animal societies are quite often ordered, where some individuals defer to others more dominant, so forming a "peck order," and it generates still more verbal confusion. Basically dominance in Man means the ability to relate confidently and unanxiously to other individuals

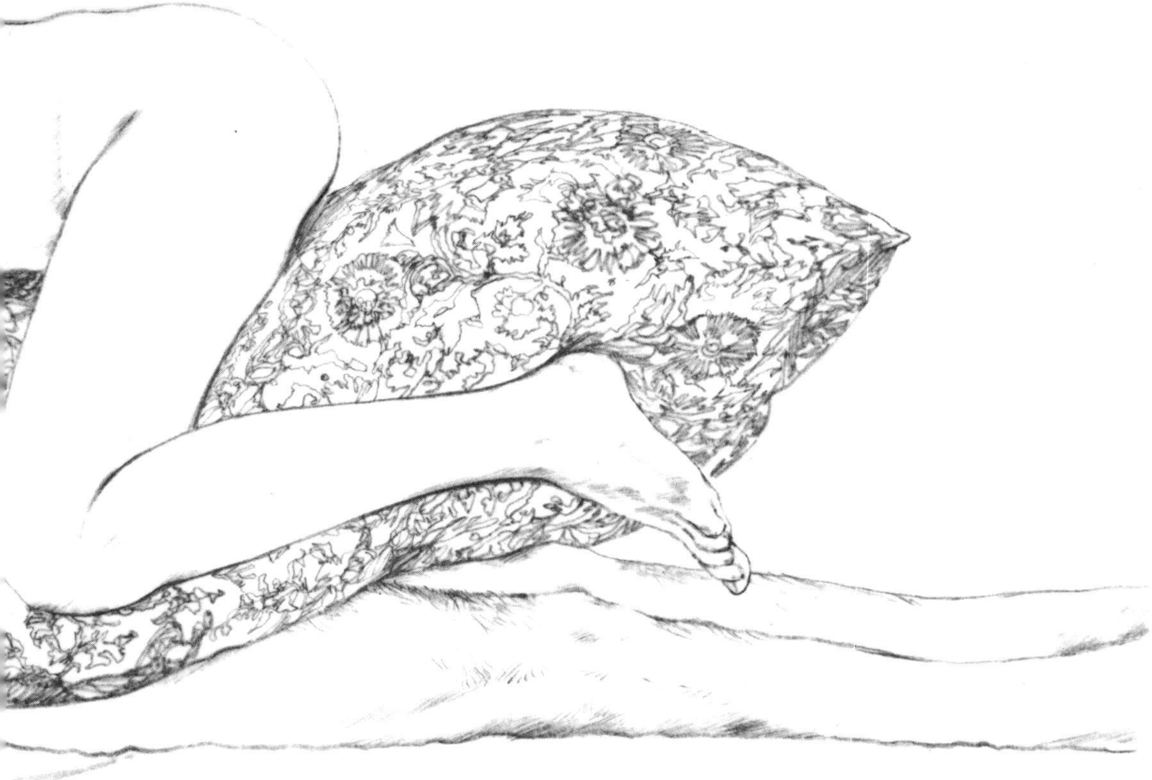

and know, intuitively and by reading nonverbal signals, what role to adopt towards them. It has absolutely nothing to do with "domination," either socially or as a sexual charade. People who have to wear jackboots and crack whips aren't relating confidently to others: they need a whole range of props in order to relate at all. The same goes when the domination is real, by way of social or domestic bluster.

One prevailing theory about aggression-hostility is that you can store it up, like garbage on a camper, and dump it at intervals. It's by no means certain that this is the case, but a lot of therapy has been based on having people take out accumulated hostility on cheap crockery, rubber dummies, or by bashing one another with pillows or batacas. Clearly a low-dominance subject (or a person in a dicey situation) who daren't show anger to a spouse or a boss may go and kick the cat, but this is less a process of storage than one of passing on one's resentment down the dominance line. Jumping up and down or smashing things are classical chimp demonstrative behaviors, and represent nonverbal expression of what we can't trust ourselves to say (for a direct view of chimp behavior, watch a footballer who just dropped a pass, and compare the expressive phrase "hopping mad"). Where dummy-bashing and bataca-fighting help is probably in teaching us not to be afraid of our own emotions.

Maslow, who studied dominance and sexuality in women, divided dominance into feeling (self-esteem) and status (being more or less strong or adequate than some other person). The only relationship between high dominance and aggression is that people with a high level of self-esteem are less blocked about expressing anger when they feel it – others keep quiet for fear of the consequences. High self-esteem in Maslow's women went with a rejection of many male-prescribed feminine performances like timidity, submissiveness, religiosity and conservatism, and with high enjoyment of genuinely feminine sex – orgasm, equal relations, experimentation. High-dominance women also had a positive attitude to sex generally, not being scared to come on top, not because they wanted the man to be underneath but because they enjoyed it that way. Where both parties had this high self-esteem, Maslow wrote, "every aspect of sex and sensuality is eagerly, enthusiastically accepted and warmly thought of . . . experiments of all kinds are made, all sexual acts are thought of as 'fun,' rather than as a serious business. Very frequently in a marriage between high-dominance people there has been experience of every form of sexual behavior known to the psychopathologist as well as the sexologist. . . . These acts [anal intercourse, homosexual contacts, oral sex, exhibitionism, group sex, etc.] have no pathological tinge nor are they pathogenic in any way. . . ." In other words, a high-dominance couple tries everything once and enjoys the lot, as fun and without fear.

Great, if you can do it, but we aren't all, and don't have to be, high-dominance people, and both halves of a couple are seldom equally self-confident, sexually or otherwise. It doesn't matter if there is a stronger party, and which is stronger in a particular situation is apt to vary. The point is that while the high-dominance person can learn to turn it down and play it tender on occasions (and would miss a whole section of sexual fulfillment if they didn't), they are the only people to get the best out of playful sex. Since a high proportion of folk are blocked in their capacity for sensuality by fears, better-not feelings, and the attempt to use love as an adhesive rather than an experience, training in reasonable assertion (aggression two) can help their sex lives, and the kind of gourmet attitude to sex which we've described can help their capacity for assertion. Very low-dominance and put-down people can react by overasserting and becoming Napoleonic bullies. Usually this shows because it also involves a lot of hostility (aggression one).

Types of sexual play are important as well. Low-dominance women regard coming out on top and other things such as digital-clitoral orgasm as "untender": they might be advised to try these things more often. Some people enjoy aggressive-looking games, either because they enjoy the try-everything self-confidence they know they have, or because it helps them to dramatize a self-confidence they haven't. A few are quite disablingly stuck with them. On the other hand, don't overdo the symbolic interpretation of turnons. For most people who enjoy struggling, bondage, simulated rape, and other non-cruel and non-dangerous "aggressions," they aren't aggressive at all, or even very symbolic, but depend quite simply on the physical kicks involved, with some references to childhood ideas of sex roles thrown in. Quite often, if they dramatize anything, it isn't aggression but trust, and overcoming the idea that the other sex is a bit dangerous.

It has been found too that women who like sadistic-looking games in which they play at dominating the male often aren't sadistic, in the correct sense of getting pleasure from hurting or humiliating someone. They are simply trying the conventional, phoney, overaggressive male role for size to see what it feels like, and to experiment at the same time with the sensation of being the stronger partner. The idea of masculinity in which he "dominates" her, by force and socially, is long out of date, but there's no harm in seeing what it would have felt like, in a secure pattern. Men who dramatize dominating women are more often trying to get over the idea that females are basically dangerous. If you have these needs, incorporate them into play and take turns – they have nothing to do with cruelty or hostility.

In any case, "being overpowered" and "being penetrated" do have a biology for women, but high-dominance women treat them as kicks and aren't frightened or devalued by them. Between self-confident people if either does any physical submitting on a given occasion it's in the interest of mutual orgasm and treated as fun, not violation, and part of a wholly equal and tender rough-and-tumble, interspersed with many much more gentle and relational passages. For them a totally unaggressive, tenderness-obsessed male who takes no initiatives without asking is a dead turnoff, as is a totally non-initiative-taking, non-penis-seizing woman. The temptation is to try to excite hostility in such a partner if you can't get any other sort of response, and needle them until they do something, even if it's only to shout.

Accordingly, "aggression" in loveplay is a good part of the human sex repertoire and only a danger-signal if it gets out of hand. As to real hostility, it's best dealt with by expressing frank anger at the time, and discussion (not nagging, sulking, no-saying or finding ways of getting even) afterward – that is, if you are adult adults.

The final attribute of low-dominance people, and perhaps, as Maslow came to think, the most important one, is insecurity. They don't express hostility or anger because they are afraid of being rejected, or that the partner will go away. Because they are using him or her as a stick to climb up, even the possibility that they might have to start on their own, that a relationship might not live happily ever after, and that they might have to be individuals is too frightening to contemplate. For these people permanence is a fetish, other people are sources of essential vitamins, and love involves possession or annexation.

This, as you will see from what we've said, makes a whole circle, because it turns relationship into a form of aggression: it is aggressive (and devaluing) to own someone, to impose rules on them, and so on. All people need other people. For high-dominance folk, love is an experience between people. If it is good they hope it will last. If it ends they will experience mourning, but not lose their self-esteem. They also tend to value experiences as they happen and not as guarantees that they will last forever: none do, if only because people are mortal. For low-dominance people love is often semiparasitic possession. Immediate joy is lost in worrying or planning ways to make sure it lasts and putting out more tentacles.

These are Maslow's "being-love" and "deficiency-love." Blake expressed it better:

> He who bends to himself a joy
> Doth the wingéd life destroy:
> He who catches joy as it flies
> Lives in eternity's sunrise.

Most of us share both the need for joy and the need for some kind of security – this is only reasonable. But it's worth pondering how love gets turned into aggression by low self-esteem people, and how high self-esteem people turn hostility into love through play. Frederick Perls put it best: "I am I and you are you, and neither of us is here to live up to the other one's expectations. But if we meet it's beautiful." Tigger was a high-dominance person, Eeyore a low-dominance person. Pooh comes between the two, on the low side.

boys

The two chief attributes of boys in our culture are that they carry a colossal load of male-expectation ideas, and that they are physically more easily excited to the point of no return than are girls. The first of these makes them extra-vulnerable to the restarting, by any kind of put-down, of childhood anxieties about being competitive and virile (girls are vulnerable to different things – though both are vulnerable to the idea of being rejected). Consequently they tend to be muscle-and-penis centered, or to make up in other ways for not being so. The knowledge that he has made it with a girl "feels different" from the girl's sensations on having made it with a boy – he has done the penetrating, she has let him in. Women's Lib may be changing this, but it's pretty basic.

The main thing about boys' responses is that girls are often unaware just how fast a really horny boy can be turned on; inconveniently fast, sometimes, if they don't know their own minds. Others end in bed because they can't believe that they are so desirable as to produce such an uncontrollable response. Quite a few cock-teasers don't intend to be so, they just don't know enough boy physiology: the sight of nice breasts and a few kisses will produce an erection in most males. If this happens and she doesn't want intercourse, she should tell him she has her period and offer an alternative. A boy can be given an orgasm by hand and if she doesn't know how, she should let him show her.

erection

Male erection can, of course, happen spontaneously, from being randy, seeing a sexy woman, a picture, etc., but it doesn't have to. Quite a lot of males at any time, most males at some times, and all males as they get older, do need direct physical stimulation of the penis to get fully hard, and will either stimulate it themselves or want their partner to do so. Worth saying because there are women who feel devalued if their man doesn't instantly erect "no hands" (and will make him flaccid for the whole session by saying so), and men who think it is somehow unmanly to ask for a rub when they need one. Both these attitudes arise from ignorance of human natural history.

The spontaneous erections which males get on waking and during periods of what is called "rapid eye movement" sleep (r.e.m.) are physiologically interesting: what sets them off is not known. The best thing to do with the morning kind is to use it there and then.

exhaustion

Something it seems almost impossible to get over to males. They get tired, and may be turned off sex by being preoccupied or anxious to a not-tonight-Josephine level, but never seem to be totally exhausted. For a start they find furious sex invigorating; and when very tired, they expect the woman to take over and rub, ride, suck or otherwise nurture them along to orgasm. But women do get genuinely exhausted, not least if, as is happening a lot in our culture, they're either expected to do two jobs, one

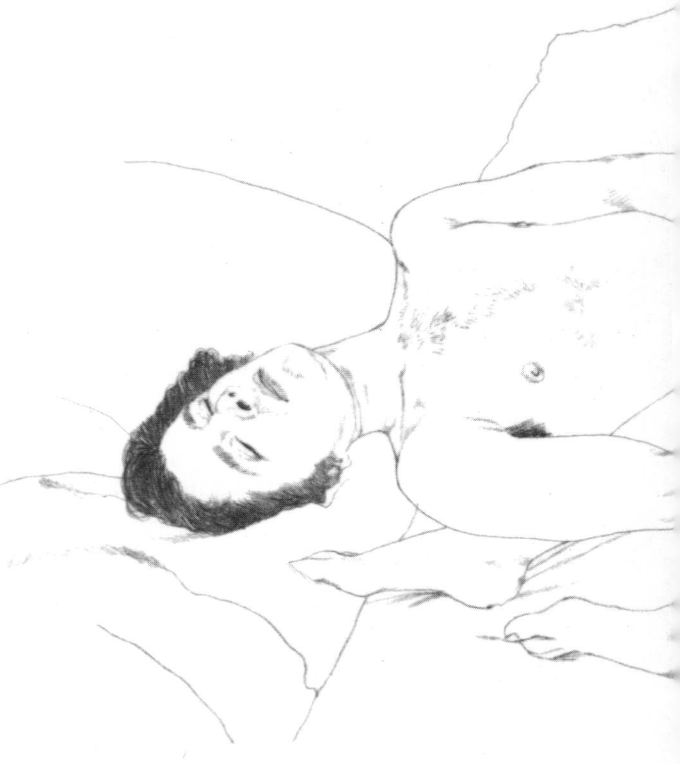

domestic and one other, or are subject to 24-hour child-demand.

Male folklore still seems to demand that the woman be at the bedroom door when he gets home, mouth open and contraceptive in place, horny as a bitch and loving with it, before leaving him to relax and getting the dinner. Afterward they make love at intervals all night and then she has to get up without waking him and fix coffee. This, it might as well be said bluntly, is not on. It may be a caricature but it's not far from the truth, and men who implicitly take the line that they do the work and all they're asking her to do is to keep the house clean and open her legs invite physical assault.

The facts are that women need sleep, and women with jobs and/or children need a lot of it. They don't respond well sexually when tired, and aren't easily able to get an orgasm then. If they do, it has a far more sedative effect than in men, and they usually need to rest and collect themselves – at which time they appreciate someone else dealing with children, getting coffee and so on, after a suitable period of togetherness. They can't convincingly

deliver any of the wilder or more active sexual performances when tired.

All of this can be dealt with by a mixture of consideration and communication, unless adjustment is economically impossible and both must work flat out to stay afloat. Even then the situation can be improved, but not if men see fatigue (which they often use themselves to give them a letout for potency anxieties) as a covert sort of rejection, and exhaustion as sexual malingering. It's great on a vacation to wake her every time you have an erection, but if she works you have to be considerate. Even a token sharing of home jobs helps to take the pardonable resentment out of the situation: real consideration with frank discussion helps a lot more.

When she's exhausted and he isn't, lovemaking can be in order, but the main part of it will be holding her and not pushing the specifically sexual part unless she seems to need it. When he's exhausted and she isn't, it might be the time for this too, or for her to be very active: play it as it comes. Exhaustion is neither ignored nor denied between really loving people.

gay or straight

If a Martian was writing a history of human idiocy, he'd start with sexual behavior, and quite probably right here. All human beings are able in some circumstances to relate sexually to members of their own sex as well as to the other. This is probably true of most other mammals (though these use homosexual-looking behaviors for special purposes). It is only odd or anomalous biologically if, like some theologians, you think that reproduction is the only function of sex: in Man and many apes it isn't – bonding, or the expression of dominance, are equally important uses of what we regard as mating.

In all societies and at all times, a certain proportion of people have related more easily, or preferentially, to their own sex and not to the other. This behavior has been differently received. In some cultures it has been simply an accepted variation which anyone might move into and out of: Spartan or Japanese warriors balled their squires on campaigns, and thereby bonded them into the warrior group; classical Athenians reckoned that men should have one kind of sexual relation with boys and another kind with women. In others, the preference made one a wizard. Our own, influenced by Jewish fears of the "unnatural" and Christian hatred of sex generally, has hanged, burned, tortured and persecuted for centuries anyone who was rash enough to express this preference in action, or even in words. We have only just quit doing this. Homosexuals overlapped with witches and heretics, excited the same fears, and got similarly treated.

After hundreds of years of idiotic persecution, it's no wonder that people aware of similar preferences today have started Gay Liberation and demanded the right to do their own thing. Of course they have a right, but the campaign is unfortunate in that it reinforces the totally erroneous idea that there are two kinds of people, straight and gay (older apologists even insisted that gay people represented a third sex). The fact is that all people are both straight and gay if they'd let themselves be; the differences of emphasis have been stamped on by society's heaviest boots so that people are forced into an either/or choice instead of the subtler range of options which are really open to them. Society hasn't bothered too much about the same classification in women, nor persecuted them about it, and in consequence they show much more of the range of normal options and aren't nearly so bothered about relating to both sexes, affectionately and physically.

Some males would call themselves emphatically gay. They prefer relating to, and having sex with, men. This doesn't mean they have a response which others haven't. It means that they don't or can't relate to women. The why of this isn't known – learning, family experience and possibly genetics and prenatal hormone exposure may all play a part, and the convention that if you're one thing you can't be the other hasn't helped. A predominantly gay male who wanted to become heterosexual (some do, if it's a bad trip for them or they feel they are missing an important range of experiences) wouldn't need help to stop being attracted by men, for this is an unused potential present in all straight men which they've trodden on under orders from society. He would need help in overcoming his nonrelation with women.

The totally normal or zero-input state for unpropagandized, unintimidated males and females would probably be like that of the Classical Athenians – they'd be bi, able to relate sexually to men and women, but having individual preferences. It's not quite as simple as that, because man-man relations don't have the same biological functions as man-woman relations. People who insisted on treating contented homosexuals instead of torturing them to make their "abnormal" behavior "normal" were actually trying to make their behavior fashionable. But the repertoire of man-man responses, which obviously aren't connected with reproduction, are connected with dominance and with bonding: situations like the bonding between David and Jonathan can get sexual play added on because humans sexualize nearly everything. This looks odd to us, because in our panic over the supposed unmanliness of being gay we've suppressed all tenderness between males. A David and Jonathan who were affec-

tionate in the way our culture outlaws, but some others don't, would naturally use some companionate sex play to express it. (If you bridle at males being allowed to be mutually affectionate, stop and ask yourself why.)

Society being what it is, and our upbringing being what it has been, it's probably not a good idea for straight males (or bisexually aware males who have a settled heterosexual pattern) to rush out and realize all their bisexual potentials, simply because they might, unless they're very hardy, find it disturbing themselves and they would excite the hostility of disturbed people. One can't change one's culture overnight. They could however look at those potentials and notice the taboos on male-male affection they've been living by. People of either sex who

are aware of their gay side, especially if they're adolescent, should be careful not to be hocused by society and by gay solidarity into taking a position, closing all other options, and settling to be gay for life. Apart from anything else, young people of both sexes often go through a normal period of relating better sexually to their own than to the other sex. If you settle to be gay you're foreclosing on options like reproduction, marriage and straight sexual experience, which are rewarding unless you really don't or can't use them; you're also buying a continuing underhand hassle from "garbage" people generally. It's quite possible to have both kinds of experience, and a bad thing to be totally blocked for either, especially for the sake of a name. You don't have to line

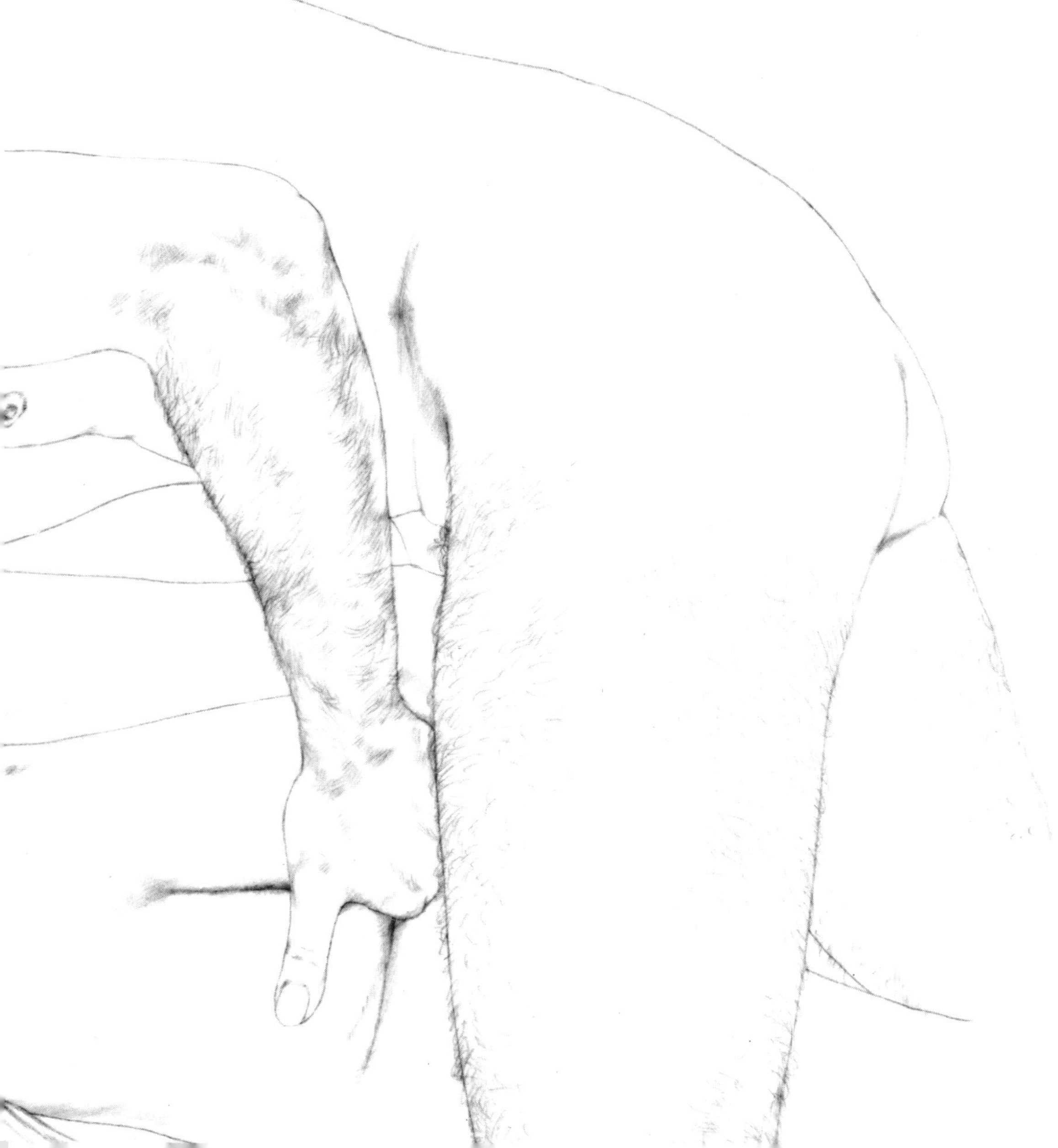

up with either battalion – the flags are phoney anyhow.

In ordinary sex relations the sanest rules seem to be: don't upset a good and stable pattern when you've got it simply to realize a potential that hasn't mattered to you before; and don't be scared or upset in group scenes if you find yourself responding sexually to someone of your own sex. The latter is wholly normal and won't alter your existing pattern, only discharge some needs you hadn't realized (but don't equally do anything which will upset you or your partners after the excitement subsides). If you've got real needs, face them.

We didn't include gay sex in *The Joy of Sex*. Males use mutual hand and oral work and sometimes anal intercourse, now ruled out by the risk of AIDS.

Women use manual, oral and breast work, embracing, and sometimes mutual genital friction. The techniques are the same as in man-woman relations and so are the extras, but a same-sex partner often has a better idea of his or her partner's physiology and uses it very effectively, a thing people with gay experience sometimes miss in straight relationships. If you want your other-sex responses boosted for any reason, behavior therapy can help – but that is learning a new skill, not treating a disease. The whole range of human sex responses is normal and healthy: a less hungup generation will probably use more of it without being anxious.

giving head

Genital kisses are only a problem because they have become a male expectation and some otherwise sexy women are genuinely put off, not by doing it, but by the idea. One gets "he expects it, I find it really difficult – do women really enjoy it or is that male propaganda?" They do indeed enjoy it, not only for their partner's response, but for the sensual part of the experience – the texture of the penis, the sensuality of their own mouths, and often the ejaculation – which mixes up babyhood with a particular adult intimacy and a feeling of receiving. All of which is hardly surprising, in that it's a universal mammalian caress (so much for it being unnatural) and the male probably has an odor pheromone to turn on the female.

On the other hand, all heavy expectation is a bad thing and leads to rejection feelings if what turns one partner on turns the other partner off. Often the distaste hangup is boosted by lack of reciprocity: he wants her to give head, but won't do it himself, and is basically as distaste-concerned as she is, though he often won't admit this and gives some other reason. Really there shouldn't be pressure on anyone to adopt any form of sex behavior – only encouragement not to miss good ones.

Oral sex has come from bad magic to an obligatory sign of sexual turned-on-ness in ten years flat. All the same there are still some clown-made state laws which constitute it a felony. (It's hard to imagine sane legislators

sitting down and seriously prescribing which part of your man or woman you may kiss.) The genitals have only just stopped being "dirty" on the sayso of generations of parents, nursemaids and schoolteachers, so it isn't surprising if some people still have problems. In people who don't wash, including some of both sexes, they are

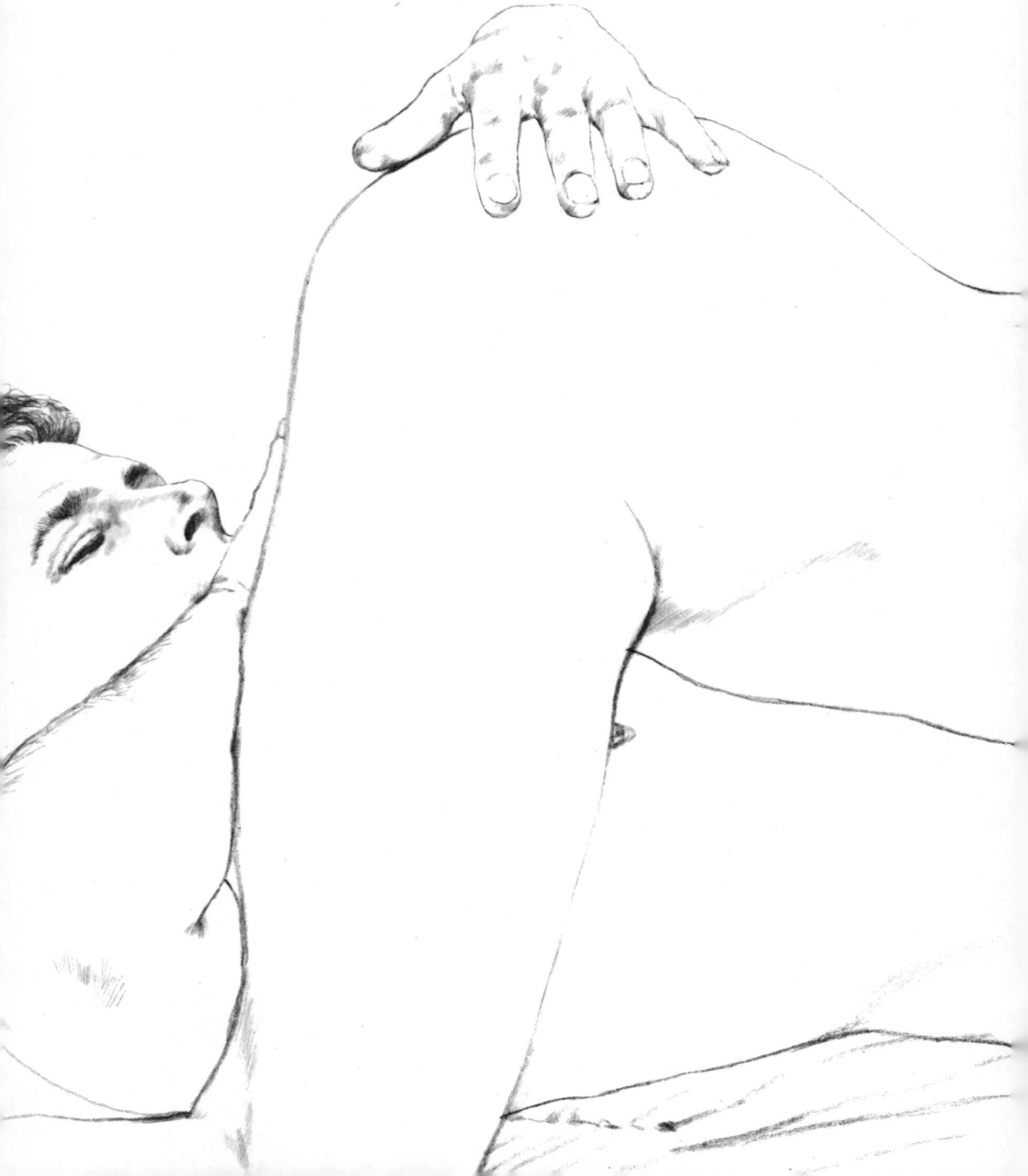

dirty, and are distasteful to kiss, like the mouths of folk who don't attend to their teeth.

Good oral sex isn't only a supreme love-gift to a partner but a potential turnon to the giver, and it is one of the sex experiences which it would be a pity to miss unless it really turns you off. Getting rid of any needless hangup isn't helped if you read hung-up psychiatrists who suggest that it's humiliating and really appeals to masochists (they say the same about women who like intercourse from behind). It's worth overcoming that prejudice. Make him wash if he doesn't. There really isn't much difference, except in the mind, between operating on a clean penis and on a thumb, so practice on a thumb. It helps to get it mutual – say "my turn now" and push his head in the right direction. But don't run any part of your

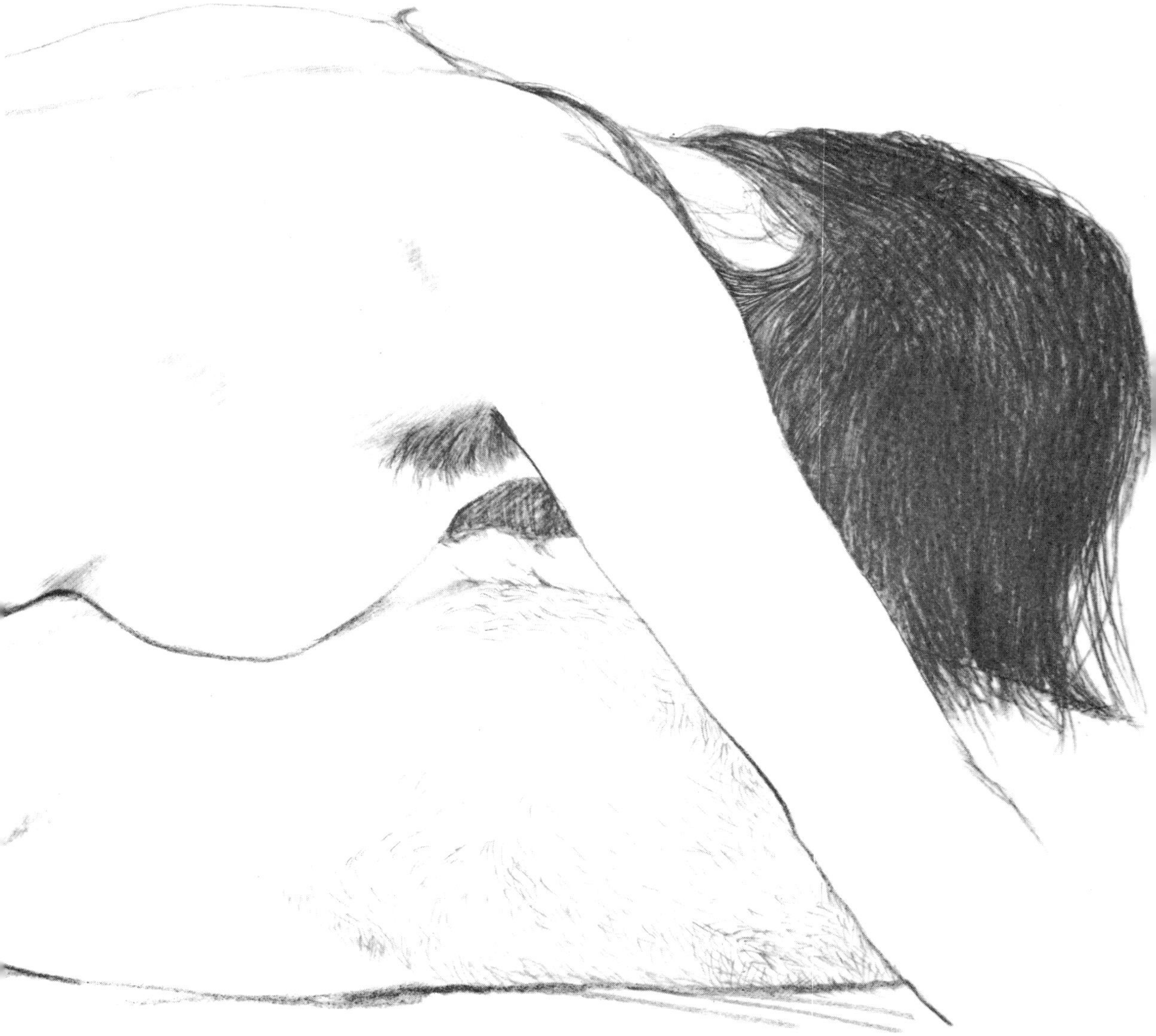

sex on a basis of "if you won't, I won't." If it's the ejaculation part which you dislike, skip that. And remember, if you have been turned off this and you suddenly do it unasked, the response is likely to be well worth the effort. It might never be your favorite sex play, but a penis is one of the world's two best playthings. Most women who give good head do it because they find it intensely enjoyable themselves, not because a demanding or insensitive man lays it on them. It's also a situation in which they have total control, not a kind of household chore.

Another consequence of male expectation is that some males expect oral sex to be the ultimate. If they don't reach orgasm with it they may say you don't know how to do it. In fact, over a quarter of males can't regularly be brought to orgasm in this way without added hand work, however skilled the operator: this includes many who have frequent sex of other kinds and simply need more friction than the tongue and lips can provide. It's worth knowing this.

As to the male side, the only reason good muff-diving hasn't become an overt female expectation leading to identical male hangups is that women have kept unreasonably quiet about their needs for fear of a bad reception. All women who have ever experienced good genital kisses will come to expect them, many who haven't would like them, and reading and franker discussion about sex will equalize the situation in which males have done the demanding until recently. There's been even more ignorant support from psychological literature here for the idea that kissing a woman's vulva is an act of submission and so on. In a good scene all genital kisses are totally mutual. She should wash (fruit essence and other muck isn't a help), but beyond that any distaste problems are in the mind and shouldn't outlive a single trial.

The clean genital odor of both sexes is a built-in stimulus. If it is distasteful, something is wrong. She should ask when she wants it – with some males it's no good waiting for initiatives. He should be prepared, moreover, to develop a lot of technique. It's no good working for five minutes and then saying "It's my turn now." Unlike men, some women can take a full half-hour, with intercourse afterward. As these are some of the most rewarding things in sex, for both sexes, it's well worth both of you making yourselves virtuoso performers.

his and hers

There are plainly biological differences between men and women – if there weren't there wouldn't be this book – but beyond the really obvious ones, the most striking thing is that among the real and the supposed behaviors and aptitudes which our culture rates as male or female, it's virtually impossible to tell which are built in and which aren't. Women might really be biologically better at intuition (meaning the ability to read nonverbal signs) or they might just have been expected to be so socially and acquired the skill. There might be a built-in reason for the predominance of male composers and painters, or it might be similar to the predominance of non-Eskimos in Congress. Even if you start arguing that men have masterpieces because women have babies, and prefer having them, you also start with a set of assumptions laid on women by a society which told them to prefer babies. Now babies aren't compulsory, more women will get time and opportunity to compete – Bach didn't have to blow the noses of his tribe of children, and the only organ Mrs Bach can have had time for was her husband's.

Almost all the subtler differences in actual response between men and women in our society are of this "probably learned" kind. In fact, we know from children brought up in the wrong sex that sex roles, and even biological-looking things like activity and choice of aggressive or non-aggressive play, are about 80 per cent learned, though hormone levels can and do affect behaviors in male and female directions. The social override in man is absolutely enormous.

We learn, therefore, to be masculine or feminine according to the rules laid down by society. As those rules change, so will the expectation that is imposed on a child as it learns its sex role. Our kids may be learning that the roles of the sexes in society are similar, and so grow up like racehorses – where the sexes look much alike and the odds on a horse and a mare are about equal. It ought to be obvious from this that there are no set human sex roles – each period forms and transmits its own. Women may be expected to scream and faint or to land with airborne troops, men to dominate women and treat them as slaves or to defer to them totally. It depends when you lived and where (though at any time there would have been people of either sex who welcomed their role or detested it). On the whole the gentle and sexuality-centered societies have struck a more reasonable balance based on affectionate equality with some variety.

We don't want here to go much into the social aspects of male and female equality because it's been widely discussed. The biological differences do remain, and are interesting. The first and most obvious is that the male gets an erection, whereas the woman lets him in. This can affect, and has affected, the attitudes of both (see *Penetration, Performance*), but it does so a great deal more in the traditional male-chauvinist setup than between people who have a different, less polarized attitude, and have learned to make love with their whole bodies. How much we build on top of a biological fact depends on how strongly we feel – and are hung up – about it.

Second, women can bear and suckle children and men can't. Moreover men aren't programed to nurture very young babies, because they lack the subcutaneous fat which provides the appropriate body texture, and this probably matters more than having or not having milk. It's also possible that they don't smell right. Our culture has bypassed some of this in that neither sex nurtures babies much when naked, though, from what we know of ape biology, it might be better if they did. It may also once have been important that a woman didn't have a beard which would conceal her facial expression.

A much more important fact is that today women "can" have babies: not so long ago it was a "must." Now that motherhood is a matter of total choice, sex can be recreational, not reproductive, at will. This is the greatest single factor in making the needs and experience of men and women more alike and more equal. Compulsory pregnancy – the sanction behind most of the other putdowns – is the main thing women have been liberated from. "Unfulfilled biological drives toward motherhood" which go beyond liking children and wanting to have one usually represent, like Kant's categorical imperatives, something the person learned before they were five, and are due to what mother said or did, not to hormones or Jungian fairies.

Thirdly, women's hormonal patterns are cyclical and men's aren't. Apart from the fact that magic about menstruation has been a prime source of female putdowns since the Stone Age, this is important, because the hormone cycle measurably affects intellectual and physical performance and mood, as athletes and examination candidates know to their cost. Most suicides and impulsive crimes among women occur in the few days preceding a period – in men, they're spread regardless of time – but though cyclical things like epilepsy, migraine and depression often synchronize with the cycle, they aren't necessarily commoner than in males. At the same time we're going, if it becomes safely feasible, to see calls for menstrual suppression. This is sometimes done now even though it still looks a little risky.

Whether there are attitudinal differences, apart from those arising from having or not having these experiences, or aptitude differences apart from the roles men and women have learned to expect, we simply can't know

until both sexes start with more similar social roles, if then. If there are, they're probably complementary.

Between lovers, the differences which matter are the muscle difference and the texture difference – the texture of each sex delights the other, and here the reproductive-maternal echo is real and valuable. She has a nurturing surface and breasts, and she smells feminine – all men had mothers, and this is a delight. He has a texture different from her own, he is often strong enough to pick her up, and all women had fathers. Harmless, semi-seductive play with a father in infancy is known to be about the best guarantee that a woman will respond fully to men when adult, and a lot of that is in the prefiguring of male contact. It can also generate turnoffs if the reminiscence is wrong. Exploring these reactions before going on to the equally fascinating visual and tactile exploration of each other's genitals is one of the best parts of the interaction of man and woman.

mess

Two competing truths here: proper enjoyment of sex involves getting over the idea that the genitals, the secretions involved and the entire business – including the human body as a whole – are messy, dirty, unworthy or repugnant in any way. At the same time, sex is messy at a practical level and in our culture women, however liberated, have often in the past had to clean up, and frequently still do. Semen isn't filthy, but it's hard to get out of furnishings, or out of one's hair, and however good sex may be it's a comedown to wake up lying in a pool or to catch your man wiping his hands or his penis on your clean covers when you have put out a towel. Some feminine fastidiousness is pretty practical.

Split the problem, and make sensuality exercises practical too. Menstrual intercourse is fine, but have it somewhere that doesn't stain, like the shower. For other purposes make a sensible use of towels, but don't thrust one into the hands of a partner who has just had an orgasm, or wipe off semen so precipitately that it looks like rejection – strike a balance. In some situations, such as slow masturbation of the male, semen is bound to go all over the place (he may look as if he'll never stop ejaculating) and the waterworks are part of the woman's turnon. Here it's better to clean up afterward than try to slam a cloth over him and lose the last spurt. You could put a condom on him if it's essential to leave no traces, but you'll miss a part of the fun.

If you have to choose, it's more important not to entertain ideas that sex and any attendant stains are "dirty." But if the practical aspects become a putdown, use the same ingenuity you'd use in a motel where you don't want to be surcharged or embarrassed. Have drip-dry sheets on the sexual bed, and put a non-crackling plastic layer over the mattress (motels do this, and not for fear of enuretics). Pick semen-proof sexual furniture (so you don't have to break off and find something to put over a chair). How far you furnish your house, or a part of it, around sexual realities is a measure of how far you've come – and how often.

penetration

There is something basic in the fact that she has to let him in – not only on to her territory or into proximity, but actually into her body. There aren't many identifiable, built-in male-female differences, but this is one of them and it does affect feminine thinking. Sex is external to a man, located in an offshore peninsula like the State of Florida, and he puts forth; it's internal to a woman – a visit or an invasion – and she has something external left with her. This doesn't mean that women unconsciously see all intercourse as a violation; the fact of having the man inside can be warm, good and reinforcing as nothing else, but he's still what the lawyers call an invitee.

These emotions are complicated, and men wouldn't easily intuit them. Positive and negative feelings about being penetrated play quite a part in patterning women's actual response, and some rather enragé Women's Libbers have suggested that every man should himself be penetrated at least once to see what it feels like. We doubt that this would work fully – anal penetration isn't really programed and doesn't feel the same.

One spinoff is that women tend far more than men to regard the place they live as a body surrogate while men regard theirs as a territory. A woman who hates letting people into her apartment is saying something – so is the woman who says, "He should be happy with me, Doctor – I've made him a lovely home with wall-to-wall carpeting." She's really talking about her body.

Being deeply penetrated by a man you love and trust, who treats you as an equal and loves you back, is about the best of all feminine experiences – it marks the end of any anxieties about who is entering whom. At that point the penis is joint property and a lot of infantile fears get resolved.

performance

Another man-woman basic is that while she, at worst, can lie back and let sex happen, he needs a positive physiological response – erection. Given all the other male feelings of anxiety, which arise from the fact that the penis isn't only for balling, but is also a dominance signal like antlers, it's almost impossible for the man not

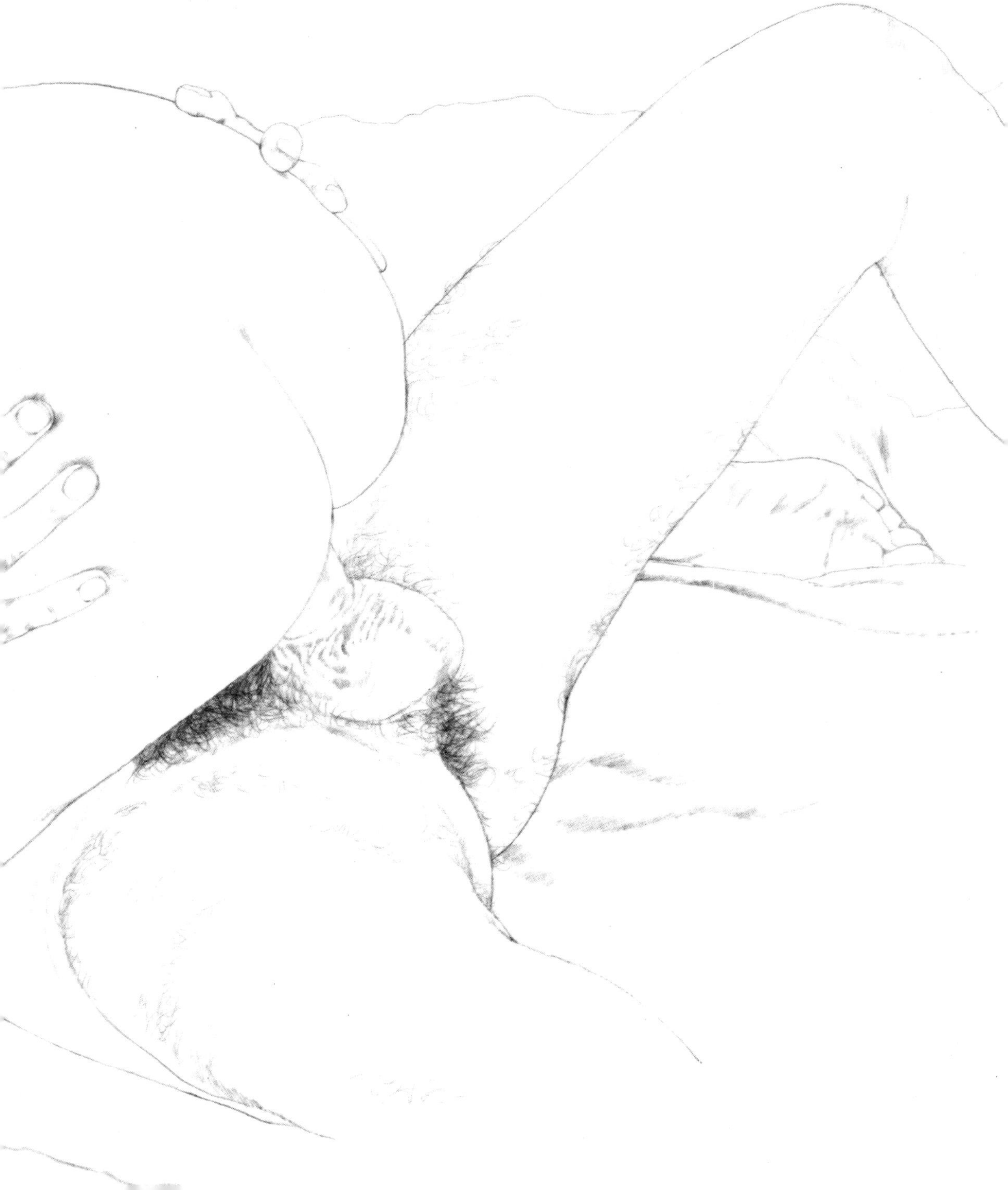

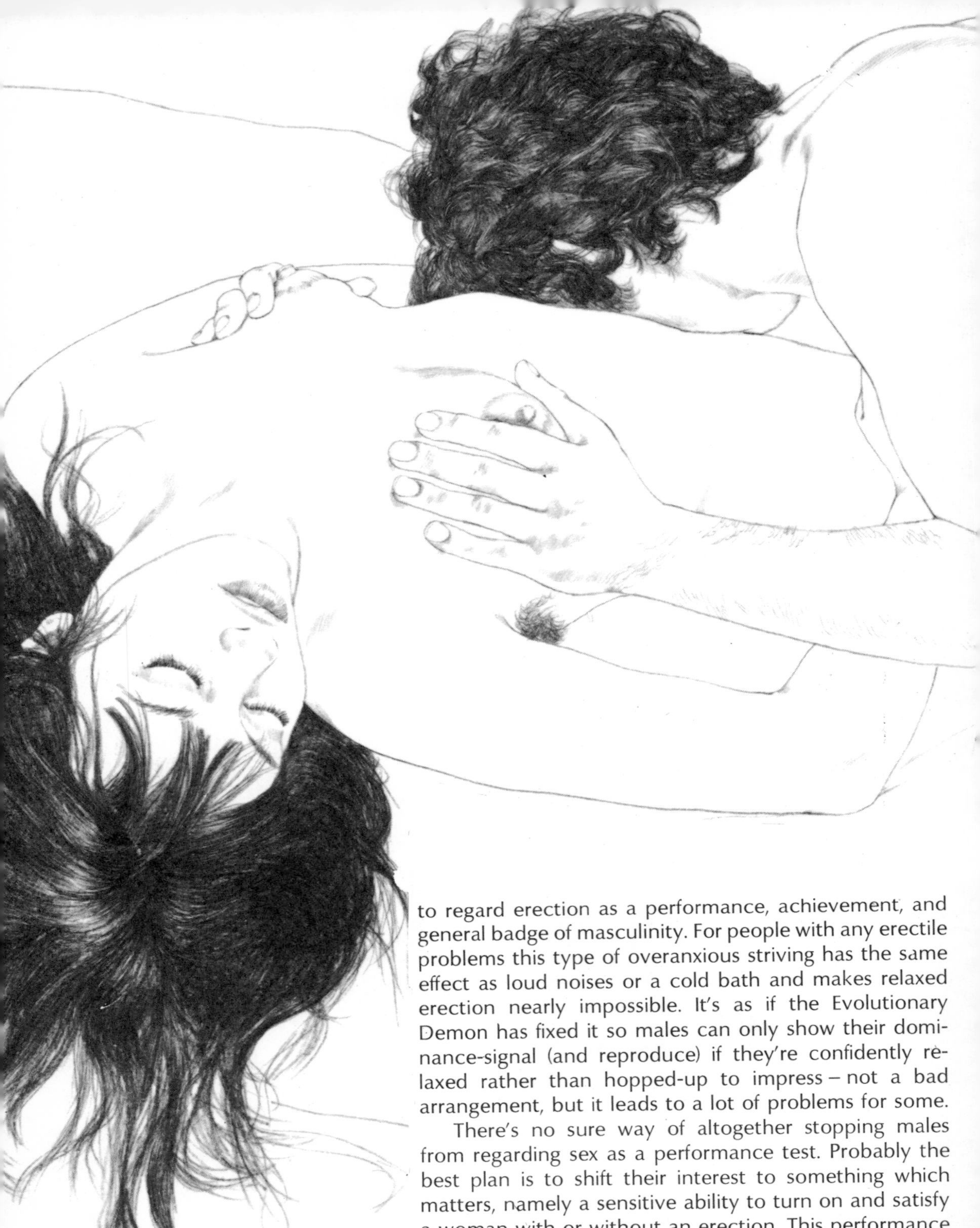

to regard erection as a performance, achievement, and general badge of masculinity. For people with any erectile problems this type of overanxious striving has the same effect as loud noises or a cold bath and makes relaxed erection nearly impossible. It's as if the Evolutionary Demon has fixed it so males can only show their dominance-signal (and reproduce) if they're confidently relaxed rather than hopped-up to impress – not a bad arrangement, but it leads to a lot of problems for some.

There's no sure way of altogether stopping males from regarding sex as a performance test. Probably the best plan is to shift their interest to something which matters, namely a sensitive ability to turn on and satisfy a woman with or without an erection. This performance is well worthwhile, and by taking off the heat it usually improves erection anxieties.

plenty of time

The one thing nobody realizes when they are adolescents is that there *is* plenty of time, and adults should point this out if they can – not that adolescents should turn

down sensible opportunities for sexual experience just to please adults or to conform to adult expectations. At the same time the boy of 16 who listens to boys of his own and higher ages bragging about the girls they've had, or the girl whose classmates boast about dates, isn't irretrievably on the shelf, though it certainly feels that way at the time. The best advice if others are really scoring more social successes is: "Notice how they do it and why you don't. It's often because they have more confidence, which comes with age, and maybe they took the trouble to acquire social skills, like dancing."

Some of the worst confidence binds are appearance-centered – spottiness or overweight – and these, too, often cure themselves between 16 and 17. If they don't, they can be tackled, sensibly, later: the main thing is to see they don't damage sexual and personal self-esteem during important years and make a youngster over-shy or wildly promiscuous in an attempt to catch up. Note that the spottiest, fattest or plainest adults of both sexes acquire mates (tell them to look around at your dinner guests – they didn't all get like that in middle age).

Body anxieties are quite the most crippling sexual disabilities – in fact there's no body configuration which can't be offset by social skills like vivacity, humor and considerateness. These, however, need learning. Everyone is gauche at 16 and if your child spends time worrying about being left out he/she won't acquire them. It's unfortunate that all but the lucky among us meet most putdowns from equally callow classmates when we're least equipped to laugh them off. Learning to address the other sex as people (without showing off or being in a cold sweat, and above all without hurrying for fear someone more confident gets there first) is the most important

skill. Adolescents shouldn't copy he-man or sex-siren approaches from classmates, who are probably quite as uptight inside as they are. In fact, they should realize that everyone feels insecure however studlike or beautiful or popular they are. Nobody tries to learn to ski in three weeks flat and love is a more complicated skill than skiing.

saying no

It's a by-product of the work that educators have done in the last few years to kill off hogwash-based notions of the dangerousness, guiltiness and unworthiness of sex that some people go to the other extreme and reverse their former anxieties. They worry that they aren't getting satisfaction when often they are, and they get guilty about saying no.

Between a couple who have regular sex it's just about the best test of the spontaneity of their relationship that either can say no when for some reason they don't really feel like sex, without anyone feeling guilty, rejected or being ostentatiously resigned. Women who are tired (see *Exhaustion*) and men who are preoccupied often agree to try and then resent it, or say no and then feel guilty. If someone says no all the time, of course, there's something wrong and you should investigate. But in a good couple either can do so when they mean no, and should agree to play it this way.

For singles, often young girls, it's a question of not being blackmailed or overpersuaded. The letter-column answer "if he wants to lay you, dear, he doesn't really love and respect you" is bunk. On the other hand, all normal men tend to want sex, at least in fantasy, with any woman they get close to, and this is even truer of boys who urgently need to prove their manhood and desirability. Girls need to feel desirable too, and there are complex emotions about not being rejected, not being left out, and so on. Routine yes-saying, however, isn't more rational than compulsive no-saying; it can lead to still more rejection if you use your body as a love-gift to lay an obligation on someone, and it's idiocy if you aren't 100 per cent baby-proof. The time to say yes is when you are fond of each other and both will enjoy it without strings or ensuing obligations. It's also better not to say yes out of sympathy. Agreeing to say yes on other terms, and especially to avoid loneliness, only works if you are strong-minded enough not to be disappointed if sex doesn't prove to be a contact adhesive and sustain the relationship.

It isn't only teenagers who need to learn to say no. One of the most valuable lessons learned by the women who went to Sandstone (q.v.) was precisely this.

security

It's part of psychiatric folklore that security acts as a releaser in women. This is by no means always true: there are quite a few women for whom danger or excitement are releasers – like the wife in *Une Femme Mariée* hugging herself in the taxi on the way to her lover each time she passed a Dangerous Corner sign. At the same time it's part true. In a recent study by Dr. Fisher a sense of security had a higher correlation with orgasm than any other sexual circumstance. What is probably true is that while insecurity is a turnoff in both sexes, society has laid socially secure partnership extra heavily on women as a prerequisite for enjoying sex. The things which make men insecure, on the other hand, except sexual nonperformance, don't enter the bedroom. Very dominant and self-esteeming women don't feel this so much, but most of them need either the stability of the relationship or a stable setup as background. Loss of the fear of pregnancy, which would be a sound biological background for a security need, might alter this.

Finally, for some people security lies not at the social level but simply in being at ease with the partner they have on that occasion, and the rightness or wrongness of their communication. For Maslow's findings on this, see *Aggression*.

selfishness

Some people might think that this is a prosperous middle-class book, meant to help prosperous middle-class white people experiment with sensuality, purely personal experiences and kicks in a world that is rapidly going to hell on wheels.

Quite the reverse is the case. Of course good sexual experiences are easier to achieve for prosperous people who have privacy, contraception, leisure and control over their lives. So is good medical care. But at the same time, acquiring the awareness and the attitudes which can come from this experience doesn't make for selfish withdrawal: it's more inclined to radicalize people.

The antisexualism of authoritarian societies and the people who run them doesn't spring from conviction (they themselves have sex), but from the vague perception that freedom here might lead to a liking for freedom elsewhere. People who have erotized their experience of themselves and the world are, on the one hand, inconveniently unwarlike – they'd rather stay and make love than kill Vietnamese or Hungarians – and, on the other, violently combative in resisting goons, political salesmen, racists and "garbage" people generally who threaten the personal freedom they've attained and want to see others share.

The obsession with money-grubbing and power-hunting is quite largely fueled by early distortions of body image and of self-esteem – distortions that carry over into a whole range of political behaviors, from hating and bullying people to wrecking the countryside for a profit you don't need and can't use. In fact, most great powers are now run by a minority of sick people, suffering from their inability to erotize and hence humanize their experience, who use the rest of us for play therapy. Somebody once challenged Marcuse, when he was arguing on these lines, "Go erotize the State of Kansas." That could be happening. Marcuse is an old-style Marxist who still sees Marxism as radical and laments the fact that existing Marxist bureaucracies are violently anti-sexual as well as antilibertarian in tone.

A generation that has erotized its experience will be radical in quite a different vein – environmentalist, science-based (because you need to study human biology to know why you function) and hopefully as ungovernable by non-people as the American Colonies were by King George. If your widened self-experience and experience of others leave you an unreconstructed Middletown don't-carer, it wasn't widened enough or human enough.

simultaneous orgasm

Great when it happens, but it is a hangup from modern sexual folklore that it has to happen every time or even often, and that you've fallen short if it doesn't. This differs as much as every other sexual attribute. Some couples always get there together, others sometimes or rarely, a few never, but this matters not a whit. Worth mentioning because the contrary is one of many counseling fantasies, due to the writing of sex books by people who haven't had much sex, or much variety of experience, themselves.

If you specially want it and want to try for it, the idea would be to time both partners' responses during your most usual pattern of lovemaking, then use some other technique before starting the ignition sequence for about the time you estimate it needs for the slower to catch up. This doesn't always work, as full arousal may depend on the usual pattern you've learned, but it may do, with adjustment. If the woman is the slower, the best thing to try is breast play followed by a long period of tongue work on the vulva (better than using the finger – a long genital kiss leaves her wet, and will slow him down when he goes in). If he's the slower, she can start with oral or hand work (building her own arousal at the same time), put him in astride to complete this, then they turn over, timing this if possible so that both are just into their home stretch, and can go at it flat out. If she can get several climaxes, he should with luck synchronize with one of these (the folklore doesn't seem to recognize that most women are or can be multiorgasmic).

size

Sex counselors, who aren't, and don't wish to appear, unsympathetic, are just about fed up with answering anxious people's questions about penile size. We've spent years telling enquirers, correctly, that penile size is, functionally, wholly unimportant; that most people who worry that they are smaller than other males aren't (they simply haven't seen other males in erection, at least since boyhood); that the only difference between penises which are large and small when flaccid, a few rare conditions excepted, is that the large kind enlarge less on

erection; and that imagination matters far more in lovemaking than a donkey-size dong. Open sex and mutual observation would cure a lot of this nonsense – large size may be idealized in Texas, but they do fine in New Hampshire, too.

The trouble is, however, that the anxiety isn't personal but programed. The penis is not only for putting in the vagina, but is also apparently a dominance signal in other primates. We don't, like squirrel monkeys, get an erection to warn off another male (or rather, there isn't any printed observation that we do, though primitives who greet by patting each other's penises look a bit as if they were checking that the other male isn't threatening), but we seem to have kept the wiring so that it forms our attitudes. Saying you are small compared with other males is a statement about your self-estimate. In fact we've probably moved the dominance-signal behavior into infancy, where Father is bigger than I am. One thinks of Cassius's remark about Caesar:

Why man, he doth bestride the narrow world
Like a colossus; and we petty men
Walk under his huge legs, and peep about
To find ourselves dishonorable graves.

One practical importance of this, and of feeling small in our relations with more-dominant males, is that if you feel small your penis will, as a result, actually retract when

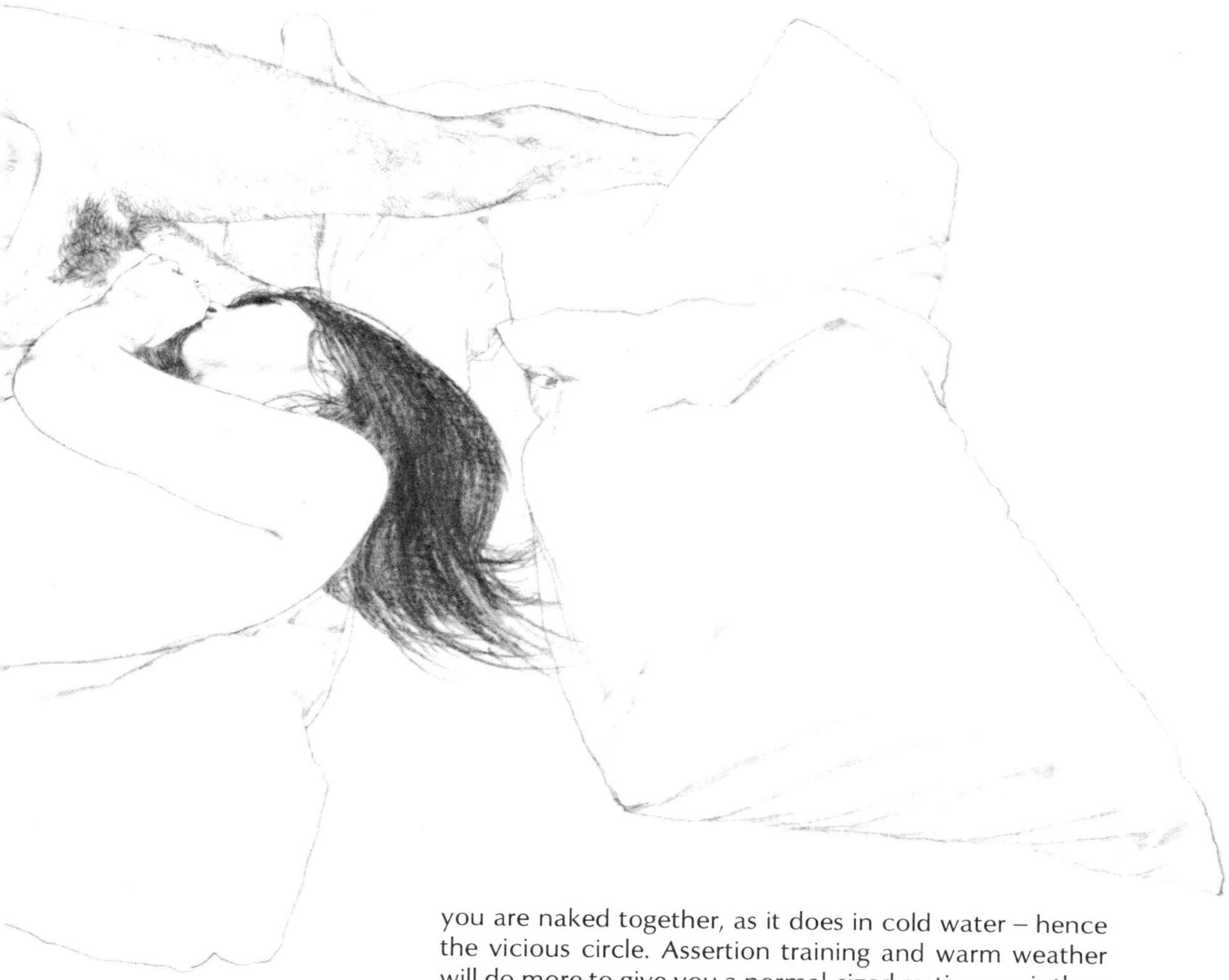

you are naked together, as it does in cold water – hence the vicious circle. Assertion training and warm weather will do more to give you a normal-sized resting penis than devices that increase the size of the makers' bank accounts. One or two good sex experiences will do still more. Women who put down a partner, either over resting size or over erection capacity, can upset unconfident people and would make bitchy partners anyway. It pays to recall that dominance isn't everything, and some kingsize flaccid penises attached to muscle-men stay flaccid at the moment of need, while many smaller specimens move briskly into an operating position.

vaginal orgasm

Some women's orgasms always feel the same, and some have an habitual pattern – one big one, or many, or a plateau in which they all run together. But even with an habitual pattern most women surprise themselves sometimes with one massive all-out climax when they usually plateau, or some other variation. Orgasms also feel different in both sexes when given in different ways, by hand or by mouth for instance. In women the clitoris and the surrounding tissues are the most usual trigger, but some find a direct stimulation of these too intense and prefer the incidental approach to them through deep penetration. Once in the mood, quite a few women can get orgasms from almost any region of the body – earlobes, breasts, fingers, soles of the feet – and even from listening to music or watching football. We know one woman who had to give up going to the hairdresser because brushing out gave her an orgasm. Luckily nobody has tried to classify all these.

Orgasms as turned-on people experience them are a little like the varieties of wine, and as hard to classify. Unfortunately, as always, the nonplaying coaches (chiefly male) have moved in: "clitoral" orgasms are immature, "vaginal" orgasms are unliberated and don't exist, etc. Apart from the fact that most of these writers can't have had a female orgasm and sound as if they have never witnessed one, they have caused a lot of anxiety in people who haven't yet learned that most admonitory writing about sex is hogwash. The best thing, if one thinks about it, is to enjoy your own pattern to the full and explore other responses to see if you can vary it.

The origin of the clitoral-vaginal hassle was in Freud's obsession with intromission as the only mature sexual activity, and his idea that the clitoris is a little penis, so that to be maturely female one had to "transfer" sensitivity to the vagina (which doesn't happen to have any sensory nerve endings). This seems to leave aside the question of what, in this case, the clitoris is for – a front door bell is there to be rung. Of course a mature female enjoys deep intercourse, and there are biological reasons for this if she's to reproduce, but Freud never appreciated the play functions of sex, and his idea of maturity was as rigid as the Catholic idea of virtue. The clitoris was installed to be enjoyed, and if it's your mascot, don't let theory worry you.

What does appear to be true is that some women, either always or sometimes, get a different, and often an even more overwhelming, sensation from quick intercourse without preliminaries but with very deep penetration, and distinguish this from the orgasm they get by clitoral stimulation or even by regular but less vehement intercourse. What seems to be happening here is that the trigger area is the peritoneum, the sensitive membrane lining the abdomen, not the vagina. This sort of orgasm produces gasping, breath-holding, and a once-for-all climax sensation, and women who know they can get either kind are often aware which, on a particular occasion, they want. Too much preliminary clitoral contact or foreplay seems to block this special response which, when it does happen, is as rapid as a man's. Subjective accounts may just mean that everyone's pattern of preference differs, but they need to be considered, even if there isn't much difference in the physiological changes – after all, the importance of an orgasm is how it feels, not its physiology.

If the peritoneum is sexually sensitive it could explain why anal intercourse works, in some members of both sexes: the only specifically feminine thing about this experience is that most men don't get penetrated routinely. It probably also explains why pressure on the abdomen can boost response in some women. But since not everyone does respond like this, it's pointless to feel disappointed if you don't.

Some very insecure women turn off to clitoral response altogether and find it nasty, oversharp or untender. Often this is a carry-over from masturbation fears, or not being able to relax sensually unless they have deep penetration, which reinforces the sense of "possessing" the partner and has maternal overtones they find reassuring. This might happen less if women and girls were encouraged to masturbate. Good masturbation enhances response by teaching the acceptance of sensuality, and doesn't impair any deep responses they may develop later. It's a pity to miss out on either. See *Masturbation and learning*.

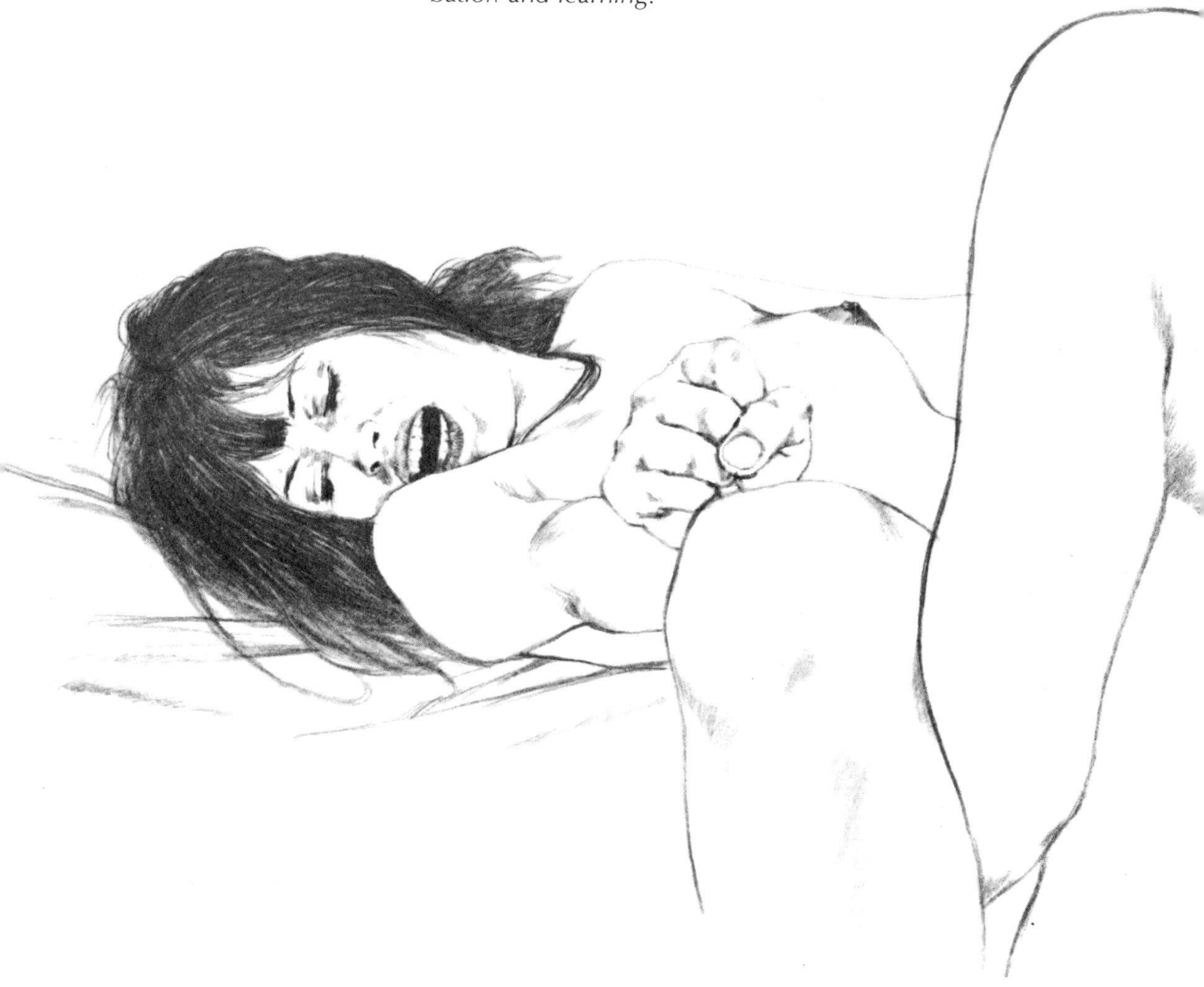

weaker sex

Sexually speaking, the male. In consequence, over the centuries, he has tended to talk women into restricting their potential sex performance, a process in which women themselves have co-operated. What has put paid to this has been the final separation of sex from reproduction: women now can realize their full sexual potential without anxiety, they can swing if they wish. Above all they can accept the fact that for both sexes sexuality can be relational, recreational, or both at different times. In other words they can claim the freedoms men have had, and out of which they have been hocused by propaganda about the inability of women to respond in any context except that of a total relationship, etc. etc. It's true of some women. It's also true of some men, but Byron's crack that love is a part of man's life but the whole of woman's is a normative generalization – in other words, propaganda.

This is a shock for some males. That a fully turned-on woman can have 10, 15 or 20 orgasms on end and still enjoy herself, with several partners if necessary, alarms them. The advent of the pill and the increased awareness among women of what they can achieve has led to a lot of impotence among spouses who nourished comparably neurotic images of maleness. Men who in theory always wanted to meet a nympho have sometimes been scared stiff (or flaccid) by their own wives.

We don't ourselves see this particular anxiety. It goes with a misconception of male performance, as well as of female; ignorance of the technique of managing longer intercourse; ignorance of the ways in which you can bring a woman to full orgasm without having an erection yourself; ignorance even of what a skillful woman can do with a non-erect penis – manually, orally and, if she has the gift of good muscles, vaginally. (In fact, women with full muscle control can perform best with a semi-erect partner who can relax and not resist their internal movements.) What we have to do now, having buried crew-cut, in-out male ideas of sexual prowess, is to see that women don't get re-hocused in the opposite sense and forced to assume that every one of them wants multiple orgasm, every one wants to swing, every one needs marathon sexual sessions. Some do, some don't. People are as different here as in every other respect. What matters is that they discover their thing, and find a partner sufficiently clued to permit them to make love so that it is sometimes his trip, sometimes hers, but always theirs.

This is one field where wider variety in partner experience really does help, though even here some people would rather not. Think what meals would be like if neither of you had ever tasted anyone else's cooking. And don't let harassing from the sidelines or the past stop you from finding your full and desired pattern of response. The folklore of the dangerous, insatiable woman expressed in locker-room ballads like "Eskimo Nell" will probably just not make sense to an unafraid generation who have learned what maleness and femaleness are in terms of co-operative self-realization. If we can make up for the hundreds of years spent in turning women off, men as well as women will learn to enjoy the results.

One point on which the male is emphatically the weaker sex is in the dependence of his sense of maleness on the role-playing imposed on him by society. Women have been afflicted in the same way (some get very upset, or feel defeminized, if the wife-and-mother role gives out), but we have the impression that long before Women's Lib they played the role-game less wholeheartedly than men. The role society has imposed on men has been varied by the preoccupations of the men. It has ranged from a crude and basically childish stereotype of constant erection (making for trouble when it isn't constant, merely normal), to invincibility with women (leading to rejection when women have other ideas, or put them down, intentionally, accidentally or by being smarter or

more successful than they). Being responsible for your wife, stereotype-pattern, and your children is no bad thing. But we now see numerous cases of impotence and depression in unemployed males which are exacerbated, not relieved, if the wife is still earning well. One might have thought they'd be glad the family income was safe and swapped roles by mutual agreement until the business outlook improved, but no – a breadwinning woman is threatening, has stolen your testicles, and so on.

One could pursue these dangerous male support-mechanisms through a whole tradition: brawling if another man insults your woman (she's quite able to put

him down by contempt without creating an ugly scene), the mania for firearms as surrogate penises and even the terrifying threat of identical hairstyles in the two sexes. There are good Freudian reasons why men should be the more anxious sex, but a lot of the reactions they have been encouraged to form against this anxiety simply have to be unlearned if we are to have reasonable relations between males and females in a society of equal opportunities.

In a clued and affectionate couple, neither is weaker except when it comes to lifting furniture. He can't have or suckle babies, and never will be able to. She can't father them. Each has special needs derived from childhood, but these will be roughly complementary. As to achievement on the one hand and chores on the other, each will be delighted by the other's success without silly or sulking competition, and who does what when (earning, children, dishes) is settled by sensible discussion – just as who takes the initiative in bed is determined by how both feel at the time.

Couples & Others

love

Love is the mutually satisfying sharing of each other's experience and the experience of each other – with no built-in time requirement. The use of affection to manipulate, cause guilt, invite sympathy, settle scores, produce or express dependence, or invade, annex or entrap another person is not love.

Many of the people who talk loudest about love, in its conventional meaning of making someone live up to their expectations, are neurotics incapable of loving anyone except themselves. So are the totally doormat-like who expect love to abolish any expectations of their own. The genuine article occurs between mutually respecting people, whether it's lifelong or for once only.

marriage

Over a large part of human history, marriage hasn't primarily been concerned with sex but with two other things – property and kinship, which had similar functions, because kin are a resource. Until the start of the last century property and kinship were still two of the most important motives in marriage among rich people, and finding an efficient workmate was the main concern if you were poor. During the 19th century a new emphasis appeared. More and more marriage and love were seen as a lifelong perpetuation of the peak experience of courtship, that of two individuals living wholly in and for each other, in a state of mutual self-absorption and mutual proprietorship. It's the kitsch version of this that figures in old movies and some unlib women's magazines.

In its original inspiration, this new or sentimental idea of marriage wasn't wholly retrogressive. It started to treat women as people rather than as bearer bonds, and it recognized the possibility of exploring sensibility and sensuousness. At the same time it badly sentimentalized both parenthood and expectation. Because living happily ever after was top of the menu it injected an element of intense insecurity. Warning lights started to come on if either partner's involvement became less than total 24 hours a day, or if either threatened to develop or change at all, and it took over and transferred to a psychological and emotional level all the old property considerations. In the old dispensation men were jealous of their wives as real estate or the producers of their children. Under the romantic dispensation they were permitted to stay jealous in the interests of total mutual involvement, and to lay loyalty, fidelity and so on upon them – note the financial symbolism when a wife is said to be cheating. Since the new concept was more equal, wives now asserted proprietorship of their husbands, who were part of *their* real estate – what has been neatly called penile servitude for life.

Much "romantic" love was in fact a good and rewarding interchange which could be lifelong, where these features weren't prominent, and where the thing was an open-ended mutual adventure. In other cases it led at worst to mutual parasitism disguised as love and masking a lot of hostility, or at best to affectionate relations with both parties aware that parts of their life were like a deposit box with two keys needed to open it, of which each partner had only one. It wasn't realistic, however, to talk about any sort of open-ended relationship, tailored to different people, so long as large families were compulsory, because fertility does impose fixity on marriage.

The positive features of this marital style were that it started to recognize men and women as equals capable of a total sensual and emotional experience. The negative features were its unsocial privacy, which overexposed people to each other and children to adults, and its insistence on total permanence, both in expectation and in social convention. This brought in an element not of security but of anxiety and proprietorship, leading to a covert custodial relation between the parties.

We don't now have this style of marriage in America. What we do have is often the pretence of it (which still makes the expectation of many naive youngsters who marry totally unrealistic) and the practice of serial polygamy helped out by adultery. The main reasons behind this shift are threefold: greater intolerance of social fictions and preference for telling it like it is; voluntary fertility; and longer lives. Victorian pietists were frequently liberated from an overpossessive relationship by the lamented death of a spouse – the lamentation discharged guilt at the fact of release. With lifespans pushing the 80s and a decline in premature deaths, until Death do us part is now one hell of a long time. The state of mutual sufficiency would have to continue through what are effectively two consecutive lives, including the sharp revaluation period (second adolescence) which most people experience in the late 40s or early 50s when children are grown and fantasy needs are re-evaluated to see if there is still time to meet them.

Security is utterly necessary in a relationship between man and woman. In youth it need only be the security that this is the right person for now. In middle age and after children, where two people have built a complete life-pattern, emotional and economic, it's still needed. Yet this is the time when for a variety of reasons it may, and sometimes positively has to, crumble or be rearranged – a prospect for which traditional expectation simply doesn't prepare people.

Marriage in Christian countries is still supposed to be

the permanent sexual union of one man and one woman to the exclusion of all others. The supposing is done not only by the Church and the State, but also by a sizeable number of people undertaking it. Others, especially among the young, would say that this isn't in fact what it does mean in modern America, and either won't go through the form because they regard advance pledges nobody can really make as dishonest, or marry with their own reservations.

It's quite true that a high proportion of modern American marriages end in divorce, that a high proportion of people have more than one spouse in a lifetime, and that few men, and only slightly more women, have sexual experience in a lifetime with only one partner. A frequent pattern is the compromise one of serial polygamy (one marriage at a time) coupled with at least some spoken or unspoken tolerance of sexual experience with other people. This adultery is often condoned on condition that it is discreet or secret and not anxiety-producing for the other partner, or that it isn't serious, that is, that it doesn't involve any competing commitment of any lasting sort.

In the general flux of experimentation at the moment it's easy to overlook the fact that even among younger people the traditional pattern not only exists but works, and that for many couples it isn't an imposition but a strong preference. Its drawbacks are the problems of the age, which we've outlined, and its outstanding advantage is that *in our culture* it seems the least harmful environment for rearing children, unless you want to experiment with them. Even authorities who think the isolated nuclear family harms children would agree that serial polygamy is about the worst system. Granted that the children of two fighting people who won't divorce may be deprived of what could be a better milieu, the many-times married couples we meet who trail around half-a-dozen kids by different people and spend odd weekends on statutory visits to others (visits they often use to perpetuate old scores) are probably laying up bad trouble for the children in their relations with the other sex and by way of general insecurity. Kids are surprisingly tough, but not all of them. The blame lies here not with serial polygamy as such but with immature adult attitudes to children and emotional self-indulgence in having them because they are cute, socially expected, or a way out of one's own inability to handle an existing relationship. Now that children are a question of either choice or negligence, it's about time we kept the word "marriage" for a life-style devoted to raising them in a stable environment, preferably not in an embattled nuclear family, but in a setup which is indissoluble until they are psychologically self-supporting.

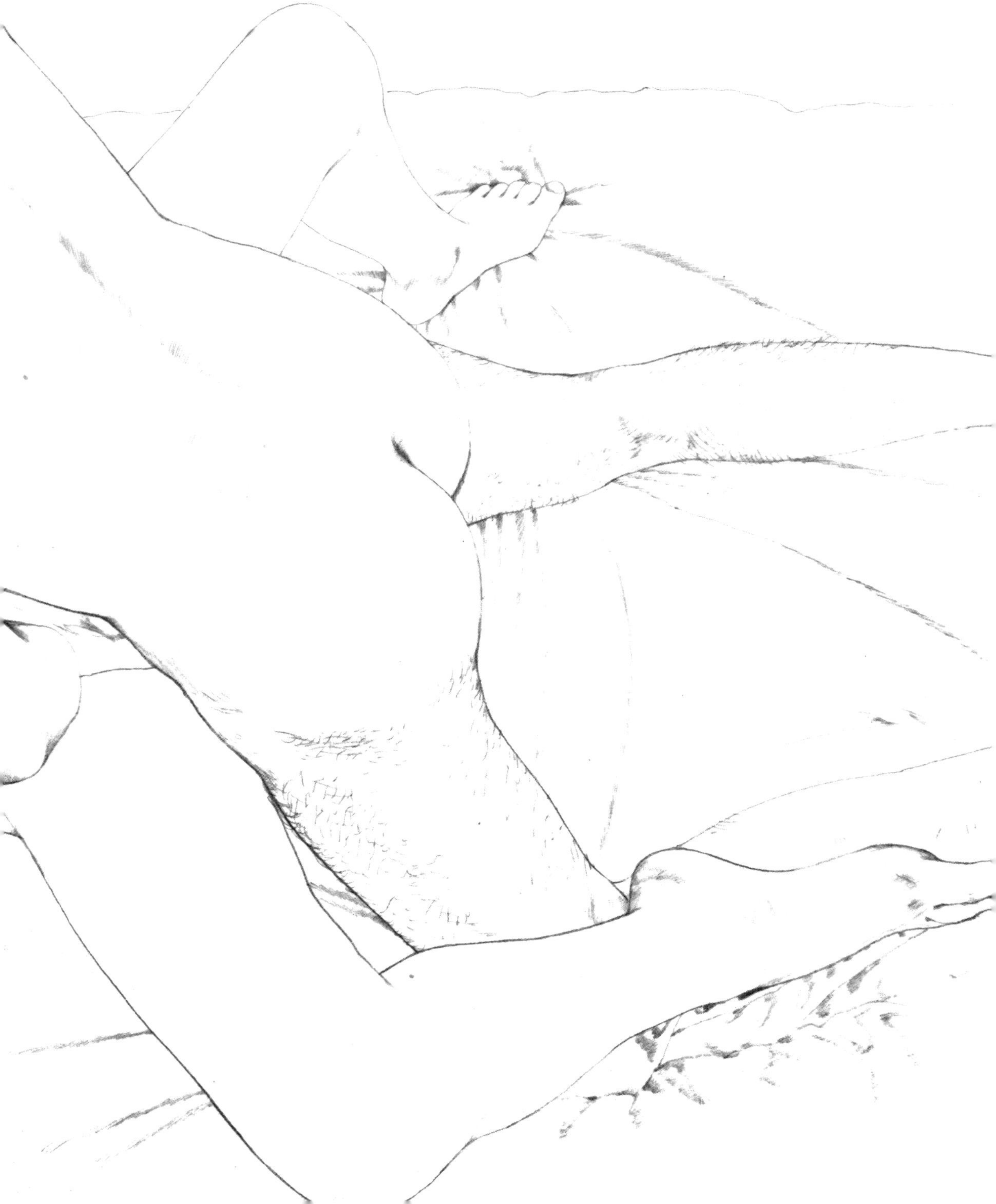

Parenthood shouldn't be undertaken unless you are willing and able to finish the job.

Marriage also has contractual advantages in that it regularizes the business side of the relations between two people who live together. But for adults whose bond is companionate and sexual, "primary relationship" is a much better phrase: it bypasses the law books, implies commitment, but is unrigid in that it is for the parties to decide what exactly that means for them. Primary relationships can change, sometimes coexist, and supplement each other. Using another name doesn't draw the teeth of human living, prevent sorrow and rejection, or stop people fighting, but it tends to the recognition that love is a relation not a romance or a margarine commercial. It also humanizes secondary relationships by insisting that they are relationships, not intrigues (in which the third party gets exploited and deserves it), nor threatening and shabby conspiracies against the other member of the primary pair. It recognizes the true facts: that while in a good couple each is largely sufficient unto the other, no two people are wholly so, nor do they own each other. At the same time one primary relationship is as much as most people want, need, or can handle. Conventional marriage modernized by depriving it of the concept of mutually jealous ownership does suit many couples even if they don't have children. What it fails to recognize institutionally is the wide variety of human needs, which include total couple-involvement but aren't confined to it. The idea that no pattern of relationship or behavior, conventional or otherwise, suits everybody is the most important one we have to get across, whether that be monogamy, heterosexuality, liberated womanhood, conventional womanhood, swinging, being a celibate monk or anything else whatsoever.

Since society is more or less bound to institutionalize relationships, it will ultimately recognize this variety in law by matching up responsibilities with obligations and dropping essentially religious differences between wives and mistresses, legitimate and illegitimate children. At present it talks monogamy but accepts serial polygamy – an instance of Herman Kahn's idea that a bit of hypocrisy tends to keep up standards. It would be better occupied in localizing marriage in the cradle, not the vagina, but that may be too much to hope for.

Open marriage, as it now figures in the literature, really represents the kind of compromise which humane folk would naturally accept in living together – in particular getting rid of sex-role nonsenses, both those imposed traditionally on the man and those which make the woman an inferior partner. The traditional man-woman roles may have been appropriate once, and were at least accepted. Basically the woman, in exchange for being obedient, chaste and excluded from male occupations, acquired a permanent right to the custodial proprietorship of the man, while he, in exchange for giving her economic security, got custodial rights over her virtue. This kind of thing is just no longer relevant to real people. Members of an open marriage are equals, support each other, divide what has to be done between them, discuss and resolve fairly the competing claims of their separate ambitions and wishes, avoid hurting or rejecting each other but don't rely on blackmail to keep property rights in one another. They are loving and committed but not jealous, and try to build security on adult instead of neurotic attitudes. That would be a fair rule-book for most sexual primary relationships, and a lot more realistic than the conventional idea of female obedience plus penile servitude for life.

mischief-makers

Avoid them. They can be especially bad news in a threesome, but you can get mischief-making couples who cause disruption wherever they go. A group usually comes to cope with them or throws them out, but they can cause a lot of harm before this happens.

We're talking about specifically sexual mischief-makers, who get satisfaction from invading and upsetting a primary relationship, not the ordinary kind – stupid relatives and neighbors, spying landlords and so on. The latter are commonly recognizable, while the sexual sort often look like friendly swingers, but tend to move in, seduce people rather than relate to them, and their own relationship to each other is that of accomplices, not lovers. There's a classic portrait of a mischief-making duo in *Les Liaisons Dangereuses*. Anyone who doesn't actively increase your couple-closeness is a bad choice for a threesome or a foursome, and make sure you yourselves don't act disruptively or intrusively with couples to whom you relate. Reinforcement is a matter of extreme tact in reading and giving nonverbal cues. Non-sharing couples can also be exposed to mischief-making, but most of this is verbal: a couple who aren't jealous aren't easily split up by tattle.

It's wise to keep clear of disturbing people, generally – judging them by the views they express. They're often as mean and vicious in their private as in their public life.

othello and all that

Jealousy, in its theater and opera sense, isn't natural, built-in, mammalian or the like. It's a social convention which people have been taught is an index of love and marital propriety.

Fear of rejection, losing a love object, being put down, outclassed or supplanted by someone else, is natural, built-in and human. It follows from this, if you think about it, that secure and communicating couples who include each other in all their fantasies and pleasures aren't jealous.

The operatic attitude goes on causing suffering. If the person you marry is highly skilled and highly attractive you might expect that others would wish to enjoy sex with him or her sometimes, and since sex isn't an asset which wastes with use, one possible reaction to this would be to feel chuffed at the compliment to your luck and judgment. The response prescribed by society, however, is that you ought to behave like a backward five-year-old who sees another child with his tricycle – and also break off the love relationship or keep it going as part of a heavy guilt and forgiveness scene. This looks idiotic and is. Love is a giving relationship, yet in our tradition the hallmark of togetherness is that you acquire unlimited rights to block the loved one's fantasies. This is topsy-turvy.

Huge tracts of European literature have been built

on this series of extraordinary conventions. The next generation may find it about as reasonable as the ritual guilt of Orestes, but the lobster quadrille ("did they?" "will she?" "with whom?" "does she know?") .goes on pathetically in middle-class society.

The trouble is that we have been encouraged to confuse fear of rejection (real) with jealousy (conventional). Now that parenthood is controllable the only original basis for hardline male jealousy is obsolete. Fidelity doesn't mean today that nothing goes on below the waist, it means real couple confidence and couple unity and not doing dangerous, rejecting, or anxiety-producing things. Sex with others (taking care also that the others concerned won't be hurt or upset by it) may or may not be involved – for some couples fidelity is really total complementarity so that the idea of any third parties turns them off. If any outside sex happens, it must include, not exclude, your primary partner – by full communication if not by participation – and the motive for avoiding a particular situation will be concern, not a species of male or female chauvinist copyright convention. Loving people are lovers not jailers to each other. They grant one another's fantasies, enjoy one another's pleasures, and speak up at once if something that either is doing

threatens, upsets, or puts them down. On this basis they can live as free but mutually concerned people, sensitive to what it is and isn't safe to do.

This is some way from strangling (or divorcing) a beautiful woman whom you love, and who loves you, because you think she may have slept once with Cassio. Nobody would blame Othello – he came from a jealousy culture, felt put down by whites because he was black, and had his ear poisoned about her fooling him. In that frame of mind he'd hardly be inclined to speculate that maybe she'd like to try it with someone uncircumcised and ask her how she had liked it. As we come to separate jealousy of the conventional kind from rejection-feelings, we may get more, not less, sympathy for Othello. Rejection is one of the worst things that afflicts us, and openness in marriage, not conventional jealousy, is the way to see it doesn't happen to us.

relational, recreational

Sex in humans has three functions. It can be reproductive (producing babies), relational (expressing love and bonding adults together), or recreational (play and fun). Most human problems over sex arise from anxiety over, and confusion among, these modes.

If human sex were "ordained for the procreation of children," we shouldn't mate all the year round and throughout pregnancy, but one or two times a year (as some rather cracked theologians would have us do). Until recently religion, which in our culture traditionally rejects pleasure as a motive, actually taught that reproduction was the only decent use of sexuality. With the growth of the romantic idea of marriage it shifted its ground, rather behind the event, so that today, together with crypto-religious psychiatry and counseling, it asserts that worthy sex can only be relational.

There has been no time in human history when either of these valuations was wholly true, though they have served to bolster up the uses to which the family has been subjected. Even in very kin-minded cultures gaps were left for sexual activity which wasn't an expression either of the wish for children or all-embracing personal closeness. Normally these gaps were provided for males only: they were the legislators and claimed the right to nonrelational sex, while prohibiting their women from doing so by means of moral codes, purdah or, more subtly, the indoctrination of girls with the notion that relational sex is the sole kind of which women are capable, and that unlike men they can't enjoy unless they possess totally. (Recreationally-minded women were obviously needed as well to make this ploy work, but they were outside good society. The whole system backfired badly, however, because a large number of men were impotent with "respectable" wives since sex was now something you didn't do to a nice girl.)

The pill has totally altered this. Safe from compulsory pregnancy, many women have now discovered that their capacity to experience sex at all three levels, either together or on different occasions and in different contexts, is as great as any man's if not greater. The adult of today has all three options – sex for parenthood, sex as total relationship, and sex for fun accompanied by no more than affection. Older folks looking at the young today realize how much their generation suffered through society's scheming to confuse these modes – when play between boy and girl led to forced marriage between acquaintances, or when one partner misread the other's mind or simulated love and concern to get a relation-minded partner into bed.

All good sex is partly relational. If it's really good it generates a relationship, even if only of warmth and gratitude, and nobody wants sex even at the play-level with a person who isn't considerate and caring. At the same time it can perfectly well express anything from total involvement to a romp between friends. The important thing is that all these are worthy aspects of human interaction provided the partners fully share their estimate of the level of concern involved. Sex may, through its intensely reinforced bonding ability, change two people who engage in it and make them closer: it can, that is, be an open-ended experience. Accordingly you have to pattern your choices by common sense and you have a responsibility to avoid upsetting vulnerable people. There are some people you wouldn't take mountaineering. For robust folk of high self-esteem, recreational sex with tenderness is good. For couples, it is best incorporated into the couple relationship so that recreational relationships involve and include them both, instead of leaving one out. Don't above all, misread recreational as trivolous or exploitative. It means playful, caring and tender.

seriousness

Seriousness about sex differs vastly from person to person. "Some take it like the Host, some like a toffee," and there are Quixotes and Sanchos. In Strauss's *Ariadne auf Naxos*, when Ariadne, who lives at the high-tragic level, is deserted by a Hero, she can be consoled finally only by a God. For her maid, the soubrette, it's simply a case of off with the old love, on with the new.

Our culture has probably greatly overvalued intensity. Some people can't help it – it is natural and proper to them – but there's no virtue and some harm in overcultivating it, and some virtue and no harm in tender playfulness. Tragic intensities tend to produce bad trips, not peak experiences.

sexual revolution

By all reasonable standards there isn't and wasn't any such thing, even though books such as this have been credited with, or accused of, promoting it. There have been changes – most of these stem from the increased explicitness of sexual behavior, the willingness to admit openly, and discuss, what was formerly done in private, at least by some people. There has also been a marked increase in the general sexual noise level, in the media and in conversation. As a result, more of the range of behaviors which always existed among the sexually sophisticated have become available to the conventional and cautious. This has brought new anxieties: people who formerly experienced anxiety and guilt if they did the things described by the adventurous now worry if they don't do *all* the things described by the adventurous. Thus do we swap one hangup for another.

What has changed is the fact that reproduction is now optional. It used to be an inevitable and restricting concomitant of any act of intercourse. Given that, the woman (who was literally left with the baby) was extremely wise to keep her feet crossed and demand guarantees. Another thing which has changed has been a steadily dissolution of responsibility in regard to children, who tend in some circles to be literally equated with pets (cute but rather tiresome at times) or possessions. The moral obloquy which used to be focused on harmless sexual behaviors badly needs refocusing upon parental irresponsibility.

Another change has been the wide availability of abortion. We see this issue cynically exploited as a political football, or insisted on as part of a women's rights package. Abortion is not a desirable social custom. Very early termination is preferable to unwanted pregnancy: the late terminations one sometimes sees now are not easy to distinguish from infanticide. One could respect the humane intention of the antiabortion lobby, and agree that destroying foetuses is likely to cheapen life in general, if precisely the same people weren't the noisiest denouncers of adequate available birth control – and hence largely responsible for the cheapening of life and parenthood which they denounce.

There are two paths we could pursue in relation to abortion, granted that it has been used as a quick fix for thoughtlessness. One is to re-ban it, derive great moral satisfaction from doing so, and pretend it doesn't occur – in which case the prosperous will go on buying it as before, and the unprosperous will go to the coathanger practitioner and die in droves, as they did before. The other is to mount a sustained campaign for better contraceptive techniques, universal contraceptive availability, and public education from school up, which will reduce the pressure to terminate pregnancies. It is a test of "pro-life" agitation to see which path it adopts. Judging from its present stance there are no prizes for guessing the outcome.

Whether sexual abuse of children has become commoner in recent years is questionable. It is unquestionably common, but many of the witnesses who have been subjected to it are now adult, and were abused in pre-revolutionary days. When Freud was astonished at the frequency with which his prosperous Viennese patients spoke of sexual contacts with relatives in childhood, he concluded that these experiences had to represent fantasy. We might now be more inclined to take them as true accounts. Probably the only major contribution to this problem from the "sexual revolution" generation, other than increased willingness to face a longstanding human failing, has been the effect of serial polygamy. This exposes children to close contact with "fathers" to whom they are unrelated, and probably lowers the taboo-level imposed by consanguinity.

Physical abuse of children was always with us: the righteous, and certain schoolmasters, have from time past knocked their charges about on principle. It is a gain in decency that this behavior is no longer tolerated by society. Child pornography is a new phenomenon – an unsightly offshoot of greater freedom of sexual depiction – but the activities of "chicken hawks" and the prostitution of underage girls are not new: in fact, they probably reached a peak in the late 19th and early 20th century, when the journalist W.T. Stead exposed them to London. The fact that we are now inclined to intervene and stop sweeping them under the carpet is a positive development.

Sexual behaviors probably change rather little. Social attitudes, which are more determined by what is respectable and admissable in conversation than by what is or is not "moral", do unquestionably change. The intense reticence and anxiety over sexual matters which was general until the middle of the century was wholly unhelpful – as the reticence has declined and the humbug has become exposed, we have the difficult and not always selfgratifying task of finding ourselves a genuine sexual morality, based on not exploiting others, assuming parental responsibility before we expose ourselves to parenthood, freeing children from having children by more practical methods than were prohibition, and generally learning to reconcile the freedom of enjoying an immensely rewarding range of human behaviors with the wellbeing of others. There is plenty of room for moral indignation, Papal injunctions, and social pressure – but we badly need to improve our aim. If half the aggro lavished by past moralists on harmless activities such as masturbation and unconventional preferences such as homosexuality were to

be refocused on bad parenting, irresponsible treatment of our neighbors, and the obstructors of contraception and sexual education, we would not draw the teeth of human sexual problems but we might produce a lot less suffering and a lot less work for psychiatrists still unborn. Here endeth the lesson.

For gays, there was indeed a revolution: centuries of idiotic persecution suddenly ended. Some of them had very much the experience of being released from jail and overcompensated for the past: it was incredibly tragic that the fortuitous appearance of a new disease about tnat time should have hit precisely that group, caused death and suffering, and given the professional gay-baiters the chance of a comeback. One must hope that they do not succeed in putting back the clock. Revolutions, real and imaginary, don't finish anything: they simply impose new agendas for change. If there ever was a "sexual revolution", it is no exception to the rule.

sharing

Sharing means exactly what it says – the sharing of sexual experience with another couple (not "swapping" which is something quite different). Some lovers find this an invasion of their privacy: others find it a resource. The essence of sharing is that two couples make love in each other's presence; no more than that. See *Watching, Massage, Threesomes.*

A couple who both wish to try it (and "both" excludes going along with a partner out of loyalty or for peace and quiet), should start by putting out of their heads anything they have read about orgies, wife-swapping and the like. Most of these are masturbatory fantasies. Next, they should forget about sexual excitement as the aim of the experience. Sex in a group scene can be exciting, but the main experience in sharing is quietude, and the intention is sensual rather than sexual. The experience of sharing we're talking about quite often involves no cross-couple contacts more sexual than touch. A sharing occasion can go on to complete sexual involvement of all the parties, but most often it doesn't. Its value doesn't depend on doing so, and the participants should be at liberty to impose any restraints which accord with their own feelings and reservations. This won't spoil the experience; if it is going too far or too fast, they can turn it aside into simple sharing of intimacy.

The fundamental consideration for everyone is to be careful when choosing the couple or couples to share with. Self-advertised swingers are the worst people, as they will try to hurry on to a sexual exchange. Best friends aren't a good choice either, unless it happens naturally. The ideal is a couple both of whom both partners like and who aren't in the throes of a marital problem. If the choice is wise none of the participants should find subsequent social intercourse embarrassing or overintense.

Usually the evening starts with a group meal – a good beginning to any religious experience, which is what this becomes if it works. Drink shouldn't be used as a disinhibitor, wine with the meal is plenty. Then the lights are turned down and the couples relax together, not in chairs. sitting-room fashion, but in a dream setting, on mattresses, in front of a fire if it's cold, and side by side.

At an early stage, they introduce shared nakedness. This can be done by swimming, sunbathing, or hot tubbing (q.v.) before the meal, or each partner can undress the other in front of the fire. Once undressed, everyone relaxes completely and talks. If it seems natural, they start to make love of the gentlest kind to their own partner – massage, touch, kisses. Sometimes they go on to intercourse if and when it seems right and natural. If it doesn't, they shouldn't. The other couple will probably follow; if not, no one should be disappointed – but go back to quiet enjoyment of each other's company. Making love in warm company isn't lascivious or embarrassing but often movingly innocent. Don't at any price give an exhibition – it would be insensitive.

Afterward is the time for some extended pillow talk (playing tapes or records all the time spoils this). In the right company the couples feel a deep relaxation even greater than after making love alone. If things are so arranged that there are pillows and blankets, they can sleep and breakfast together. Next morning is often the best part.

This simple sharing is more often than not a safe and beneficial sexual and sensual experience for any two normal couples all of whose members want it. It's neither embarrassing nor disturbing, and if it's unpleasant or unrewarding they picked the wrong couple. Quite obviously, however, the potential is there for such an experience to go on perfectly naturally to express the sensual (not necessarily sexual) involvement between them. Girls being loved side by side often hold hands. A couple sitting close to a lovemaking couple (and they should be close, not on opposite sides of the room) can become involved in touching, massaging and being touched. If this happens they need both to feel that all of them are securely in control of the situation (so that they can quite gently put a hand aside if they don't want it there – "no" isn't a put down), and at the same time not block the growth of the experience. Sometimes the two girls embrace, then invite the men in. But the pace isn't horny or excited, more like that of mutual sensual massage. The cautions we've mentioned over AIDS clearly apply here, but nothing is lost by couples who agree to stay sexually exclusive but still enjoy sharing. It is a different operation from partner exchange, and far less threatening at all levels. The slowest member of the foursome sets the pace. If one person doesn't want to be more involved, the others should cool it back to touching and resting, or simple massage.

There is no scenario for sharing. It is ruined by expectation, or attempts to stage-manage, seduce or push. Taken at this level of cool and control, there is no reason why any normally robust couple should find it harmful to their relationship, provided neither of them was positively turned off by the idea and pressured into trying it. (Being doubtful isn't the same thing, for doubt can be relieved when they see that the experience isn't turning out to be what they thought.)

Sharing can help rather than harm people with sexual (not marital) problems, but a couple should not go into business as amateur therapists, or persuade people to share, even at the least sexual level, because they think it would do them good. With the right people, and even without any intense sexual involvement, it can be a charismatic experience, but it's only for couples who communicate fully, know their minds, and are willing to follow their feelings in saying yes or no. The really important thing, especially where the interchange does become sexual, is that the couples act as couples and reinforce each other's couple bond. If one person sits there hating it while the other three make furious love, it's a bad and destructive scene.

It's not obvious why having sex in company should have so big a beneficial effect on some people, a question which is bound to be asked by a culture brought up on privacy. That in fact may well be the reason – privacy means that we experience others as hostile to our sexuality. Either they would disapprove and punish it, or they're Peeping Toms, or they would try to take our partner away. To drop privacy, stop checking if there's a crack in the shades, and experience others outside our sexual relation as approving, enjoying, encouraging, even applauding, and only joining in to reinforce, not threaten, our primary relationship can well be encountered by some people as a total reversal of attitudes they've learned to their hurt. Most of us have learned such attitudes, even if we rationalize them by saying that love is a secret and private thing which would be devalued if other people saw it – which is another way of saying that it would be threatened or disapproved of.

swinging

In primitive societies – or what we call primitive, meaning societies that are technically simple but emotionally sophisticated – people exchange wives and husbands under fairly strict conditions. Lending a (willing) wife may be a gesture of hospitality, but it's a convenient one. Like any other favor it imposes obligation, and because this favor is sexual it increases the number of your kin – he borrowed your wife, so you can borrow his canoe or his help in hunting. Orgies (meaning no-taboos, no-holds-barred sexual fiestas) occur on set occasions, often against a background of strict propriety at other times. They counteract the repressive and disruptive effect of hard-line morals, make all the participants children again for one limited occasion, and perhaps boost the general fertility of the crops (if crops were moralistic they might not grow). Everyone comes out of these occasions breathless, guiltless, and ready to return to propriety. Easy-going people who treat sex as a gentle sport also hold what look to us like orgies, but these are just the relaxed enjoyment in company of what they already enjoy in private – as Devereux said of the Samoans, it's the equivalent of football, the movies and the Saturday night binge.

Our society – technically advanced and emotionally naive – doesn't think in this way. If in America and in other countries increasing numbers of married couples are getting courage from media accounts of swinging to try to develop rituals that involve others in their sexuality without sacrificing the primary relationship, overwhelmingly the biggest motives are greater emancipation (leading to impatience with the proprietary idea of marriage as mutual ownership) and sexual restlessness. Another is probably that which inspires wife-swapping Eskimos, namely shortage of kin. The double standard seems to us merely disgusting, and the conventional American solution of serial polygamy with adultery (see *Marriage*) merely dishonest. Accordingly, the search to fulfil the need for experience outside the couple can represent honesty and mutual concern rather than lust – when it works, that is, and when it is reciprocal.

In a culture still overtly disapproving, swingers, like nudists, became a charismatic subculture with a shared turnon and a shared secret. This form of experimentation too has been nipped in the bud by the appearance of AIDS – although, fortunately, there is no medical evidence that it has played any part in spreading the epidemic. Any sexual involvement with unknown quantities is now wildly imprudent. Two uninfected married couples who know each other incur only psychological risks. For some people these can be real and disruptive. Psychologists are equally split between those with participant experience, who tend to be favorable, and those without, who are denunciatory or apprehensive. The few impartial studies are downbeat in assessing ultimate results. Swingers may have discharged fears and fantasies to their benefit, felt closer because their spouses are seen as giving them back their freedom, and – more rarely – acquired genuine surrogate kin. Others kept all their prejudices intact, and simply added swinging to a rather limiting life-style as they might add golf, sometimes with equally divisive effects.

That a sizeable minority claimed to find swinging rewarding is good anthropological evidence that there is something there, but it seems the wrong, or not the best, initial way to go about the search for that something, except for very robust and secure people. Having sex is a powerful experience and by ritualizing it with virtual strangers one is unable to tap some of its power – notably to transfer sex and its anxieties from the "hot" category prescribed by an irritated culture to the "cool" category based on nonanxiety, noncompulsion and recognition of personhood.

It is beneficial to realize that in some sexual contexts we and our partners temporarily become unpersons (in making no socially prescribed demands), but it is also limiting to ritualize this too much.

The small-ad, casual contact scene is clearly hazardous and apt to be squalid when enacted. AIDS apart, swapping with strangers was always a bad start, and swapping with close friends can be divisive unless it happens absolutely naturally, and sometimes even then. The most rewarding experiences, if you aren't too obsessed with scoring, are those with people who can relax with you until anything that happens happens naturally and nobody is disappointed if nothing does.

threesomes

A threesome involving a permanent couple and a third party can be a uniquely moving sexual experience if the conditions are right (and a complete turnoff if they are

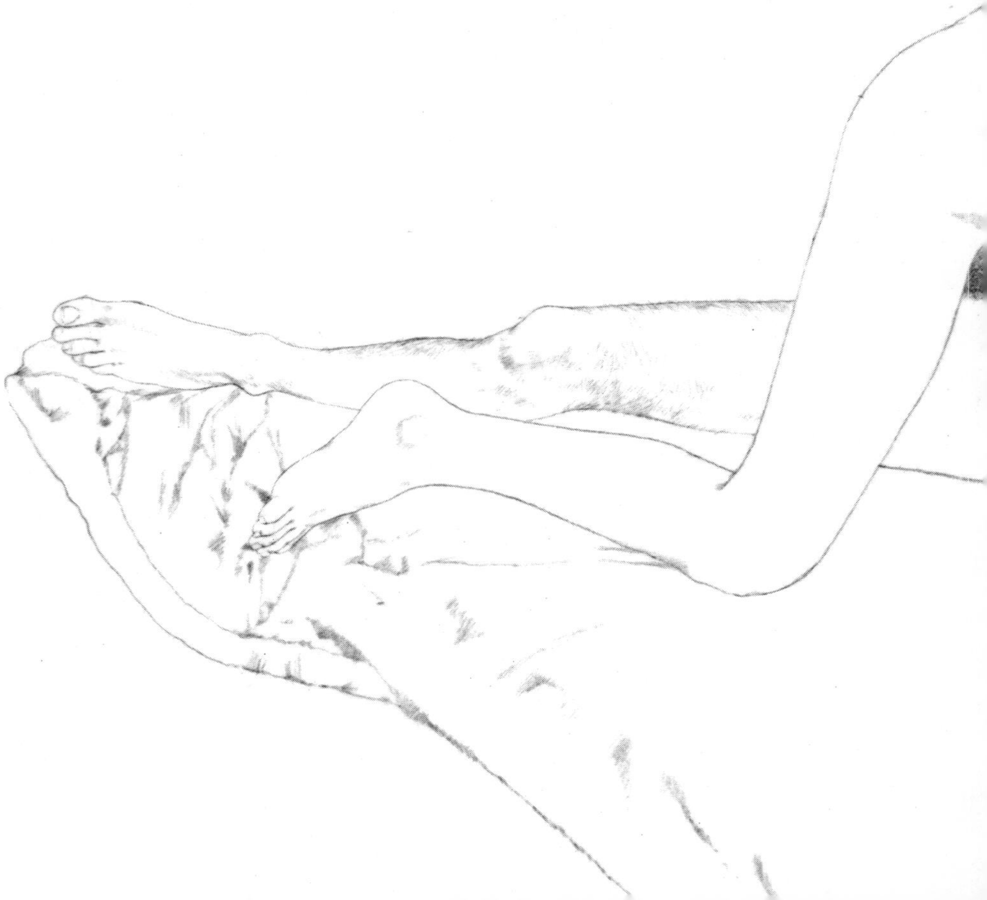

wrong). It also represents by far the commonest first experience of extended sexuality.

Threesomes do, and will continue to exist – they carry a substantial hazard, however, arising from the fact that a third party who is male, or a male who desires to involve another male, may have had bisexual experience, and falls in a high risk category for the HTLV virus. The issue of partner choice is here exactly the same as in couple relations – the more people you involve, the higher the statistical risk of contact with a carrier.

Given healthy people, the issues are emotional and psychological.

The third member can be of either sex. The two like-sex participants, instead of experiencing the jealousy expected by society, often become extremely close even though nobody has any sex at all – a kind of sisterhood or brotherhood. In the case of women this can lead to quite unexpected mutual sex-expression that has nothing lesbian about it, and may greatly excite the man. They shouldn't be upset afterward if this has happened – it's wholly normal. Most men stay at the level of strong friendship; avoidance of

male-male contact is not a safeguard against infection, one should add, since the AIDS virus is present in semen and could pass via the shared woman.

A threesome will not work if one partner imports a lover whose aims are intrusive; if a couple mischievously seduce a third party who can be thoroughly upset by the experience, or try to use the occasion to spite the other or prove something ("you don't know how to make love – you should see me with Mabel"). Equally, it won't work if they try to fuel it with gin against everyone's better judgement. This ends with disgust and recriminations. It can work when a thoroughly secure and loving couple who already have good sex mutually invite someone they both like, and about whom they know enough to be sure that it is safe for all three. The relationship is a rather subtle, two-way gift – the woman who invites another that her man fancies is giving him a present (not least the feeling that she is totally secure and doesn't need to be jealous), and both are giving the third party the gift of sharing their secure intimacy – and their sexual knowhow. The same applies when the man does the same for his woman.

There is no sexual innovation which escapes from the human capacity to generate, and try to relieve, anxiety, even if it appears to happen on impulse or by its own momentum. One reason for the efficacy of the one man, two women

scenario is, oddly enough, the intense relief of the male in relating to two women who aren't fighting. In polygamous cultures this experience was general. The two man, one woman situation, apart from its bisexual overtones, may involve a relief of performance anxiety and an element of load-shedding. All such unconventional situations have overtones which go beyond the simple desire for variety.

A permanent threesome (*ménage à trois*) is obviously a totally different situation. It can and does work for some people, but only when the three individuals involved all relate to one another. Often they may do so for rather special reasons: one or more of them may be strongly bisexual; an older woman, especially if childless, may treat a younger one with children as a sister or daughter; two men may have a David-and-Jonathan relationship, sexualized or not, in which they reinforce each other. The situation is unconventional for our society but not for Man – sororal polygamy (marrying two or more sisters simultaneously, like Jacob) is a widespread human pattern. It tends to be "economic," based on convenience in managing work and child-rearing, while fraternal polyandry (marrying several brothers, like Draupadi in the *Mahabharata*) has to do with male comradeship and bonding. Neither necessarily goes with a particular view of sex roles, and doubtless people who adopt it now would make it fill other needs. One can enumerate the kind of stresses it might lead to, especially if one of the parties was only grudgingly willing to accept the pattern. Whether these are greater than the stresses of a one-to-one relationship would depend on the people concerned.

Pair-mating animals seem to have found the same thing. Threesomes either way are fairly common in normally monogamous birds, and apparently just happen (without any deep Freudian needs on the part of the birds). Infants can bond same-sex adults – a cat whose kittens have died will take turns minding and rearing another cat's litter. Usually where two males share a mate, it is because such sharing makes them allies, not rivals, as society seems to expect, and able between them to outthreaten any third party. This could go for us, too.

Resources

behavior therapy

Nearly all human behavior is learned. It can accordingly be unlearned by training, and it is to this that behavior therapy addresses itself. Classical behaviorism (which is a psychiatric ideology, though that doesn't impair its results) is sceptical about things like emotions, feelings and drives – after all, we can only observe these if they give rise to behaviors. In rejecting "mentalism," old-style behaviorism assumes that states of mind are at least as much a result of behavior patterns as they are causes, and sets out to change the behavior. All normal people are scared in a battle. If by training you alter their behaviors, not only so that they don't run away, but so that they don't go pale, sweat, have dilated pupils and a raised heart rate, then according to the theory you've abolished fear. In fact you can alter their behaviors in this way, but through the fear of being afraid they commonly get obstinate nightmares later and need to be allowed to experience the emotion of fear, by reliving, in order to lose them.

This instance indicates the uses and limits of behavior modification by learning, though sometimes the classical theory works better than this. If you teach a downtrodden person to show dominant behaviors, his self-esteem rises through response from his fellows. Much that has been written is merely oversimple – if you reward a dog each time it raises its head above a line you can rapidly train it to jump (on the basis that rewarded behaviors tend to be repeated). However, in the course of this process there comes a time when the dog quite obviously latches on to what the experimenter wants and does it – a cat doesn't. Dogs and dolphins, but not cats, are social animals and programed to be sensitive to approval and disapproval. So are we.

We aren't, however, concerned here with theory, but with the fact that behavior therapy is uniquely good at tackling handicapping sexual behaviors and teaching new skills. It works on the assumption that behaviors which are followed by unpleasant results are less often repeated, and – much more important – that behaviors which are even nominally rewarded are reinforced and more often repeated. Society has for centuries tried to turn off unpopular forms of behavior by aversion (punishment) without much success, because they usually managed to reinforce not being found out. People changed their verbal behaviors but not their tastes. A few eager beavers have tried to treat homosexual people by aversion – involving such things as a mild shock accompanying a same-sex picture, and even tapes of mockery and abuse (a great idea, in dealing with a behavior which may reflect low dominance). Amazingly, they have been surprised at their low success rate in anything but making the sub-

jects stop admitting to being gay. The Inquisition got similar results with redhot irons, which are a stronger aversive stimulus. The fact of setting out to treat a normal component of human response tells you something about the motivation of these quite humanely-intended studies. One sportsman tried to cure a masochist by aversion, and found to his astonishment that the patient rather liked it.

Punishment as a training method is as old as man. Far more important is the idea that where possible you should operate by reinforcing a wanted behavior by reward, not trying to turn off a complicated behavior you don't want. Aversion has its uses, but only when you've analyzed the pattern you are dealing with, and it usually calls for building up an alternative. You can avert an alcoholic from whisky and from going to the cupboard to get it (by trying to associate it in his mind with nausea), but you usually need to build up his dominance so he doesn't require it and can refuse it in company. If somebody's homosexual orientation is a bad trip and bothers him (not society – it's none of society's business), you can reinforce his heterosexual skills.

Some people have behaviors which bother both them and society – exhibitionists or child molesters. One can argue philosophically that no normal female should be upset by a normal set of genitalia, and that much of the harm to molested children (who may have been surprisingly and precociously seductive themselves) is in the consequent panic and uproar. At the same time, people are incarcerated for these things. You can help them turn off the behaviors, but a more productive attitude is to be less bothered by society's fears than the subject's problems. You set about reinforcing the normal sexual approach to adult women which they lack.

Behavior therapy using the whole range of methods is excellent at turning off unproductive hangup behaviors, turning on new sociosexual skills, getting rid of destructive behaviors like smoking, alcoholism and overeating, and helping people overcome irrational fears – of flying, of dogs, of particular situations. It's particularly good with what are called functionally autonomous habits, like impotence or frigidity. The psychoanalytic view of these, and of hangups generally, is that they represent persisting infantile anxieties – surface the anxiety and you should lose the hangup. Unfortunately this rarely works – a habit once set needs to be unlearned, or it persists long after the cause which started it. While psychoanalysis aims to improve sex by giving insight, behavior therapists realize that if you improve performance, a lot of the feedback-generated consequences of the problem go, and the subject is better able to get wise to him or herself. Naturally it can't make someone over from scratch. If the old problems are still alive they may cause new symptoms, and some patients would benefit from another form of psychotherapy as well. But at least they've lost the presenting problem. People who go to an analyst may get much information about themselves – and stay impotent or frigid.

The technique with frigidity is basically a retraining

of the body in sensuality – learning to relax, learning to masturbate, first alone, then with the other partner, and a gradual carry-over into regular sex. This progression does actually alter the person from tense and denying to relaxed and accepting. The treatment of impotence depends on the fact that we can control and condition not only behaviors we can see, but also involuntary ones like blood pressure or bowel movements, provided we can monitor them. If we're yogis we may get this knack from ten years of meditation. For others it's quicker to use some sort of display system. The impotent man has a strain gauge or a volume recorder put on his penis. He is told not to think about sex but to concentrate on moving the needle. Many men can thus acquire something which doesn't normally exist, namely the ability to produce erection at will. Since most impotent men have been anxiously willing an erection in a way that stopped it occurring spontaneously, they can learn in this way to make a problem beat itself, and the buzz they get from success on a few occasions is often enough to turn off the anxiety and unblock the normal mechanism. If their self-estimate has been distorted as a cause or a result of their handicap, they may need more counseling, but at least whereas they were impotent, now they can ball. By a similar technique, women can get delightful control over their pelvic muscles.

As with analysis, how good a trip you get in consulting a behavior therapist depends on whom you consult: if he's uptight he'll try to make your behavior fashionable rather than rewarding. It's expensive, like all other help in America, but you get results in a few weeks, not 15 years, and the results are tangible. Unfortunately, the sexually reabled don't advertise like other patients, or it would be more widely known and used.

biofeedback

Doctors and yogis have long suspected that there are precious few body processes which can't to some extent be controlled by the mind. The trouble about controlling, say, one's blood pressure by taking thought is that one has no way of monitoring it. We have a full set of muscles to move our ears, but as we can't see the results of using these muscles it's difficult to learn specific movements. If, however, you watch your ears on closed-circuit television, which doesn't reverse like a mirror, you can learn to waggle them in a single session.

It's now known that blood pressure, skin blood flow, erection, and even brain electrical activity can be controlled voluntarily if you have a readout of what is happening and play hotter, colder with it. Fooling about with brain waves has become a West Coast party trick

(luckily it seems to be harmless, and even an aid to meditation), and the same device can be used to teach sufferers to turn off epileptic fits. Biofeedback-based control of sexual processes has a growing use in teaching women to co-ordinate their pelvic muscles, and impotent men to produce voluntary erection like a yogi. See *Behavior therapy*.

books

We're not knocking competitors, but the main thing here really is to avoid being badly misinformed. Sex books are mostly written by nonplaying coaches of limited experience, some of whom never saw an act of intercourse, or by sexually active and quite humane people who don't, however, know any human biology and get their medical information from old books. Both tend to be based on the psychiatry and sexology of 1874 not 1974. This doesn't of course apply to all books – modern field studies like those of Kinsey or Masters and Johnson, for example (though some of these are deliberately written in goon-language so that local policemen won't understand them: if they were interesting they might get banned – it doesn't do to let ordinary people read about sex). Magazines are getting franker about sexual behaviors, but contain a lot of fantasy and hogwash about rejuvenation remedies, potency pills, etc. The most realistic source of sexual comment is often the cartoons in *Playboy, Oui* and similar publications.

Moral and medical ax-grinders are fairly easy to spot. Beyond that, it's safe to say that any alarmist comment, or comment which suggests that something you both enjoy doing is immature, mentally unhealthy, etc., is likely to be bunk. The best test of a book is whether it's obvious the author really enjoys sex himself, and recognizes its infinite variety.

If you have straight questions or want book lists, try the Sex Information and Education Council of the US, 1855 Broadway, New York, NY, or the National Sex Forum, 330 Ellis, San Francisco.

doctors

We pointed out in *The Joy of Sex* that doctors aren't trained in sex counseling, or are only just beginning to be. On the other hand, they could do it well if they were, and in any case they're the first people to be consulted over sex problems.

You can get some idea of the quality of the advice a doctor gives you by noting his general demeanor. Reassurance is a proper medicine, but be a little doubtful if you get hormone pills for impotence in the first instance, and very doubtful, to the point of consulting someone else, if you're told that it's your age, or nothing can be done and you should live with impotence, frigidity or premature ejaculation. With tricky problems doctors will refer you to a reputable sexologist, if there is one and the doctor is clued (referral to a teaching hospital is always a good move), to a gynecologist, a genito-urinary (g.u.) surgeon if you're male, or a psychiatrist. A gynecologist is obviously right if the trouble is pain, an anatomical thing, or subfertility. If it's the latter, don't go back to that clinic if they don't ask to see your husband too. You can save unnecessary investigations on yourself – he may have no sperms and will enjoy masturbating into a test tube more than you enjoy being insufflated, etc. The g.u. surgeon is a counsel of despair for all but anatomical male sex problems – some g.u. men are good on counseling the impotent or the over-quick: others aren't. The psychiatrist is often a cop-out – he may well be the best person if you have a problem such as depression (q.v.) or big emotional difficulties, but some doctors are liable to refer to him any behavioral problems that they can't handle themselves.

It is much better to insist on seeing a reputable sex counselor for any of the more common malfunctions – he'll call in the psychiatrist, the endocrinologist, the gynecologist, or whatever, if he thinks that they will be able to help you.

With reluctant counselors, change your doctor or be a nuisance until you get satisfaction. Don't let a major hangup become a way of life.

encounter groups

These have become an immensely popular West Coast sport. Basically, they're group psychotherapy sessions run by amateurs in a high atmosphere of expectation with self-chosen members. Professional training doesn't guarantee good reading of human communication, and some amateurs are intuitive therapists of a high order. Others aren't, or are working off problems of their own on the other group members – a psychiatric training at least makes the trained therapist aware of this possibility. The amateurs also tend to be optimists. Being amateurs they get everyone straight counseling has failed to help, and they don't screen their entrants. In consequence unless they're lucky they can collect really mentally ill people, expose them without skilled direction, and send them right round the bend. Accordingly, though encounter doesn't hurt, and can benefit, the mentally robust, regular psychotherapists spend a fair amount of time undoing the damage done to disturbed people by equally disturbed group-leaders.

The general effect is of the apocryphal small ad, "Teach

yourself brain surgery – all you need is a mirror and a saw." An aggressive leader can do real harm – his group usually turns into a wolf pack and reduces the least dominant and most disturbed member to tears instead of increasing their self-esteem. There are encounter pundits who are immensely proud of this technique. Others turn into mutual admiration societies around a guru who basks in the parental role and hasn't the skills to make constructive use of it, including turning it off when no longer needed. Such a leader doesn't really want his disciples to be able to do without him, and he creates a disabling addiction.

Methods and theories apparently don't matter, as a controlled study by Professor Yalom at Stanford has shown – the personality of the leader does. Many are badly disturbed themselves. The good ones try to teach their method to disciples, but as their results depend on the kind of people they personally are, the disciples get indifferent success.

If you want to learn awareness in a context of social interaction, it's better to do it either in social interaction where the atmosphere is less excited, or in group sessions with a therapist who has been properly trained as a moderator. Training doesn't make all therapists good, but you don't hire an amateur heart surgeon.

exercises

It would be perfectly easy to draw up a schedule of structured experiences which would take a couple through all of the things which sexuality can express – maleness/femaleness, weaker/stronger, muscle/skin, trust, assertion, helplessness, oneness, tension, relaxation and so on. The best exercise is to do this yourselves.

If you've played through the sexual resources in *The Joy of Sex* for pleasure, play them through again for pleasure but also with the conscious intention of improving your ability to read and speak the language implicit in them. This doesn't make sex either self-conscious or spoil its spontaneity, any more than it spoils *Madame Bovary* if you read it both as a masterpiece and to improve your French.

You can set up your own exercise plays based on the ordinary resources of sex plus what we've said in this book. Quite small changes when you are fully excited – like having intercourse with one or both of you blindfold, or the woman fantasizing that she's a man and trying to get inside maleness – can greatly deepen and alter the ordinary pleasure experience. Don't confine yourself to experiences which immediately turn you on. Try experiencing maleness if it doesn't specially attract you, or femaleness if you're self-consciously male. If you're

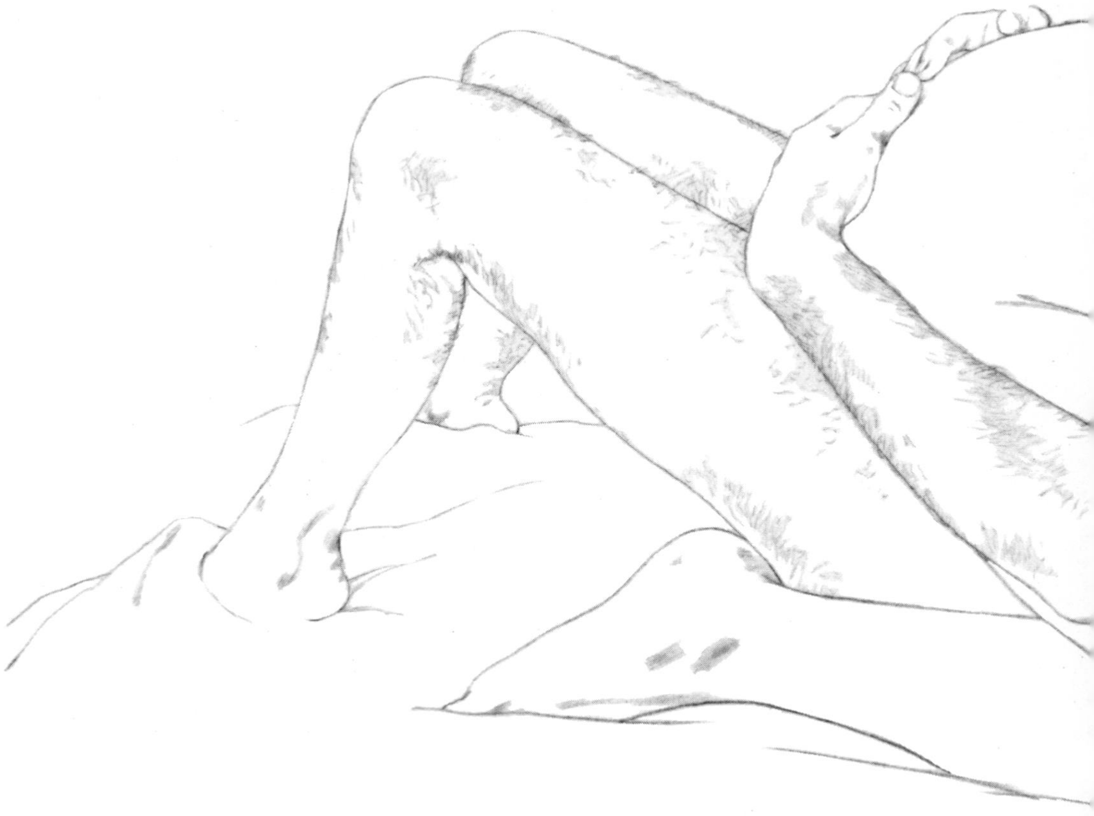

very aggressive, in the positive sense, and a little untrusting where you don't control, try experiencing complete helplessness; or, if you're very unassertive, complete control of your partner. Do these things in the play and coital situation so that the experience is reinforced by orgasm. At the same time maximize any potentials you have but don't use; a very muscular man who doesn't already fully use his muscularity in orgasm should work out with his partner ways of doing so, but also work on total relaxation.

Rather than telling you exactly how to do these things by a set of exercise situations (which people are bound to try correspondence-course fashion), the best way of making sexuality into a development experience – super-gourmet sex if you like – is to devise them yourselves using the materials and the knowhow we've quoted, and angling what you do to your particular needs. Handled like this the joy of sex can be assertion training, relaxation therapy, encounter and sex-identity reinforcement as necessary.

Some examples:

bathing, sex in water	total skin experience body is weightless, flying infantile and possibly prenatal reminiscences
blindfold intercourse, massage, etc.	anonymity of partner sex of partner hidden surprise effect (cannot predict partner's initiatives)
bondage	weaker/stronger experience helplessness/assertiveness/trust not being responsible partner's initiatives outside your control: you control partner erotization of struggle
breast play	infancy flashback lover/child experience closeness, heart contact

clitoral play	sharpness of orgasm
	not being penetrated
	female fantasizes having a penis
matrimonial	relaxed oneness
oral sex	pleasure of sucking
	pheromones (odor hormone stimuli)
	intimacy, incorporating one another
	worthiness, cleanness of genitals
	going back to the womb
	taboo-breaking
rear entry	perineal stimulation
	back available for touch
	female invitation
	partner is anonymous
slow masturbation	total control of/by partner
threesomes	inviting a guest
	love-gift, non-jealousy
	dramatizing bisexuality
	relaxing male dominance (with a second male)
woman superior	better control for her
	trying-out sex roles
	he relinquishes responsibility
wrestling	muscular turnon
	weaker/stronger
	man stronger, dramatizes being taken
	woman stronger, dramatizes infancy reminiscence

meditation

Not at first sight an obvious resource for people with problems. It doesn't mean sitting and thinking about something, but rather achieving mentally a kind of zero-input condition. When this happens one becomes able to monitor internal brain traffic, to achieve altered states of mind, and – if one is a mystic and meditates systematically – "oceanic" states very similar to those induced in some people by LSD, but without its risks.

Peak experiences, if you happen to get them, do alter people beneficially, but the reason we include this as a counseling rather than a religious resource is that the meditative state, even at a very low level, has big effects on the autonomic nervous system and can relieve tension, while the more advanced experiences can help turn people off drugs or alcohol if they have the stamina to persist that far. You need an instructor to get started, and continuing instruction if you want to get further (otherwise some of the LSD-like effects can be scary for an unprepared person who isn't a natural meditative saint). Tantrics combined meditation with slow, non-orgasmic sex as an exercise in body-image manipulation, by which each one experienced himself or herself as simultaneously male and female. How far you go will depend on your religious talents – as a simple exercise in relaxation most people find meditation of quite a rudimentary kind rewarding.

psychoanalysis

A high proportion of prosperous Americans appear to visit the analyst weekly, as they visit the hairdresser – often with the expectation of getting help with personal or sexual problems. It is therefore worth looking at what analysis is, and what it isn't.

Freud's original technique of treating patients sprang from his discovery of infantile sexuality and repression. Adult sexual behaviors spring from extremely powerful emotions and responses existing in early infancy, in which the parents figure as sexual objects and the subject of desire, jealousy and so on, far ahead of any capacity for sexual performance. Repression is the programed putting out of mind by adults of a whole series of these infant experiences which nonetheless surface unbidden and influence behavior. Freud analyzed dreams, behaviors, attitudes and free-associations in order to make relevant parts of this infant experience conscious – explanation being used to enable the patient to experience (and hopefully come to terms with) those portions of this repressed background that were affecting his performance. Of all the subsequent psychoanalytic theorists who have modified these ideas, Freud still stands up best in the light of modern biological knowledge.

One key Freudian finding was that at one stage male toddlers experience intense anxiety about, and fear of losing, the genitalia, coupled with jealousy of the father – the so-called castration anxiety and Oedipus complex. We would now talk more about infantile sensuality instead of, or as well as, sexuality, and see the castration anxiety as a special case of a dominance situation. The penis is a dominance signal, and the mother's vulva is both an invitation and a threat – highly appropriate to a young prehuman male primate who had to stay with his mother, because he was immature, but avoid approaching her sexually because of the risk of being treated by the father as a competing adult male and vigorously attacked.

The reason that the penis is an obsession of Freudian interpretations is that it's an obsession of man. In most animals it takes adult plumage or voice to set off competition with other males, and one would expect beard anxiety rather than penis or castration anxiety. Man seems unique in picking a structure present from birth as a dominance signal – hairlessness, growing intelligence and upright posture may all have conspired to make a male recognizable, and hence competitive, while immature. What seems to have happened is that in evolution this whole package of behaviors has got moved to an irrelevantly early age.

Dominance anxiety *vis-à-vis* the father is, therefore, in all probability a temporary organ like the tadpole's tail, but it does profoundly affect adult behavior, as well as all human myth and literature. If avoidance of the female as your mother and a tabooed object is not satisfactorily reversed when the time comes to mate, a male may treat all women as a threat, and either prefer males, or need a transitional object (a fetish) in order to face them, as a child needs a teddy bear when anxious.

As to women, Freud postulated that they see themselves as already castrated and in search of the penis they have lost, while males are anxious to provide them with one in order to make them less threatening. Some of this sounds right and there's a fair amount of this thinking in folklore. Women do in some senses seek a penis, and men find phallicized women reassuring – witness the preference of some men for one-legged women, which is a simple schematic signal of the kind seen in animals. On the other hand, Freud himself didn't feel satisfied with his psychology of female sexuality, and we may well feel less so (we could do with a moratorium on theories about female sexuality devised by men). If you want a proper account of Freud's own ideas read his *Introductory Lectures on Psychoanalysis*, not what someone else says he said.

Both Freudian analysis and later variants (including that of Jung, who was interested in archetypes, or preferred patterns of human thinking, and in the male and female selves concealed in every individual) can be instructive and rewarding experiences and deepen self-comprehension. If they work, they are emotional or feeling experiences, not the equivalent of a lecture. In the course of self-comprehension some of our more irrational behaviors, such as being a perpetual loser, hating the other sex, or being accident-prone may be seen for what they are and relieved. For most concrete sexual problems, such as impotency, they're unfortunately far more instructive than beneficial. After ten years of analysis one may have garnered a lot of insight – and still be impotent or whatever other problem prompted you to seek help.

As an education analysis is well worth it if you can afford the time and the high cost. As a treatment for functionally autonomous habits that one is stuck with, whatever their infantile origins, the results are poor, and other kinds of attack are both quicker and more certain – scientifically operated relearning, for example (see *Behavior therapy*). At the same time many people who are cured of a symptom by behavior therapy could do with more insight (and can get it from nonclassical analytic methods like brief analysis and analytic group therapy, which are quicker and cheaper than Freud's original routine). Idiotic hostility occasionally reigns between analytic and behavioral practitioners, but they're both examining a programed learning process, and a primate biologist would knock their heads together.

All modern sexology and primatology has to take account of Freud. All discussion of human behaviors also has to take account of Jung, who was more sensitive to the realm of feelings but apt to take off into a kind of Wagnerian stratosphere, and of Adler, who was the first to point out (in other words) that a lot of what Freud classed as sexual anxieties in fact relate to dominance. These three weren't on speaking terms. It has taken primatology and anthropology to put them together into a general biology of human thinking and behavior – the way science gets delayed by dogma and ego-trips was a subject that none of them, unfortunately, tackled. Accordingly, the brand of analysis you get, if you have it, may depend on the school to which the analyst adheres, unless you get a sensible eclectic who knows all the theories. This matters less than you might think, because analysis is a sensitive experience in communication and intuition between you and the analyst, and it is this that imparts any benefit you may get from the sessions.

psychotherapy

Almost anything that makes you feel better mentally – from reassurance to ten years of analysis. It's mainly used of specific situations of dialogue or interaction which are designed to impart insight and overcome problems, and nearly all of it depends on the language of human nonverbal as well as verbal communication. Even going to the doctor with a pain somewhere can be a form of this (quite a lot of symptoms are messages or demonstrative behaviors) and a good doctor, beside giving you some aspirin for the pain, will read your body language and deal with the message through his own verbal and nonverbal communication to you.

Psychiatrists didn't invent what are called transference and counter-transference (the interaction of the patient's image of the doctor and the doctor's image of the patient – the doctor is a person, too): it's a normal form of human communication. More specific psychotherapy can involve letting someone talk (and make up his or her own mind over courses of action), while the therapist listens both to the verbal and the nonverbal information and responds helpfully. This can be a little like holding the mirror to enable someone to see into his own ears. Only you can get your head together, but a skilled outside observer can see things you don't, and enable you to see them.

Group psychotherapy saves time and maximizes the flow of this kind of information because there are several individuals of both sexes and a number of different make-ups interacting. A single therapist can only be of one sex at a time (so can't witness your reaction to the other sex) and starts with a built-in "parental" role. You came to him or her as an authority or a magician with the expectation of relief, and this doesn't expose, for example, your degree of dominance in a group. A really expert group therapist usually stays pretty quiet, reads the group interactions, and intervenes either to keep order (protecting anyone who gets picked on, asking an overtalkative member to give others a turn if the others don't ask him), or to guide the interaction so that members see for themselves what is occurring between them. It's a valuable experience to test yourself in such an environment even if you don't have gross problems.

You can learn even more about yourself through psychodrama in which members of the group act out their feelings to one another, or to figures like parents, spouses or employers. This can go on to straight social training: a shy person can learn to address a person of the opposite sex by playing a little charade, with the others giving comment and suggestions. An office doormat can learn to deal with his boss and colleagues by letting other group members play them, and seeing where he is going wrong. This is rather the way in which some schools teach salesmen. One form of psychodrama is assertion training, which teaches you the skills and signals of higher dominance (without being overaggressive) when your self-esteem is low, using games and support from the group.

All psychotherapy aims to give you accurate information about yourself (insight), pinpoint hangups, and substitute more appropriate social skills. Its main use is in getting rid of general problems arising from your attitude and behaviors. It doesn't usually attack specifically sexual hangups directly, though problems like frigidity, if they're based on fears or mistaken beliefs about yourself and about sex, often improve, and so do physical symptoms which arise from things like constant anxiety or low self-esteem. The skills you learn from good group therapy make you a more fully interacting and signal-reading human being and better able to interpret your sex role *vis-à-vis* others. It is, however, a living and a learning process, not magic, and it won't undo a lot of bad learning experiences overnight.

sex therapy

Good sex therapists use – or know about – all of the techniques in this section, and fit horses to courses. At clinics treatment is of three main kinds: giving straight reassurance and information; giving specific treatment schedules for managing a particular problem (this is often really a form of behavior therapy); and couple-counseling. This is best done by the technique pioneered by Masters and Johnson, where a couple counsels a couple, so nobody is in a minority of one. All sex therapy involves seeing both partners and going into their attitudes, fears and expectations – not just into the presenting problem.

Quite a lot of couples come not because someone is impotent, frigid or otherwise in trouble but because they want to improve their sexual relationship in depth. Accordingly, one excellent kind of background therapy, specific problems or not, is for the counselor to put together a group of couples and let them talk, in the course of which they find that all of their problems are shared. For more detailed overcoming of a specific difficulty, the best practical helper is your normal partner (if not, you've got the wrong partner). The therapists talk through attitudes, get rid of nonsenses, and brief the couple on the best way of giving themselves the requisite behavior therapy. Showing videotapes or films of a really relaxed couple can help others who are uptight or lack knowhow.

Good sex counseling is badly needed, and doctors unfortunately are not trained to give it. The problem in finding the right person to consult is that freaks and

quacks aren't uncommon. If you want an address in your area, try calling the Sex Information and Education Council of the US. When you go to a clinic you will not forthwith be handed over for instruction to a surrogate partner: you should both be interviewed, together and separately (distrust a therapist who doesn't suggest this) and you should get an estimate of the expected cost and duration of treatment. Some church bodies support sex therapy clinics which are open-minded and not committed to religious dogmas of behavior. Any therapist who suggests sleeping with one or both of you is a phoney: that isn't the therapist's role.

If you can't afford help or get it in any other way, you could well try to convene a group of couples in your area, by way of a small ad or otherwise, and try to get them talking. This in itself is therapy, and people help each other, even if they don't know the answers. You could then try to get someone who does know some answers in to assist. Try to include one knowledgeable, uninhibited and sexually alert pair, both to get the others talking and to put down common misconceptions – that oral sex is abnormal, for example, or that impotence is a physical disease. This is a second best but better than nothing, and the group can supplement their experience by reading. We don't want to sound like a commercial, but this book and *The Joy of Sex* could be used in this way. Unlike most other matter written about sex they represent modern knowledge, not obsolete folklore, at least as far as the range of normal behaviors is concerned.

And don't be deterred from seeking help if the idea of any kind of group discussion offends you. Good therapists work in complete privacy, and won't suggest talking to others or taking part in group discussion unless you both wish it and think it would help you.

We've talked here about therapy with couples. If you have no partner, have a problem, and need help with it, you can be helped by other techniques, so don't be deterred from seeking advice.

surrogates

The best way to learn to have sex if you're new to it or have problems is to have it with a clued, experienced, undemanding and turned-on partner. Unfortunately, most of our regular partners are also learning, don't as a rule have all that much experience and have hangups. They are also involved in the bind over "Am I pleasing him/her?" "Why isn't he/she pleasing me?" which gets worse the more the other party has performance troubles. Hookers are clued, experienced and sometimes turned on, but the scene is wrong, and a lot of them, by motivation and by experience, are basically hostile to the oppo-

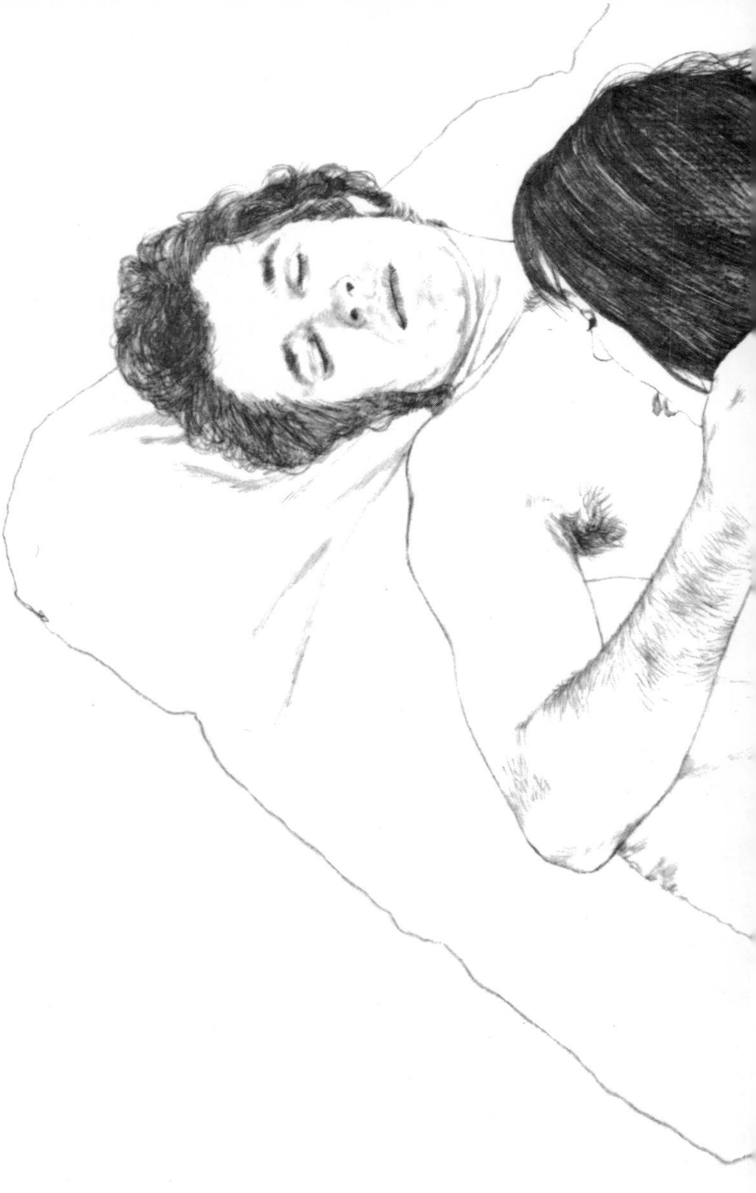

site sex – also, unless you go to very expensive call girls, their time is money and they time-stress you.

When someone consults a sex therapist over a problem such as premature ejaculation, if he has a partner the therapist will instruct the couple. How about a male who has gay experience only and wants to acquire heterosexual skills? Holy society used to tell him to get married (which could be heavy for the wife if he has made the wrong decision in trying), less holy used to suggest prostitutes or pickups, risking a lot of mischief if a failure led to a putdown. Unless you think sex can be taught by correspondence course, a sane therapist would send him to a woman with the necessary skills, who enjoys sex and is supportive but doesn't make demands. (We say "he" and "woman" because that's the way around it is now: there are male surrogates, but from a cultural backlog women are very often less able to accept them

than men are female surrogates, and there are psychodynamic differences. We don't know enough male surrogates to be able to judge how this will go.)

The woman who is a surrogate has to enjoy sex, be clued about handling male problems, and be warm and caring, but tough enough not to get overinvolved with clients. She always works with the therapist who referred the patient to her, and takes responsibility for the line of treatment. Surrogate and client are introduced – first names if they prefer – and spend the first few sessions getting used to being naked together. He may never have had the chance to explore a woman's body. Her job is to reinforce him without scaring him, to cultivate his potency, to teach him social as well as sexual skills in bed, and to concentrate on his presenting problem (premature ejaculation is perhaps the one surrogates most often tackle). Quite as much as training in performance he gets training in unhurried relaxation, and catches her confident, undemanding attitude toward sex.

So far from being an exploitation of women, some surrogates find their job an ideal expression of their own needs, though it's hard work, like any other wet-shoulder assignment. They and their clients don't become mutually dependent or fall madly in love, but stay close friends. One surrogate we know wept with pleasure, not jealousy, at getting a letter to say that an ex-client was happily married and owed it all to her. It's a warm, rewarding human relationship, given the right people, with nothing clinical or prossy about it.

Sensible doctors have used surrogates for years but kept quiet about it. Now they can do so openly, which is much to the good.

Special Needs

alcohol

Alcohol is one of the common causes of impotence: people forget that it's a powerful sedative.

What commonly happens is that a male has an off night – they come home from a party, and he finds he can't get it up. She may or may not say something which hits his ego, but he spends next day getting up steam to show her (or himself), has several drinks to fortify himself, then tries the virility bit – meaning straight-in intercourse with no relaxation, no preliminary touching, and no help from her. This is failure number two. With luck he will wake with an erection, but we've known males who failed to use this, insisting that they must produce one when they wanted. This kind of self-frustration can rapidly build into habitual impotence, with an equally habitual two or three martinis an evening guaranteeing that failure will continue.

Most Americans simply don't realize how much they do drink. It can easily run to half a bottle of spirit, in one form or another, per day, and this is enough to cut male response quite heavily, in spite of the status of sub-intoxication as a virility symbol. Most males survive this, but many more would be multiorgasmic if they cut down on the ingestion of a sexual blunting agent. Moreover, since premature ejaculation is a form of nascent impotence, drink doesn't help that either – it's more liable to turn it into the complete variety.

Alcoholism, in an alcohol culture, is difficult to recognize. Basically anyone whose behavior is altered by drinking in a way deleterious to himself or others is an alcoholic. Alternatively imagine that it were announced that as from tomorrow the world supply of alcoholic drinks had dried up: a normal reaction might be "damn!" – an alcoholic's reaction would be "how do I get through the day after tomorrow?"

Alcoholism is a disease, not a weakness of character or a fault. It's quite one of the most disruptive things which can affect a couple's relationship because of the long stretches of non-communication, the unreality of the drunken party's behavior, and the character changes that go with it. It's useless to pose a choice between drink and you, because drink will be chosen. There is no alternative to treatment, either through community psychotherapy with Alcoholics Anonymous, or by other methods such as behavior therapy (q.v.). The main problem is to get it recognized early by the sufferer – at the stage when the other partner starts a game of hide and seek to avoid drinking occasions or liquor in the house, and the sufferer starts playing to circumvent these efforts. Often nothing is said during this game, but it's diagnostic and the time for plain speaking if serious problems are to be avoided.

depression

Depression is probably the commonest cause of sudden loss of sexual feeling in people who have so far been functioning well.

In severe depression, which can come on gradually or suddenly, there is a loss of all satisfaction in life. Surroundings appear drab or tasteless, there may be a sensation of cut-offness, tiredness is intense, and is accompanied by feelings of despair, misery, guilt and so on which can lead to suicide. This is a medical emergency. Some people have recurrent attacks, others one only. It can follow normal grief at a bereavement or a putdown, but is quite different in feel. Depression of this kind is a biochemical illness affecting brain amines. It doesn't respond well to psychotherapy, but can almost always be relieved by drugs. These take about two weeks to act, and it may be necessary to try more than one kind of drug before finding one appropriate to a given person. Recurrent attacks can be prevented by the mineral lithium, but this must be taken continuously and the blood levels monitored by a laboratory. Some of the drugs used to treat depression can turn off sexual performance, increasing anxiety and despair if they do, but this is a side effect and soon passes off.

Severe depression often but not always leads to loss of libido, as it leads to loss of appetite generally. It is also usually obvious that the person is ill – to others, if not to them. The depressions which present sex problems are mild depressions; the patient doesn't feel depressed so much as ill (without symptoms), tired and turned off. They may suddenly become frigid or impotent, and that doesn't help. A lot of the trouble in treating them is in persuading them that they are depressed, not just glum and unlucky, and it's only when medication lifts the mood that they realize how depressed they were. Untreated mild depression can drag on for years. If you suspect it in yourself or your partner, get it treated.

A lot of counselling and psychotherapy have been wasted on these mild, long-lasting changes in brain chemistry. The treatment is the same as for the severer kinds and is within the competence of any doctor. The trouble is that some psychiatrists are apt to turn on the entire talk show when what is needed is one of the types of drug which restore the normal chemistry in your head. You may indeed need counseling as well, but that should accompany or follow medical treatment of the main illness. Always suspect depression if you or your partner cease without any good reason to function or to enjoy. Depressions get better in the end, and any therapy you have had over the years gets the credit. Tricyclic or MAOI drugs do the job in between two weeks and two months. In severe depression, electroconvulsion therapy is safe and effective. It is about as unpleasant as a dental extraction.

disablement

Disabled people – even severely disabled people – can use both this book and *The Joy of Sex*. At first sight, since we obviously describe a lot of things one can't do if badly paralyzed or otherwise handicapped, they might look depressing to anyone with these problems. But in fact, because they cover the whole range of sex behaviors, not simply straight intercourse, you will realize, if you think about it, that you can use them as a dyspeptic or a diabetic can use a cookbook.

Minor disability may only limit your choice of positions, etc. Major disability will mean that you may have to carve out a whole special form of sex for yourself. Virtually nobody is too disabled to have some pleasure from sexuality – with a partner if you can, without one if you must. Generations of disabled people have been hocused out of this by other people's embarrassment, the pattern of institutions, and the desire of society to suppress any sexual expression which was suppressible. Everyone needs tenderness and contact, but it needn't stop there. If you are immobile, or if you have difficulty using your genitalia in the usual way, you can still beat the handicap, by using non-genital sensation, by finding out what resources you have got. Your biggest problem, after that of getting well people to treat you as a person, will be in getting it through their heads that you have the same needs as they have. How to do this is a constant topic of conversation where badly handicapped people get together (usually not in front of the hospital staff, who pretend as often as not that "we don't have those problems here").

Gradually, however, things are getting better, and counseling help is being made available if you insist (don't settle for Pollyanna or talk about coming to terms with reality if that means accepting that a physical disability means you have to be an involuntary monk or nun and like it). Your first big problem isn't the disability but other people's hangups – most nurses won't help two disabled folk to get into position for lovemaking, and few institutions provide privacy, even if they recognize the need, even for masturbation. But given determination you can beat this. We know one badly handicapped couple who have a really tender sex life, even though they only have the hospital bathroom – she uses her mouth and he his big toe.

If your disability goes back a long way you have a lot of fears and worries to live down; if it's recent, like a wound or an accident, you've got the shock of picking up the pieces. It's easier if one partner isn't disabled, and if you've already had a sex life; you'll have to reprogram it in terms of what you still have. Paraplegics can often make love and enjoy it – males can usually get an erection even if they can't feel below the waist, and extragenital sensation grows with practice in both sexes. We can't counsel here in detail, but at least we've described many ways of getting sexual pleasure, some of which almost any disabled person can manage. The big thing is to resist the pressures to become an unsexual unperson.

Above all, get rid of the idea that nobody can love, or have pleasure with, a disabled person. It simply isn't true. Thousands can and do. In fact, the need to give special help to people with impaired mobility, etc., may be the beginning of a general move in medicine to give proper sexual help to everyone who needs it. It has been the need of these people which has brought home to doctors that at the moment there is little or no proper sex counseling at a practical level for anyone. In your case, couples with the same kind of disability as you who have fought their way through could probably help most, plus a change in the attitude of institution and nursing staff. In the last resort you can only get this by fighting.

How far sexual prostheses can help disabled people is a matter for research: cultivation of skin, breast and other sensation and straightforward couple ingenuity are a better bid. We think that swinging couples with good experience could help more than psychiatrists or doctors here, and we wish there was an organization through which they could give this sort of help – there must be many who would be willing and glad to do so.

disablement practicalities

Preaching is unproductive, and it is difficult, beyond what we've said, to help with the emotional side of disablement simply through books. With the physical side and at the purely mechanical level one can do a lot more. Often the first disability to be overcome, especially in males, is one which affects plenty of robust and uninjured people – the idea that sex is about the genitalia, and that sexualizing any other part of the body is perverse. We have to take it that you know that this is hogwash, and that you are ready to use your skin, hands, feet, mouth and whatever, and so is your partner.

That accepted, start with an analysis of what, in the normal range of sex, you can't do. For minor disabilities one often finds that the whole problem arises from fanatical adherence to the missionary position. A woman with an arthritic hip who can't bend or open her legs can often be taken from behind, with a lot of clitoral and breast play to help arousal. A man with a bad back can let the woman come astride. Some disabilities, in one or both partners, may mean you can't use the penis at all – if so, go for hand, mouth and skin work (but if the man can get any erection, don't assume intercourse is impossible until you've thought of, and tried, all the possible forms of apposition). One group with special problems are the paraplegic, who have impaired or absent sensation and little voluntary movement below the waist. Nearly all paraplegic males can get erections and ejaculate but can't feel what is happening, but they can and do enjoy intercourse, especially with a partner who can evoke skin sensitivity in the upper parts of the body. Women, especially if they have been sexually experienced before they were injured, can often get a full orgasm from breast play, and intermammary intercourse can give them still better participation. With severer disabilities the scope can be still further reduced. But if you have any sensation in your clitoris, penis, breasts or mouth, you can experience sexual arousal, and if you can move your tongue, fingers or big toe you can do something to arouse a partner.

For everyone, disabled or not, partner arousal and climax is at least half of the reward of sex. Set about outwitting the problem by fantasizing a kind of sexual play either within, or better, just outside, your capacity for physical movement, and then see if you and your partner can bring it about. Allow for quite a few failures. If you *can* in privacy make a game of it, do so (hard as it may be to take this advice from an undisabled counselor. If it helps, the author of this piece lost most of a hand in boyhood. The surviving thumb is a marvelous and reliable sexual implement). Make full use of fantasy, pornography and the like if they turn you on. With a widespread special problem like multiple sclerosis or paraplegia, contact your national organization or talk to other couples with the same problem. Best of all, try to get a group together who can break down reticence over all this and share their experiences – with a sex counselor on hand if you can find a good one. The National Sex Forum in San Francisco are already doing this. For some very disabled people, 69 gives a greater feeling of mutuality than intercourse, for others really creative mutual masturbation. For yet others, a combination of these with full or partial insertion becomes a pattern rewarding to both partners.

This assumes, of course, that you have a partner. For the lonely or the institutional disabled – some of them incapable of masturbating, a particularly cruel defect, or even watched by moralistic idiots to see they don't attempt it for lack of privacy – hope has to lie with society. In some Scandinavian institutions the caring administration of orgasm is the responsibility of the physiotherapist – certainly to our knowledge for males, and, one must hope, for everyone, despite the sick idea that women don't need it or would find it immodest. Is anyone going to oppose this openly? Probably not, but they'd oppose it secretly, arguing that the patients would be embarrassed, the therapists would leave and all the usual repertoire of reasons. But progress can be made. When one patient openly demanded privacy to masturbate, nobody spoke up at once in support, the authorities blushed, and arranged it unobtrusively for everyone. It can be done, while society learns the abc of concern for sexual realities. Undisabled people could take a hand too – it would be a bigger sign of caring than taking round library books. In our view, nobody need feel embarrassed either to give or to receive.

heart attacks

There are two points here – avoiding them and coping with them sexually.

All exercise protects to some extent against heart attacks provided it isn't too violent and intermittent in sedentary people. Sex is good exercise but is intermittent, so you need walking as a backup. There's no numerical evidence that it favors longevity to be sexually active, though one would expect it, and there's plenty of anecdotal evidence, not it's true that horny people live long, but that long-lived people are unusually horny. In the present state of the art, it looks as if the main causes of the epidemic of coronaries in males are cigarette smoking, tension and the excessive consumption of animal fats. On the evidence, cigarettes are probably the top hazard (the fact that it is possible that heavy smokers are constitutionally tense doesn't explain away the incidence figures), dairy products the second, and obesity and tension the third. No sane person would now eat butter, cream, bacon or saturated fats generally – the answer to the question why our peasant forebears ate them with impunity is probably that they took vast amounts of exercise and didn't usually live into the coronary age.

If you have a heart attack, you need to get gentle sex started again as soon as you can start gentle exercise. Heart attacks don't affect potency but, apart from anything else, are commonly followed by depression (q.v.), partly because they're frightening and depressing and partly for physical reasons, and a return to sex combats this. There's not much risk in a wife giving even a recumbent man an orgasm in bed (heart attacks in women are much rarer, so it's usually this way round), and early intercourse can be lateral, or with her astride, or by gentle but fairly rapid masturbation or mouth work. You can judge whether medical advice is being overcautious or not from what you know of the doctor. If he says "no sex" ask why – sex is an important part of rehabilitation, and a clued cardiologist will only advise waiting if he has a reason.

Relaxed sex, even if it's violent, only rarely provokes a heart attack – very anxious sex scenes more often do. Either is far less hazardous than gardening, or even having a severe nightmare, which seems to account for some nocturnal attacks.

later life

In *The Joy of Sex* we explained that sexuality doesn't run out with age, that given good health and an expectation of carrying on, potency doesn't decline, but that male response changes.

In organizing your sex life from about 60 on, the things to remember are these:

1 Men normally attain fewer orgasms and slower erections as they get older. If their normal frequency of intercourse is high, they may get one orgasm in three to five instead of every time. They can get an orgasm every time if the couple switch techniques after she has come, and change to oral or manual stimulation; though if you use hard rubbing, the orgasm rate in coitus may fall further, through desensitization. Don't cut your rate of intercourse below what you've been used to, because with age sexual response, like muscular strength, is very susceptible to disuse, and never drop it altogether or you may have trouble restarting. In partnerless periods, use regular masturbation, but don't hurry it: practice holding a full erection each time. The fall in orgasm frequency means that you must reprogram in the expectation of not coming every time, and concentrate on your partner's feelings.

2 Spontaneous erections also get fewer. All normal males over about 55 need some direct tactile stimulus to the penis on many or most occasions. A lot of older males who say they often can't get it up are waiting for divine inspiration when what they need is hand work. Get it up yourself – better still, your partner should do it.

3 Women's sexual feelings only decline after the menopause if they are upset about it or think that they should decline. However, over the menopause itself hormone changes plus psychic factors can produce libido swings, and a longish time after there may be vaginal dryness. Regular sex seems to keep hormonal balance going, but many women now get proper substitution therapy. This is cosmetically good, preserves their feeling of well-being if that was impaired, and avoids the loss of bone minerals which leads to the little old lady condition in the 70s and 80s with shrinkage of the skeleton. The only snag about this, with a couple who are both in later life, is that hormone therapy often makes the vagina a lot wetter than it was premenopausally, and the man, used to a fair degree of friction, may suddenly find he

gets virtually no feeling from insertion. This calls for a change in the prescription, but it's worth mentioning because males who've been scared by propaganda about aging often think they're going impotent.

4 A regular partner who ages only gets ugly and undesirable to a loving man if she really lets herself go. Familiarity and experience more than make up for magazine looks, and older men who've had both find young girls' lack of knowhow offputting. On the other hand, men do get turned off, and can become impotent, as a result of disfiguring obesity, slobbishness or sudden adoption of a senile style of makeup. Good and responsible plastic surgery (to immense pendulous udder-like breasts, for example) can help here if the problem is gross, but don't be talked into expensive face-lifting maneuvers unless you really trust the surgeon. This is a very bad area for con-men, and you can get robbed and disfigured as well as disappointed. If you need plastic surgery, consult a university medical school, not a clinic operator.

Ultimately, and especially with ill-health, your frequency of intercourse will go down, but it will never pinch out until you do, and you may find yourself developing the skills of touching, hand work and so on which you learned but didn't use so much when you were more coitally active. All you are doing is shifting your repertoire to meet a less vigorous style of lovemaking. Fifteen per cent of married people over 78 in a recent study were having regular intercourse, and that makes no allowance for couples where one partner was sick, or where they'd never had much of a sex life anyway. In fact, since highly active people sexually remain highly active (either because they were sexy to start with, or because practice improves function, or both), that 15 per cent was probably made up of couples who had really developed their sexuality earlier. Violently muscular and fantasy-based sex play probably does decline, but new modes take its place if you are versatile.

Where the couple is of unequal age the man is usually the older. If there's a big difference in age, the wife needs to be clued about the normal changes in male response. If for any reason her preferred orgasm frequency is higher than his at this stage, she shouldn't push it, but they should talk, and cultivate nonerectile extras to make up the trade gap: similarly in the reverse situation – though a woman who doesn't feel every time isn't as vulnerable as a man who is trying to outdo his erectile physiology.

masochism

A masochist, contrary to folklore, isn't necessarily a person who likes being beaten, jumped on by people in boots, and the like. Krafft-Ebing borrowed the name of a

Viennese novelist with these and other fantasies to make a self-adhesive label for a big range of behaviors, most of which, when dramatized sexually, are unimportant. The beatees and jumpees may be acting out all or part of a spectrum which involves straight skin and muscle exploration, trying out various roles for size, and real masochism, which is the desire to be punished in expiation of sexuality (and even, with some dedicated masochists, in expiation of existing at all).

Society has succeeded in laying a little of this feeling on most of us, but when it links up with other infantile mislearning about the body image, or with psychosis, it can be heavy. Real masochists may prefer sexual plays associated symbolically with pain, low self-esteem, worry over sex roles and punishment, but, far more important, in daily life they are defeatist and accident-prone. This can be bewilderingly consistent, in that they manage somehow to be involved in misfortunes that couldn't have been organized, like being robbed or mugged. Accident-proneness is in their body language and attracts lightning.

People like this make dangerous partners not because the same pattern of fantasy appears in their sexual play, but because of their capacity to arrange their own and other people's unhappiness, and the way they seduce partners into noncommunicating exploitation. Accordingly, don't bother about preferences for rough or submissive sexual play – these often fulfill other quite normal exploratory needs and act as a lightning-conductor for traces of guilt in healthy people. Look out rather for the person who is a wholetime willing dog's-body overtaken by an unreasonable number of Job-like misfortunes – accidents, car crashes, getting gypped, bankruptcies, you name it. Being emotionally kicked around by one or by a succession of exploitative partners is more important as an index than the character of directly sexual fantasy, though this, as with everyone, will match the person.

Being guilty at a deep level over sex and body feeling is a grave disability, sexually and socially. It leads to an inability to express any kind of aggression (q.v.) except against oneself, and often ends in a fatal accident or in actual suicide. If you notice the traits we've listed in yourself or a partner, get help. This is an instance where psychoanalysis (q.v.) or some briefer form of psychotherapy (q.v.) is probably the best resource.

"Feminine masochism" (the idea that women are naturally masochistic) is a nonsense based on a misreading of the ethologically submissive behaviors – being penetrated, dramatizing helplessness and so on – by which female animals, including humans, turn on the male, turn off his hostility, and overcome (in humans) infantile anxieties about the dangerousness of women.

Liking him to take you, mini-rape style, isn't masochism – only the use of good mammalian equipment. Liking him to exploit or humiliate you socially is. With the social pressures withdrawn, modern women are only masochistic if they're really suffering from a deep-seated disorder of normal self-esteem.

The name masochism has outlived its use and should be returned to its owner. At the moment it's chiefly used to cause alarm and despondency over normal play behaviors. For the actual disorder, we prefer simply low dominance.

We have talked about masochists, not sadists, because normal people won't maintain a couple relationship with a person who, for reasons exactly like those which make the masochist a loser, tries to act out a dominance he or she doesn't have by hurting or humiliating others. If such a situation persists, the persisting half is a masochist. Sadists can and do hurt people sexually, not so much by violence, though this can happen, as by humiliating or rejecting loving people who don't recognize their abnormality. But the violent or subpsychotic kind are a real hazard of sex play with strangers, particularly symbolically aggressive sex play, which may stop being play and turn to earnest. Child play can do the same if there are no adults around to control it. Any situation in which one person plays at dominating another as a sexual game is safe only on a basis of perfect trust, or in the presence of sane people who can see it stays playful. Anything else is dangerous.

overweight

Overweight can be genetic (there are fat families); it can be due to a disorder of the body image which leads to overeating; or it can be due, quite simply, to gluttony. In our culture gross overeating is a norm. Anyone who lived on full restaurant portions would be overweight.

Fatness due to too much food shortens life in both sexes and can interfere considerably with potency in the male. The only way to lose weight is to eat less. No gimmicks work. Either you do it voluntarily, with some community support from bodies like Weight Watchers, or you get a diet (from a doctor, not a cranky paperback) and adhere to it, or you are put on appetite-reducing drugs. Commercial ripoffs usually act by making you lose water. There is no way, advertisements notwithstanding, of losing weight locally. Gross cases can have an intestinal bypass operation, but this is an emergency measure. For healthy women, having the fat scraped off by a cosmetic surgeon is an example of unnecessary surgery in search of a fool to exploit. It can disfigure you for life, and often does. Don't fall into the opposite error, if you're female, and be hocused by fashion into adopting the Belsen line – it's no more sexy than a family of chins. Women normally have subcutaneous fat and are cello-shaped – don't tempt the Almighty. Most cultures appreciate normal curves, and ours will if you resist sales talk.

In young girls, Anorexia can be a fatal disease and calls for emergency treatment.

Fat people often need to develop their own sexual techniques: for the man, intercourse with someone who is moderately overweight is pleasanter than with someone underweight. If approach is tricky, she can lie face up over the edge of the bed and he can stand or kneel. It's often worth developing rear approaches making full use of her buttocks. If he has a belly, she will need to be at right-angles to him, either on their sides with her leaning back or astride, or with him over the bed edge and her standing astride – he won't be able to come on top, and will quite often prefer to avoid male-active positions because of breathlessness. As with disablement (q.v.) play this as a game and try to find your own best-fit positions. Meanwhile do something about the overweight, in the interests both of sex and of general health. It's ridiculous and dangerous to carry a permanent 50 lb girdle.

pregnancy

The normal human pattern is to go on having sex all through pregnancy, and the pregnant woman is more, not less, attractive to many males, increased tenderness and closeness apart. You may need to switch to different postures (and avoid very deep or violent ones) when she gets really big. Some women get markedly decreased desire during pregnancy – in most it tends to swing more than usual, both for hormonal and psychic reasons. If she gets morning sickness she'll need gentleness first thing on waking.

If you miscarry easily it may be wise to avoid not only orgasm but even intercourse around the twelfth week and in the last two months. Take medical advice on this if it's your problem, but distrust total offhand prohibitions, and at least discuss them. You need sex at this time for closeness.

Pregnancy can have quite odd psychological effects on the male, from the immature guy who feels left out and goes on the tiles when his wife is in labor, to the man who stakes his share in the process by getting toothache or stomach cramps – or even a dummy pregnancy by swallowing air. Don't be surprised if you feel this way – it's a common human behavior, ritualized by some cultures, who put the father as well as the mother to bed for delivery (the *couvade*). Its function is to include the father and not make him feel guilty that she has the labor while he has the fun.

Quite the best pregnancy position for intercourse is on your sides from behind, though both of you may need intelligent handwork as well. In other positions the man will have to control depth; she can help by putting her hand round the penis root. Use the occasion to cultivate the shallow techniques – they are worth it for their own sake. After delivery, you can usually restart as soon as healing is complete and discharge has stopped.

prostate

The prostate gland enlarges with age in many males. If it comes to obstruct the passage of urine, it may require surgery. This usually happens in the 60s and 70s. The vital thing is to have a full discussion with the surgeon before consenting to the operation, and avoid like the plague any surgeon who doesn't realize that 60- and 70-year-old people are still sexually active. Some kinds of prostatic surgery can interfere with potency, and it's up to you to insist that your potency be conserved, and the mode of operation planned with this in mind. If you do insist, you'll probably be able to enlist full co-operation, unless there is some absolute surgical indication for the riskier type of operation. Older men used routinely to be made impotent by younger men who think the old don't or shouldn't ball at their age. Sex itself doesn't hurt the prostate, though constant frustrated sexual arousal without orgasm possibly may.

Cancer of the prostate has to be treated by surgery, as a rule, and/or hormones, and the hormones given are apt to turn off potency quite apart from surgical damage. Discuss the options with the surgeon, and insist that the discussion be a full and a two-sided one.

vaginismus

The outward and visible sign of inner and spiritual uptightness – it's a condition in which a woman's muscles go into such intense spasm that she can't be penetrated at all. Often she is married and wants to be penetrated, but the reaction, like ticklishness, is beyond voluntary control. This condition explains the quite common cases in which a couple in love, with the male fully potent, have ended by giving up all attempts at penetration and either dropped sex or settled for half measures.

Don't settle for these, or let them get to be a habit, but shout for help early. The first step is to get the rest of her sensual and relaxed, and in this many of the forms of submedical body-awareness can help. The second is to tackle the spasm. This can be done by a behavioral therapist, or she can do it herself by buying a set of glass dilators, covering them with K-Y jelly, and learning to insert them, starting with one of little-finger size. She should do this lying over a bed edge in a warm room, alone (it's better if he doesn't help) and combining the process with learning to give herself good feelings manually (see *Masturbation and learning*). When she has got up to one rather bigger than a penis, let him try to insert it, with her eyes first open, then closed or covered, then some other object, such as a vibrator, and then his penis. A couple can do this themselves, or they may feel (especially if she's very nervous or it's gone on a long time) that they'd rather have skilled help from the start. Behavior therapy (q.v.) nearly always works if do-it-yourself desensitization doesn't.

Women with vaginismus aren't all basically unwilling to have sex, even at an infant level. In some there's a clear history of things being forced into the anus in childhood to cure constipation – soapsticks and the like. Luckily people don't do this any more, since it evidently can derange adult function quite badly.

violence

Both women and men have always run the risk of violence from a sexual partner. For evident reasons, women are overwhelmingly the more vulnerable – in our society, intensely so, since injury by a husband or lover is one of the commonest medical problems they experience. Society offers them remarkably little support. The police are traditionally uninterested in "domestic" violence, and folklore treats it as a sign of passion.

We've stressed that passion can be athletic and even boisterous, but that has nothing to do with wife-beating. Outsiders such as the doctor or the social worker often wonder why abused women give second and third chances, and attribute it to love or feminine masochism. They fail to recognize the immense economic and social difficulties experienced by a woman with children and no job in breaking with a violent partner. The break has to be made, simply on grounds of selfpreservation; often it could and should have been made before marriage, because violent men very often indicate their propensity at the outset. The rules are very simple – don't give second, and certainly never third, chances, don't accept alcohol as an excuse, and don't expect to reform the offender or look on the bright side. Dumping him forthwith, after the first assault, and resort to prosecution or an injunction if the offender persists, can be lifesaving. As to children, a wife-beating male is likely to abuse his children too, so they are at risk. The offenders may be acting out previous abuse or hatred of women, or copying a parental situation, but if you are being victimized you are unlikely to succeed as a therapist. Get in touch with one of the women's organizations who can offer you support at the first incident, not after you have had bones broken. This is a hard saying for some, but it can be lifesaving.

Index

skin sensitivity, 16, 77, 94, 202, 204